W9-ACS-197

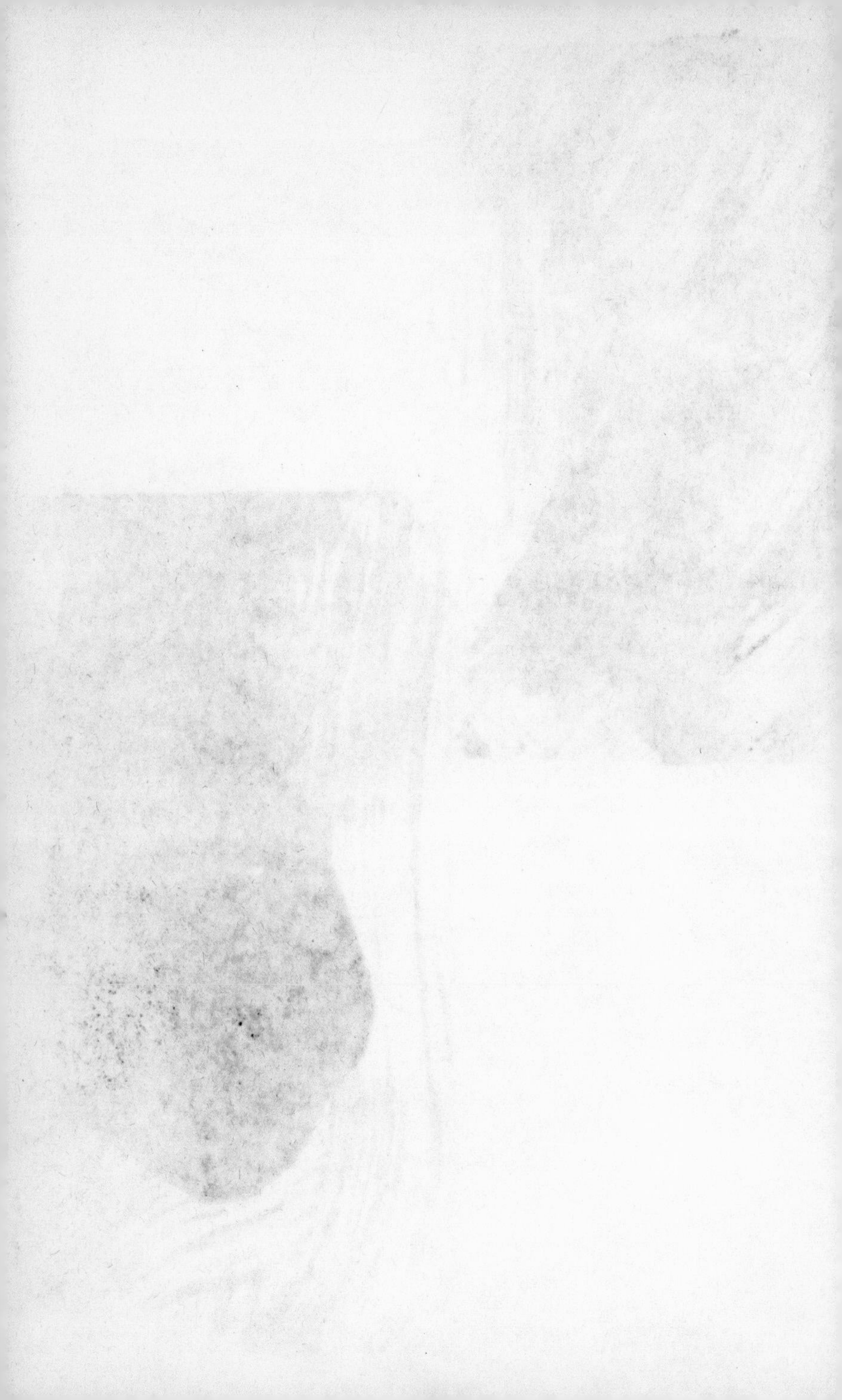

BRITISH MEN OF SCIENCE

General Editor
Sir Gavin de Beer F.R.S., F.S.A.
membre correspondant de l'Institut de France

Charles Darwin

CHARLES DARWIN

EVOLUTION BY NATURAL SELECTION

Sir Gavin de Beer
F.R.S., F.S.A.

Doubleday & Company, Inc.
Garden City, New York
1967

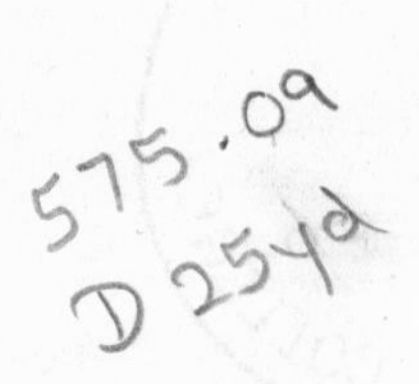

First published 1963
Second impression 1964
Third impression 1967

Library of Congress Catalog Card Number 64–10233
Printed in Great Britain

Preface

My introduction to the name of Darwin took place nearly sixty years ago in Paris, where I used to be taken from my home in the Rue de la Paix to play in the Gardens of the Tuileries. On the way, in the Rue Saint-Honoré near the corner of the Rue de Castiglione, was a shop that called itself *Articles pour chiens* and sold dog collars, harness, leads, raincoats, greatcoats with little pockets for handkerchiefs, and buttoned boots made of india-rubber, the pair for fore-paws larger than the pair for hind-paws. One day this heavenly shop produced a catalogue, and although I have long since lost it, I remember its introduction as vividly as if I had it before me. It began, 'On sait depuis Darwin que nous descendons des singes, ce qui nous fait encore plus aimer nos chiens.' I asked, 'Qu'est ce que ça veut dire, Darre-vingt?' My father came to the rescue and told me that Darwin was a famous Englishman who had done something or other that meant nothing to me at all; but I recollect that because Darwin was English and a great man, it all fitted perfectly into my pattern of life, which was built on the principle that if anything was English it must be good. I have learnt better since then, but Darwin, at any rate, has never let me down.

For over forty years I have studied, taught, and carried out research on evolution in the fields of comparative anatomy, embryology, palaeontology, and genetics, and on Darwin's unpublished manuscripts, and I served as president of the XVth international congress of zoology that met in London in 1958 as a compliment to Darwin and Wallace, on the centenary of their first publication on evolution by natural selection. As director of the British Museum (Natural History) I was reminded every day for ten years of Darwin and his work, and I have enjoyed the great benefit of the friendly help and criticism freely given to me in my work by Darwin's grand-daughter, Lady Barlow. I have tried to put the essence of all these experiences in this book without using technical language or exceeding the length that I have allotted myself. My aim has been to ensure that the biographical treatment was sufficient to situate Darwin in his period and his circumstances, but that the emphasis should be on his scientific achievements without going into minutiae of his private life.

An experiment was recently carried out on two hundred and forty television viewers who were asked what name they associated with evolution. One-third of this number of persons could give no name at all, another third suggested Huxley or Einstein and other names, beginning with Aristotle, while only the remaining third associated evolution with the name of Darwin. Even more remarkable, among the answers to questions at a recent examination for the General Certificate of Education at Advanced level was the following: 'Darwin's theory was based on three good solid pints [*sic*]; 1. the struggle for the exits 2. the survival of the fattest 3. maternal selection.' It is difficult to decide whether this was the result of cramming on poor intelligence, or a masterpiece of wit on the part of a candidate who was prepared to jeopardize his success in the examination for the satisfaction of a good joke. As a further example of how unfamiliar Darwin's work may still be, it has sometimes been said that Darwin never used the word 'evolution'; but he did, in the *Origin of Species*, which brings me to my final point. How many, even among professional biologists and geologists, read Darwin's original works? They would be astonished to find that in addition to the demonstrations of fact and theory for which they are justly famous, they contain an inexhaustible supply of problems for research of central importance at the present day.

GAVIN DE BEER

Contents

Acknowledgments

The author wishes to record his thanks to Miss Maria Skramovsky, who found a key missing page of Darwin's Notebooks on Transmutation of Species, and to Mr Robin Darwin, C.B.E., for permission to use this; also to Sir Geoffrey Keynes who owns the original drawings by Admiral King (Figs. 1 and 2) and to Lady Barlow and the syndics of the Cambridge University Press for permission to include them. For information about H.M.S. *Beagle*, Captain FitzRoy, and Captain Beaufort, his thanks are due to Rear-Admiral K. St B. Collins, C.B., O.B.E., D.S.C., the Record Office of the Admiralty, Mr F. G. G. Carr, C.B.E., Director of the National Maritime Museum, and Commander W. E. May, R.N., F.I.N.

The following have kindly supplied material and given permission for the use of illustrations Pls. 1, 10, and 11, The late Sir Charles Darwin; Pls. 2 and 3, The National Maritime Museum, Greenwich; Pl. 4, The Royal Naval College, Greenwich; Pl. 5, Miss Marjory B. Sirl; Pls. 6, 13, 17, and 18, The Royal College of Surgeons of England; Pl. 7, The Board of Trustees of the National Portrait Gallery; Pl. 8, The Royal Society of London; Pl. 9, The British Museum (Natural History); Pl. 12, Cambridge University Library; Pl. 14, Mr. A. J Russel Wallace; Pl. 15, Sir Julian Huxley; Pl. 16, The Department of Geology, Cambridge; Pls. 19 and 20, Dr H. B. D. Kettlewell; Pls. 21 and 22, Dr N. Tinbergen; Pl. 23, Lady Barlow; Pl. 24, The Linnean Society of London.

List of Plates

List of Figures

Chapter 1

Biology before the 'Beagle'

In the seventeenth century John Baal, seedsman, of Brentford near London was brought before the court at Westminster because cauliflower seeds that he had sold grew into cabbages. Today this would cause no surprise if cauliflower and cabbage plants grew near each other, because cross-pollination of cauliflowers by cabbages would be expected to produce this result. The significance of pollination was unknown before Rudolf Jakob Camerarius discovered it in 1694, and the part played by insects in pollination was first recognized by Philip Miller in 1721. Before these discoveries had been made, the judges at Westminster could only come to the conclusion that Baal had been guilty of negligence or fraud, and they condemned him to pay a fine and compensation to the buyers of his seeds who had wasted their money, time, and labour. The case had one further effect, however, for John Ray was then working on the problem of *species*, the different kinds of plants and animals, each of which was held in accordance with the precept of Holy Writ and the experience of common practice to reproduce after its kind. Ray therefore defined species as groups of individuals that breed among themselves, so that 'one species does not grow from the seed of another species'. Yet here was the case of John Baal, which Ray did not attribute to negligence or fraud, but to the possibility that seeds might degenerate and produce plants different from the parent plant. The concept of *variation* had thus arisen, and it meant a step towards the possibility that species might become transmuted into other species.

Presently, in 1715, Jean Marchant, a French horticulturist, found that a plant of dog's mercury had seeded and given rise to plants that differed from the parent in size, shape, and arrangement of the leaves. Today this would be attributed to genetic mutation, but by Marchant it was interpreted to mean that new species might arise by variation from old species, although the *genera* to which they belong had been created on fixed models. Linnaeus was driven to the same conclusion in 1742 by his observation that toadflax could produce plants with circular tubular 'peloric' flowers in place of the normal snapdragon-like blooms. The new peloric plants, which had been observed to arise more than once, set seed and bred true. This 'mutation', as Linnaeus called it, was therefore no evanescent effect of changed environmental conditions but a hereditary variation. Today this also is regarded as due to genetic mutation, but Linnaeus ascribed it to hybridization of toadflax plants with pollen from an unknown father resulting in new true-breeding species. This view enabled him to accept the species of the original Creation as themselves immutable but capable of producing new species by hybridization. In this way he was led to abandon his old view that 'species are as numerous as the Infinite Being created in the beginning', and to conclude that 'species are the work of time', without restriction on the number that may subsequently have been formed. Linnaeus's views were contested by other botanists, including Michel Adanson and Joseph Gottlieb Koelreuter, on the strength of their experiments in hybridization which gave different results, but their own interpretations were defective, as indeed they needs must be, in ignorance of the particulate mechanism of heredity that Gregor Johann Mendel was to discover a century later.

The position adopted in regard to the transmutation of

species by Georges Leclerc de Buffon, one of the greatest naturalists of his time, is difficult to determine, but he introduced novel and unorthodox views on the evolution of the solar system. Edmond Halley in 1694 and William Whiston in 1696 had speculated on the possibility that the Biblical Flood was the result of a near approach to the earth by a comet which altered the earth's shape and ruptured its crust, thereby releasing the 'waters under the earth'. This desire to provide a 'scientific' basis for the Scriptures was abandoned by Buffon in the first volume of his *Histoire naturelle* published in 1749, when he attributed the formation of the solar system to an oblique fortuitous collision between the sun and a comet that forced sufficient material off it into space to form the planets and their satellites. Four years later, under pressure from the Faculty of Theology of the Sorbonne, Buffon was obliged to retract these views. This circumstance makes it difficult to evaluate Buffon's treatment of the relationship between the horse and the ass when he asked whether they 'originally stemmed from the same ancestors,' and, if so, whether 'man, apes, quadrupeds and all animals could be regarded as members of the same family,' only to answer his own question with the disclaimer, 'No, it is certain through Revelation that all animals have shared equally in the grace of creation and that each emerged from the hands of the Creator as it appears today.'

Meanwhile, the subject of mutability of species had been taken up in speculative manner by a group of French philosophers including Montesquieu, Maupertuis, and Diderot. Basing themselves on certain facts such as the gradations that can be imagined between different species arranged in series, the appearance of new varieties of cultivated plants and domestic animals and of hereditary sports such as six-fingered men, the significance of monstrous births and imperfections of development, and the changes undergone by animals during their own life-histories, these thinkers concluded by deduction that species must have been mutable. Diderot even suggested that there was a prototype from which all living beings were descended and that the agent responsible for change was the age-old folk-belief that characters impressed on an organism during its life were transmitted by inheritance to the offspring. This, in his view, would account for the supposed perpetuation of the effects of use and disuse of organs, while the principle that if an animal experienced a need this need would provoke the formation of an organ that satisfied the need, accounted for the origin of such an organ.

In substantial agreement with these speculations was Erasmus Darwin, physician-philosopher-poet, whose work *Zoönomia or the Laws of Organic Life* was published in 1794. Like his French predecessors, Erasmus Darwin believed in the mutability of species because of the changes undergone by animals during embryonic development, particularly the metamorphoses of the caterpillar into the moth and the tadpole into the frog, because of the changes brought about by domestication and resulting from hybridization, because of the significance of monstrous births, and the similarity in plan of structure of vertebrate animals. He believed that the modification of species was brought about by the satisfaction of wants due to 'lust, hunger, and danger,' and as a result of 'their own exertions in consequence of their desires and aversions, of their pleasures and pains, or of irritations, or of associations; and many of these acquired forms or propensities are transmitted to their posterity.' He recognized the importance of adaptation of organisms to their environments in the struggle for existence, of protective coloration; of artificial selection and sexual selection in bringing about change; of cross-fertilization in maintaining vigour; of the significance of vestigial organs that were without function in their possessors but presupposed a former

(2,629)

function; of monstrous births as disproof of the notion that the embryo is preformed in the germ; and of sports or mutations such as six-toed cats and rumpless fowls. But when it came to explaining how adaptations were produced in an organism, Erasmus Darwin had nothing to offer but 'the power of acquiring new parts, attended with new propensities, directed by irritations, sensations, volitions, and associations; and thus possessing the faculties of continuing to improve by its own inherent activity, and of delivering down those improvements to its posterity, world without end.'

Independently, although heir to the same speculative background, Jean-Baptiste de Lamarck came to conclusions very similar to those of Erasmus Darwin. A soldier of outstanding gallantry in the Seven Years War who had subsequently become fascinated by the luxuriance of plants in his garrison stations in the south of France, Lamarck abandoned the army as a profession and took up the study of natural history. In his book *Hydrogéologie* published in 1802 he opposed the 'catastrophic' theories of geological causes then in vogue which required fantastic catastrophes to explain the state of the earth and, like James Hutton, advocated the uninterrupted continuity of past and present causes and effects. Lamarck recognized the unlimited amount of time required to account for the history of the earth, deduced the organic origin of sedimentary rocks, and pointed out the importance of fossils for the estimation of past changes of climate, valuable services to science, largely ignored even today.

It is for his *Philosophie zoologique* published in 1809 that Lamarck is remembered in the history of science. Confronted with the task of classifying the collections in the Paris Museum of Natural History, he experienced such difficulty in distinguishing between species and varieties of species that he concluded that there was no basic difference between them. He argued that if enough closely related species were studied together, differences between them could no longer be made out and they merged into one another. In fact this is not the case, because the barrier between species is always discernible even if very difficult to detect, but the appearance that species graded into one another led Lamarck to put forward a full theory of 'transformism' or evolution, which he was the first to do, invoking descent of species during long periods of time from other species, so that the Animal Kingdom could be represented by a genealogy of branching lines, the last branch being that of man. Fossil organisms he thought had not become extinct but had been transmuted into their living descendants.

Lamarck accounted for evolution by means of the action of two factors. The first was a supposed tendency to perfection and to increased complexity, which he held responsible for the existence of the scale of beings from the simplest organisms at the bottom to man at the top. He regarded this concept as so self-evident as not to require proof, of which in fact it is incapable, being inaccessible to scientific investigation. It led him to suppose that as simple lowly organisms exist today without having been perfected or made complex, they must have arisen recently by spontaneous generation. Lamarck's second factor was introduced because the scale of beings is not a perfect series graded from the lowest to the highest but shows anomalies, deviations, and branchings from what it might and in his view would have been if the environment had not interfered. Like Diderot and Erasmus Darwin, Lamarck supposed that as a result of new needs experienced by the animal in its environment, its 'inner feeling', comparable to Erasmus Darwin's 'internal impulse' or 'living force', set in motion bodily movements and instituted habits that produced new organs satisfying those needs, in other words, adapting the animal to its environment. These organs, and the effects of their use and disuse, he thought were then transmitted by heredity. As this explanation could not be applied to plants or to the lowest animals, Lamarck concluded that their evolution was conditioned by the direct effects of the environment. He was therefore unable to provide a unitary theory of evolution.

These views led contemporary scientists to reject them, and with them the theory of transmutation. Even Étienne Geoffroy-Saint-Hilaire, who accepted the transmutation of species, regretted that by his speculations Lamarck had compromised it. Scientists like Baron Georges Cuvier who rejected transmutation were even more opposed to Lamarck. It is, however, only fair to say that Lamarck has been treated with less than justice by history, for his name is associated with a hypothetic cause of evolution that he did not invent and that is unacceptable, whereas it was his genius in proposing a scheme of evolution that deserves commemoration in the term Lamarckism.

As a result of his extensive researches in comparative anatomy and palaeontology published in 1812, Cuvier was struck by the fact that in the rocks of the Paris basin some strata contained fossils of marine animals, others fossils of freshwater animals, and others again no fossils at all. From the apparently sudden appearance and equally sudden disappearance of these remains of bygone life, Cuvier concluded that catastrophes similar to the Biblical Flood had repeatedly destroyed life, and that after each catastrophe it had blossomed out afresh through successive creations and immigrations of such organisms as had escaped destruction because they had previously lived elsewhere on earth, out of reach of that particular catastrophe. There had therefore been extensive extinction of species, which was a new concept involving the abandonment of some objects of creation to their melancholy fate by the Supreme Being. It was not many years since John Wesley, in 1770, had written, 'Death . . . is never permitted to destroy the most inconsiderable species,' and Thomas Jefferson, referring to fossil bones of the American mastodon, which he refused to regard as extinct, wrote, 'Such is the economy of nature, that no instance can be produced, of her having permitted any one race of her animals to become extinct; of her having formed any link in her great work, so weak as to be broken.'

It was also obvious to Cuvier that after each 'catastrophe' there was an advance in the complexity of life, so that each new wave of living beings showed a superiority of organization over their extinct predecessors. The younger the strata, the more fossils they contained belonging to animals similar to those living. A transcendental principle of progressionism had therefore to be invoked to account for this, since two reasons prevented him from accepting transmutation: the absence of any known intermediate forms, and the fact that organisms found in the oldest tombs of Egypt were identical with those still living and had therefore undergone no transmutation during the intervening period of time. Finally, Cuvier showed that the anatomical diversity exhibited by different groups of animals could not be accommodated on any single plan of structure undergoing progression from the simplest to the most complex. He therefore introduced the concept of four major groups or *embranchements* into which the Animal Kingdom was divided: Radiata (jellyfish, starfish), Articulata (worms, insects), Mollusca (snails, octopus), and Vertebrata. In other words, for the single scale of beings Cuvier substituted four plans of structure, which introduced the concept of divergence.

Another concept introduced by Cuvier was that of correlation of parts. His mastery of comparative anatomy enabled him to claim that 'the smallest fragment of bone, even the most apparently insignificant apophysis, possesses a fixed and determinate character, relative to the class, order, genus and species of the animal to which it belonged;

insomuch, that when we find merely the extremity of a well-preserved bone, we are able by careful examination, assisted by analogy and exact comparison, to determine the species to which it once belonged, as certainly as if we had the entire animal before us.' Cuvier was in fact remarkably successful in this.

The different organs of an animal all collaborate to adapt it to its 'conditions of existence'. The carnivore has sharp claws and shearing teeth with which it catches, kills, tears to pieces, and chews its animal prey. Cattle have cloven hooves and grinding teeth with which they chew grass, and horns as defensive weapons. There is a well-known apocryphal story of jokers dressing up like devils and surprising Cuvier at night with the words, 'Cuvier, we are going to eat you,' to which Cuvier replied, 'Hooves, horns—herbivore—you can't.'

Cuvier's principle of correlation was, in fact, based on his recognition of the fact and importance of adaptation; organs serve functions that adapt the organisms to their environments or conditions of existence, and in his view, as in that of many of his contemporaries, this fact of adaptation was evidence of purpose or of final causes: organisms had been created with their organs as they are in order that they might exploit their several ways of life and enjoy their environments. Teleology had been introduced into the details of anatomy and physiology.

To the geologist Charles Lyell, Cuvier's theories of catastrophism and progressionism were unacceptable, first because Lyell's observations and researches had convinced him that the geological agents that were to be seen operating in the present could, given sufficient time, have caused everything that had happened in the past history of the earth. This was the principle of uniformitarianism, first introduced by James Hutton in 1785 and developed independently by Lyell in his *Principles of Geology* (1830) to a point where it could not fail to prevail over the speculations of catastrophism. Lyell's objection to progressionism was due partly to its association with catastrophism and partly to his opinion that the palaeontological evidence obtainable from the fossil record as known in his day was insufficient to support progressionism. Dicotyledonous plants, the highest types of the vegetable kingdom, had been found in coal measures of the Carboniferous period, and mammals in Secondary strata. Lyell therefore rejected progressionism and, with it, Lamarck's theory of transmutation, all the more because 'if we look for some of those essential changes which would be required to lend even the semblance of a foundation for the theory of Lamarck, respecting the growth of new organs and the gradual obliteration of others, we find nothing of the kind.' In his view, the theory lacked evidence, no intermediate forms were known, he thought it extravagant to claim that organisms could vary sufficiently to account for the differences between species, and the notion that when organs were needed they arose, removed the problem out of the realm of science into that of fanciful speculation. It must be added that Lamarck's inclusion of man in his scheme of evolution could not fail to disturb Lyell, for he was not yet prepared to contemplate unorthodox opinion where man was concerned, notwithstanding his scientific approach and rejection of scriptural interpretation in problems of geology. The result was that Lyell accepted the fact that species could become extinct, as a result of failure in the struggle for existence, and he knew that extinct species had been replaced by other species, but as to how this occurred and by what process fresh species originated, he had nothing to offer.

The problem of the origination of fresh species had, however, to be answered somehow, and the inability of the uniformitarian view to provide an answer drove its critics to adopt the only alternative known to them, namely miraculous interposition by the Creator. In his review of

Lyell's *Principles of Geology*, William Whewell could only regard the appearance of new forms of life as 'a distinct manifestation of creative power transcending the known laws of nature'. Although William Buckland did not believe it possible to reconcile geology with Genesis, he nevertheless asserted that the appearance of new forms of life was ascribable only to the direct intervention of the Creator. The curious situation had been achieved that in the early decades of the nineteenth century, men of science felt obliged to have recourse to miracles which they admitted being unable to understand, in order to account for natural phenomena.

While Lyell's views involved no such extravagances to explain the structure of the earth's crust, they involved other consequences from his rejection of progressionism. This led him not only to deny that there had been improvement in the structure and level of organization of living organisms since the beginning, but also to assert that geological agents had merely rung minor changes on a permanent pattern of events. These agents had always been the same and the products of the action had been the same; there had been elevation and subsidence of land, erosion and deposition of sediment, earthquakes and volcanoes; but Lyell believed that nothing else had ever happened, the earth had never been molten, there had never been a primitive lifeless condition, there had been 'no inconsistency in the general condition of our planet, such as is assumed in the hypothesis of its passage from a chaotic to a fixed, stable, and perfect state.' There had been only endless repetition without progress, and variation about a mean. It was inevitable that such a view must come into conflict with new discoveries not only in the realm of living beings but also in that of inorganic nature and the physical universe. Cases in point were the nebular hypothesis by which Laplace sought to give an explanation of the origin of the solar system that involved considerable transformation, and problems connected with the future condition of the sun.

Nevertheless, the magnitude of the services that Lyell rendered to geology may be gauged from the extent to which his British contemporaries regarded geology as a handmaid to theology, for they were little more than speculators on *a priori* grounds and amateur observers who considered their prime duty to lie along the path of reconciliation between the book of Genesis and what they could make of the crust of the earth. Geology in Britain was the exegesis of the Creation and of the Flood, interpreted in the light of Bishop Usher's chronology, with the ocean as the chief agent of geological changes brought about by catastrophic inundations. Indeed, the Flood has a great deal to answer for in the history of geology, for it focused so much attention on the origin of sedimentary strata by deposition under water that even igneous rocks like granite were regarded as of aqueous origin by the majority of geologists, who belonged to the 'Neptunist' school. The true method of origin of igneous rocks, as a result of the action of heat, had been recognized by a few geologists such as Nicolas Desmarest, Jean-Étienne Guettard, Rudolf Erich Raspe, James Hutton, and Lyell, but these exponents of the 'Vulcanist' school had a hard furrow to hoe before their views prevailed. Meanwhile, in the first thirty years of the nineteenth century, William Buckland, Adam Sedgwick, and William Conybeare, the three leading British geologists, whose observations and descriptions of various geological formations were of great value, all believed that the principle of uniformitarianism as advocated by Hutton and by Lyell was unacceptable because contrary to the tenets of religion and morality.

Geologists were not alone in these contentions. Natural history in Britain during the twenties and thirties of the nineteenth century was bedevilled by what can only be described as a hallucination that seriously hampered its progress. This was the quinarian theory advanced by William Sharp MacLeay, a mystical system of classification of animals built on the supposition that at all levels the animal kingdom is based on five groups arranged in a circle, each with 'relations of analogy' to neighbouring circles, each containing five sub-groups arranged in comparable manner, and so on, composing 'the whole province of zoology'. For instance, in the circle Annulosa, one of the five groups was Crustacea, of which the sub-group Decapoda (lobsters) has 'relations of analogy' with the sub-group Araneida of the neighbouring group Arachnida, while the latter's sub-group Acaridea (mites) has 'relations of analogy' with the sub-group Diptera (flies) of the neighbouring group Insecta. William Swainson applied this fantastic principle to birds and mammals, classifying each into five groups with 'relations of analogy' to each other: birds of prey with carnivores, penguins with whales. Presently Edward Newman improved on this system by substituting the number seven for five as the basis of natural history because God rested on the seventh day, Noah took seven clean animals into the Ark, there were seven plagues, seven years of famine, seven years of plenty, seven golden candlesticks, seven churches, seven angels, seven spirits of God. 'Most groups of animals with which we are tolerably acquainted are divisible into seven; we shall never find the number greater, and when less, we shall invariably perceive that the deficiency exists in groups of which our knowledge is particularly limited.' There would be no need to make mention of such abject nonsense were it not that these notions passed as 'science' and were current: the theory of evolution had to triumph over them also.

So far in this study, attention has been confined to scientists and philosophers. In order to appreciate the importance of later events in the history of evolution, it is now necessary to turn back a few years to consider the works of a sociologist and a theologian, published during the early years of the French Revolution. Far more than a purely political upheaval, that great crisis in human history provided opportunities for the application and, for all that anyone then knew, possibly for the fulfilment of some of the speculations of the *philosophes*, including Jean-Jacques Rousseau, concerning the perfectibility of man, in itself an evolutionary concept. This was the burden of Antoine-Nicolas de Condorcet's work, translated into English in 1795 under the title *Sketch for a Historical Picture of the Progress of the Human Mind*, in which he enumerated nine epochs in the history of man, from the pastoral state to that of Liberty, Equality, and Fraternity that the Revolution had achieved, each marked by the shedding of a moral, social, or theological prejudice that had hampered its advance, which depended on the abolition of inequality between peoples, classes, and the sexes, and on the spread of education for all and the progress of science. Similar ideas had already reached England and been propagated by William Godwin in his *Enquiry concerning Political Justice* published in 1793.

In this manner the subversive ideals of progress established a bridgehead in Britain, where, like that other notion evolution, brewed out of the witches' cauldron of the French Revolution, they were rejected with increasing horror and revulsion as the guillotine continued to drop. Willynilly, the theory of evolution was tinged with political overtones that still persist. Then, they resulted in the writing of two books that had profound though unexpected effects on the future of natural history. On the sociological plane, a valiant attempt to stem the tide of the French ungodly was made by Thomas Robert Malthus with his *Essay on Population*, while on the theological side William Paley set out in his *Natural Theology* to prove that the study of natural history inevitably led to belief in a divine Creator.

When Malthus was barely a week old, his father received a visit from his friend and idol Jean-Jacques Rousseau, who was then looking for a house in Surrey. The principles advocated by Rousseau, Condorcet, and Godwin became a bone of contention between Malthus's father, who defended them, and Malthus, who execrated them. The result was the *Essay on Population*, first published in 1798, in which Malthus took up ideas put forward by Sir William Petty, Benjamin Franklin, Robert Wallace, and others, and generalized the principle that 'Population, when unchecked, increases in a geometrical ratio. Subsistence increases only in an arithmetical ratio. . . . I can see no way by which man can escape from the weight of this law which pervades all animate nature.' Unwittingly, no doubt, Malthus here placed man on the same plane as the rest of the animal kingdom. Among plants and animals the growth of population was kept down by mortality due to 'want of room and nourishment' and falling a prey to predators. In man, if in spite of famines and epidemics and the preventive checks imposed by reason, population nevertheless increased too fast, those of its members who could least afford the necessities of life were doomed to misery and death. On the other hand, if the checks to the increase in numbers of a population through delayed marriage and abstinence were artificial and too effective, there would be no competition or compulsion to work exerted on those whose livelihood depended on it, and the results would equally be misery from the effects of immorality, idleness, and sloth.

It followed, as H. N. Brailsford has pointed out, that all attempts to preserve life were contrary to the correct application of principle, charity was an economic sin, altruism 'unscientific', and presumably the medical profession pursued an anti-social aim. Since the possibilities of variation, shown by cultivated plants and domestic animals, were in Malthus's view strictly limited, progress was impossible; attempts to achieve it as in the French Revolution were doomed to failure; and mankind could neither improve nor be perfected. Malthus's book was reprinted several times and the main lines of evidence on which his argument rested were on his own admission more and more undermined, but he nevertheless stuck to the slogan-like antithesis between geometrical and arithmetical rates of increase for growth of population and of subsistence. In this, Malthus performed a service to science, because most of those of his contemporaries who were aware of the struggle for existence in nature ran away from the horrors of tooth and claw and tried to veil it, minimize it, or moralize on the greater resulting happiness for the survivors. As will be seen, this aspect of Malthus's work had far-reaching effects.

Among Malthus's adherents was William Paley, who based his *Natural Theology* (1802) on the argument that a contrivance implies a contriver, just as a design implies a designer, and illustrated this analogy by means of a watch. Passing from horology to natural history he pointed out that the lens of the eye in fishes is more spherical than that of the eye of land vertebrates, which showed that each eye is *adapted* to the refractive index of the medium, water or air, in which the animal lives. 'What plainer manifestation of design can there be than this instance?' he asked. The function of the iris diaphragm, accommodation for distance, the fact that the blind spots of the two eyes of an individual are not at conjugate points on the retina, that the eyebrow and eyelid protect the eye, all pointed to intelligent construction: 'it is only by the display of contrivance, that the existence, the agency, the wisdom, of the Deity *could* be testified to his rational creatures.' The same argument applied to the ear and to the function of all organs and tissues: down-feathers for warmth, flight-feathers for flight, webbed feet for progression in water, poison-fangs for defence in snakes, pouches for containing the young in marsupials, the long tongue of the woodpecker for catching grubs, the complicated life-history of mistletoe. Some adaptations are even anticipatory, such as migration in birds, a contrivance to avoid and survive a cold season that has not yet arrived, or the foramen ovale and ductus arteriosus of the mammalian embryo, which enable it to switch instantly at birth from the intra-uterine to the aerial type of respiration and blood-circulation. All these were adaptations and Paley summed them up with the words: 'The marks of *design* are too strong to be gotten over. Design must have had a designer. That designer must have been a person. That person is God.' A century earlier, Bernard Nieuwentyt had also concluded that the marvels of Nature proved the existence of God.

With clear reference to the First Commandment, Paley notices that however diversified the products of creation may be, they never 'indicate that we are come into the province of a different Creator. . . . I think, no difference has been discovered in the properties of *blood*, from whatever animal it be drawn,' a very unfortunate excursion into haematology. He also saw design in the relations of men and animals to the physical world, such as the alternation of night and day and the adaptation of sleep to night: 'It is happy therefore that for this part of creation [human beings], I mean that it is conformable to the frame of their constitution, that nature by the very disposition of her elements, has commanded, as it were, and imposed on them, at moderate intervals, a general intermission of their toils, their occupations, their pursuits.'

Paley's work serves as a catalogue of adaptations, some very far-fetched but many genuine, and as he had drawn attention to these and used the analogy of the watchmaker to argue that they could only be the result of design by an intelligent and benevolent designer, it was also natural that he should regard them as evidence of purpose and of final causes. Whatever they may be regarded as due to, the *facts* of adaptation remain, although there was one important respect in which Paley's descriptions of them were to need correction in the light of later research. Paley regarded the adaptations shown by plants and animals to their environments as perfect; indeed from his theological point of view it would have been sacrilege to have concluded otherwise. As for the significance to be accorded to adaptations, while it was and remains true that organs that enable organisms to be adapted to their environments are useful to them, and therefore purposeful, it did not follow that for that reason they were evidence for design or final causes, a point of philosophy to which David Hume had drawn attention some decades previously when he showed that the existence of order in the universe and of adaptations in animals could not be used to justify any inference on how that order and those adaptations had come into existence.

But although he had no valid argument to oppose to Hume's philosophy, Paley had a very cogent reason for opposition, for he correctly appreciated that the only possible alternative to design was fortuitousness or chance, at which he levelled his heaviest broadsides. Diderot had contended that the whole universe, including life and man, had originated from fortuitous events: another example of the ungodly views of French philosophes. Buffon's theory of the origin of the solar system from a chance collision between the sun and a comet came in for special attack: 'Beside that this is to attribute to chance the fortunate concurrence and velocity and direction [of rotation of the planets] which we have been here noticing, the hypothesis, as I apprehend, is inconsistent with the physical laws by which the heavenly motions are governed. If the planets were struck off from the surface of the sun they would return to the surface of the sun again.' In short, the solar system 'requires an intelligent interposition, because it can be demonstrated concerning it, that it requires an adjustment of force, distance, direction, and velocity, out of the reach of chance to have produced.'

It is in the treatment of the problem of suffering that Paley had the greatest difficulty in making his case. 'Pain, no doubt, and privations exist . . . Evil, no doubt, exists; but it is never, that we can perceive, the *object* of contrivance. Teeth are contrived to eat, not to ache.' The 'aches' caused in what teeth kill and eat are ignored, although the undeniable carnage of nature forces Paley to admit that 'We cannot avoid the difficulty by saying that the effect was not intended. The only question open to us is whether it be ultimately evil. From the confessed and felt imperfection of our knowledge, we ought to presume that there may be consequences of this economy which are hidden from us,' a form of argument that will be met again in very different circumstances. In an attempt to minimize the horror of the war of nature, he continues, 'I believe the cases of bites which produce death in large animals (of stings I think there are none) to be very few.'

Again, 'Pain also itself is not without its *alleviations*. It may be violent and frequent; but it is seldom violent and long-continued; and its pauses and intermissions become positive pleasures. Of *mortal* diseases the great use is to reconcile us to death.' In any case, by Malthus's principle, death is necessary to prevent over-population, and therefore beneficial. In compensation, 'The Deity has superadded *pleasure* to animal sensations, beyond what was necessary for any purpose . . . it is a happy world after all.' Then, as a parting shot, 'The appearance of chance will always bear a proportion to the ignorance of the observer,' with which Paley was confident that he had defended his religion and confounded the infidel. When Shelley was expelled from Oxford for publishing a pamphlet on *The Necessity of Atheism*, his father could think of no more potent remedy for his son than 'Paley's Natural Theology' which, as he wrote to John Hogg, 'I shall recommend my Young Man to read.' Shelley's reaction to this proposed treatment is to be found in the Preface to *Prometheus Unbound*: 'I had rather be damned with Plato and Lord Bacon, than go to Heaven with Paley and Malthus.'

What Paley had, in fact, done was to provide a catalogue of adaptations that was shortly to come in very useful, and this is why it has been necessary to allot to Paley, as to Malthus, more space than would be justified by the intrinsic merits of their special pleading masquerading as science. Furthermore, Paley's works, which were prescribed reading in British universities for many years, represent the prevailing points of view and attitudes of mind that had to be overcome by hard scientific evidence before the theory of evolution could be established, and, by an astonishing irony of history, his and Malthus's works unwittingly contributed more than any other publications to the establishment of that theory.

Such were the tides, currents, and backwaters of thought when on 27 December 1831 H.M.S. *Beagle* set sail from Plymouth.

Chapter 2

Enter Darwin

H.M.S. *Beagle*, third of the name in the Royal Navy, a ten-gun sloop-brig of 235 tons, 90 feet long and 24 feet 8 inches beam, was built at Woolwich and launched on 11 May 1820. In the service of the Hydrographer of the Navy she made a voyage to South American waters surveying the coast of Tierra del Fuego and the Straits of Magellan from 1826 to 1830, during the last two years of which she was commanded by Captain Robert FitzRoy R.N. Grandson of the third Duke of Grafton and nephew of Viscount Castlereagh, FitzRoy was no ordinary naval officer. Imbued with the most deeply ingrained sense of duty and zeal to be of help to his fellow men, his life was devoted to a number of causes serviceable to mankind and of value to posterity which, unfortunately, has failed to associate his name with them. For example, it was in the *Beagle* under FitzRoy that the expression 'port' was substituted for 'larboard' to assist mariners because larboard was so easily confused with starboard. FitzRoy instituted a system of weather forecasts and storm warnings that persists, and he became head of the Meteorological Office; he was secretary of the Lifeboat Institution, which provided great scope for his activities, and it was he who drafted the Merchant Navy Act. As Governor of New Zealand, however, he was less successful because his personality was too forceful and uncompromising to accommodate itself to a civilian administration.

During the first voyage of the *Beagle* a curious circumstance occurred that involved consequences out of all proportion to its importance. The natives of Tierra del Fuego had stolen one of the ship's boats, and as a punishment, FitzRoy had taken two of the savages on board as hostages for the return of the boat. Later, two more Fuegians came on board, but the work of surveying the channels had taken the *Beagle* away from the shores inhabited by the tribes to which these savages belonged and towards a district inhabited by different and hostile tribes who would without any doubt have murdered FitzRoy's four Fuegians had he put them on shore there. As FitzRoy was unable to turn back again, he determined to take the Fuegians to England with him in the *Beagle*, with the intention of having them taught the elements of Christianity and the use of tools at his own expense. By this means he hoped to make the fate of any mariners who might be shipwrecked less precarious if they should have the misfortune to be cast up on the shores where these cannibals lived.

At the same time, FitzRoy found another outlet for his humanistic zeal that is best expressed in his own words, written in 1830: 'There may be metal in many of the Fuegian mountains, and I much regret that no person in the vessel was skilled in mineralogy, or at all acquainted with geology. It is a pity that so good an opportunity of ascertaining the nature of the rocks and earths of these regions should have been almost lost. I could not avoid often thinking of the talent and experience required for such scientific researches, of which we were wholly destitute; and inwardly resolving that if ever I left England again on a similar expedition, I would endeavour to carry out a person qualified to examine the land; while the officers and myself would attend to hydrography.' It should be added, that in the spirit of the Bridgewater Treatises, then in course of publication, on the 'Power, Wisdom, and Goodness of God, as manifested in the

Creation,' FitzRoy expected and intended that his naturalist should provide further evidence to confute the geological sceptics who impugned the strict and literal truth of every statement contained in the Bible.

When he had got his Fuegians back to England, FitzRoy had them vaccinated, from the effects of which one of them died, but the others, who were called Jemmy Button, York Minster, and Fuegia Basket, made good progress with their rehabilitation as human beings and were received in audience by William IV and Queen Adelaide. The problem then presented itself of returning them to their homes, where they were expected to spread the benefits of the training, both moral and social, that they had received. FitzRoy even contemplated taking a ship at his own expense to repatriate them, when he was commissioned to command the *Beagle* again on a new voyage to survey the coasts of Patagonia, Tierra del Fuego, Chile, and Peru, to visit some Pacific islands, and to carry a chain of chronometrical stations round the world. True to his resolution to take a naturalist with him, FitzRoy made the appropriate request to the Hydrographer of the Navy, Captain Francis Beaufort R.N., whose name is commemorated in the Beaufort scale of wind strengths. The files of the Admiralty contain the following letter referring to FitzRoy's request:

1 September 1831

Captain FitzRoy

My dear Sir, I believe my friend Mr Peacock of Trinity College Cambridge has succeeded in getting a 'Savant' for you—a Mr Darwin grandson of the well known philosopher and poet—full of zeal and enterprize and having contemplated a voyage on his own account to S. America. Let me know how you like the idea that I may go or recede in time.

Francis Beaufort.

Darwin had entered on the scene.

Charles Darwin was born on 9 February 1809 at Shrewsbury, the second son and fifth of the six children of Dr Robert Darwin and Susannah Wedgwood. Darwin's father, a successful physician and formidable character, was the son of Erasmus Darwin, already mentioned as author of *Zoönomia*. Darwin's mother was the daughter of Josiah Wedgwood the celebrated potter. She died when he was eight years old and his home upbringing devolved largely on his elder sisters to whom, in spite of their persistent fault-finding, he was ever grateful, as he said, for instilling in him the spirit of humanity. In 1817 he was sent to a day-school in Shrewsbury kept by a Unitarian, Mr Case, where he was found to be slower at learning than his younger sister Catherine, which is not without its importance because Darwin was a striking example of the fact that in educational matters the race is not always to the swift; he was an outstanding late developer. He had, however, already acquired a taste for natural history and started to collect pebbles, plants, birds' eggs, shells, and minerals. After reading Gilbert White's *Natural History of Selborne* he could not understand why every gentleman did not become an ornithologist. His powers of imagination were already well developed, and in addition to childish fibs, he invented a bogus story that he was able to produce variations in crocuses, polyanthuses, and primroses at will, by watering them with coloured liquids, which was of course, as he admitted, 'a monstrous fable,' but also shows that he was not unaware of variation, even at that age.

In summer 1818 he was sent to Shrewsbury School, the headmaster of which was then Dr Samuel Butler, grandfather of the author of *Erewhon*, with whom Darwin was later to come into contact. Darwin remained at Shrewsbury until the summer of 1825. He was taught nothing but classics, a little ancient history, and geography. 'The school as a means of education to me was simply a blank,' he afterwards said. His elder brother Erasmus was interested in chemistry and had improvised a laboratory in a tool shed at their father's home, where Darwin helped him to prepare various substances. Because of this, he was publicly rebuked by the headmaster for wasting his time on such useless subjects, and his father upbraided him with the words, 'You care for nothing but shooting, dogs, and rat-catching, and you will be a disgrace to yourself and all your family.' He took him away from Shrewsbury and sent him to Edinburgh University to study medicine. Darwin had already started attending on poor persons in Shrewsbury and noting their symptoms which he read out to his father who prescribed for them, Darwin making up their medicines himself.

At Edinburgh Darwin signed the matriculation register on 22 October 1825, and with his brother Erasmus, who was already at the university, took rooms at 11 Lothian Street at twenty-six shillings a week. His age was 16 years and 8 months. He attended courses of lectures on materia medica, dietetics, and pharmacy given by Andrew Duncan, on chemistry and pharmacy by Thomas Charles Hope, and on anatomy, physiology, and pathology by Alexander Monro, clinical lectures by Dr Graham and Dr Alison, and principles and practice of surgery by Alexander Monro. The lectures he found 'incredibly dull with the exception of those on chemistry by Hope.' Materia medica left on his mind nothing but the memory of 'cold breakfastless hours on the properties of rhubarb', at eight o'clock on a winter's morning 'something fearful to remember'. Two bad operations that he witnessed, of course before the days of anaesthetics, nauseated him to such an extent that he rushed away before they were completed. A good indication of Darwin's general interests can be obtained from the titles of the books that he borrowed from the University Library during this session. They included Young's *Philosophy*, Fleming's *Philosophy of Zoology*, Kerr and

Foster's *Entomology*, Wood's *Insects*, Brookes's *Conchology*, Newton's *Opticks*, and Boswell's *Life of Johnson*. During the summer vacation he went on a long walking tour in North Wales when he climbed Snowdon and indulged in his favourite sport of shooting.

In the following session at Edinburgh, whither he had returned without his brother, Darwin signed the matriculation register on 10 November 1826, and was entered for courses in the practice of physic and midwifery, and in natural history including zoology and geology given by Robert Jameson. Jameson had studied in Germany under Abraham Gottlob Werner at the Freiberg School of Mines, and had adopted his master's view that all rocks of the earth's crust had been formed by deposition under water, for which reason Werner and his followers were known as 'Neptunists', in contrast to the 'Vulcanists' who attributed the origin of rocks like basalt and granite to the action of heat and extrusion onto the surface, or intrusion beneath the surface, in a molten state (see page 12). Jameson brought the Wernerian theories to Britain and, at the time when Darwin knew him, defended them stoutly although at a later date he abandoned them for the views of Hutton. A famous teacher, Jameson attracted many pupils and fired their enthusiasm, but he failed to do so with Darwin who attended his courses on geology, on the natural history of man, and, perhaps ominously, on the origin of the species of mammals. Darwin found Jameson's teaching so distressingly dull that he made a resolution never as long as he lived to read a book on geology or in any way to study that science. It will be seen how he kept that resolution.

More important for Darwin was his membership of the Plinian Society in which he took an active part. Its secretary was Robert Edmund Grant. On 26 December 1826 Darwin commented on W. A. F. Browne's paper on the natural history of the cuckoo, on 16 January 1827 on

W. F. Ainsworth's paper on principles of natural classification, and on 13 March he took part in a discussion on observations on the milky appearance of some spots of water in the Red Sea. From these unofficial activities, the directions of Darwin's interests were already clear. He used to go out with fishermen dredging in the Firth of Forth and became acquainted with methods of catching marine animals. On 16 March he caught a lumpsucker fish that he dissected with great care and entered into considerable detail in its anatomy. On 18 March he got some hydroid polyps and sea slugs, and on the 19th he obtained specimens of the polyzoon *Flustra* with its eggs. On examining these under the microscope he saw that they had the power of independent movement by means of cilia and were in fact larvae. In great excitement at this observation he rushed to announce it to Grant, and it was with astonishment and dismay that he heard Grant reproach him for working on his subject, saying that he would take it ill if he published his findings, a rebuke that made a deep and lasting impression on Darwin. It was the first time that he had experience of a scientist staking out his claim for priority. Grant read a paper 'regarding the anatomy and mode of generation of Flustrae' to the Wernerian Natural History Society of Edinburgh on 24 March 1827, while Darwin communicated to the Plinian Society on 27 March 'two discoveries that he had made: 1. that the ova of *Flustra* possess organs of motion. 2. that the small black globular body hitherto mistaken for the young *Fucus loreus* [seaweed] is in reality the ovum of *Pontobdella muricata* [leech]', but he did not publish them.

The little tiff with Darwin does not seem to have left any bitter feelings with Grant for he mentioned Darwin when he published his observations on *Pontobdella* in the *Edinburgh Journal of Science*, and he took him to the Wernerian Society where he heard John James Audubon lecture. Darwin also attended a meeting of the Royal Society of Edinburgh and saw its first president, Sir Walter Scott, in the chair. Grant had studied natural history in Paris where Lamarck was still alive, and one day when walking with Darwin, Grant burst forth in high admiration of Lamarck and of his views on evolution. Darwin listened 'in silent astonishment, and as far as I can judge, without any effect on my mind. I had previously read the *Zoönomia* of my grandfather, in which similar views are maintained, but without producing any effects on me. Nevertheless it is probable that the hearing rather early in life such views maintained and praised may have favoured my upholding them in a different form in my *Origin of Species*.'

Two other acquaintances that Darwin made in Edinburgh were significant for his future career: William McGillivray who was keeper of the Royal College of Surgeons' Museum in Edinburgh and had published a book on the birds of Scotland, and a negro taxidermist who had accompanied Charles Waterton on his journeys in South America and now taught Darwin how to prepare and mount skins of birds. But Darwin had also learnt that his father would leave him property enough to subsist on with comfort, and this thought was sufficient to check any strenuous effort to learn medicine, to which he had an aversion. At the same time his father realized that Darwin did not relish the prospect of practising medicine and proposed instead that he should take holy orders in the Church of England. Darwin asked for time to consider this proposal as he had scruples about accepting all the Thirty-nine Articles, but he soon became persuaded that they must be accepted. Indeed, at this time in his life, he felt so convinced of the truth of his religion that he 'found himself inventing day-dreams of old letters between distinguished Romans and manuscripts being discovered at Pompeii or elsewhere which confirmed in the most striking manner all that was written in the Gospels', which is further evidence of his powers of imagination.

The change of plan for Darwin's career necessitated a change of university also, because candidates for ordination in the Church of England were required to take a degree at one of the two English universities, and Darwin left Edinburgh in late April 1827. In the following month his uncle Josiah Wedgwood went to London and thence to Paris with the intention of fetching his daughters Frances and Emma back from Geneva where they had been staying with their aunt Jessie de Sismondi, wife of the historian. Darwin accompanied him but went no further than Paris and returned, the only occasion when he set foot on the continent of Europe.

Darwin was admitted to Christ's College, Cambridge on 15 October 1827 but did not go into residence before Christmas because he found to his dismay that he had actually forgotten, incredible as it may appear, almost everything which he had learnt, even to some few of the Greek letters, so that between October and Christmas he was with a private tutor at Shrewsbury. At Christ's College he was with his brother Erasmus and his cousin William Darwin Fox who introduced him to the pleasures of entomology. He had to attend a few lectures on classics, algebra, and Euclid: 'I attempted mathematics . . . but I got on very slowly. The work was repugnant to me, chiefly from my not being able to see any meaning in the early steps in algebra. This impatience was very foolish, and in after years I have deeply regretted that I did not proceed far enough at least to understand something of the great leading principles of mathematics; for men thus endowed seem to have an extra sense.' He also had to study Paley's works, which delighted him by their logic. 'I did not at that time trouble myself about Paley's premises; and taking these on trust I was charmed and convinced by the long line of argumentation.'

All in all, however, Darwin considered the three years that he spent at Cambridge 'wasted as far as the academical studies were concerned, as completely as at Edinburgh and at school.' His greatest pleasure was collecting beetles for the sheer joy of collecting; he liked listening to music although he had no ear, and he appreciated looking at pictures. His passion for shooting and hunting led him to associate with a set of sporting young men of high spirits, a companionship to which he afterwards looked back with pleasure, but he also met a number of men of higher calibre, foremost among whom was John Stevens Henslow, professor of botany, who kept open house and provided opportunities for undergraduates to meet men of distinction in many fields, including William Whewell, Leonard Jenyns, and Adam Sedgwick. Henslow also introduced Darwin to botany. One day when Darwin was examining some pollen-grains he saw the pollen-tubes being extruded and instantly he rushed to tell Henslow of his surprising discovery. This time he was not reproached as he had been at Edinburgh by Grant. Instead, Henslow very kindly explained to him what the extrusion of pollen-tubes meant and equally gently let him understand how well known this phenomenon was, 'so I left him not in the least mortified, but well pleased at having discovered for myself so remarkable a fact, but determined not to be in such a hurry again to communicate my discoveries.' This was a lesson that he learnt almost too well.

After passing his examination in January 1831 when he was placed tenth in the list of candidates who did not seek honours, Darwin still had two terms of residence to put in, and on Henslow's advice he went back on the resolution that he had made in Edinburgh and studied geology. He had recently read Humboldt's *Personal Narrative of Travels* and John Herschel's *Introduction to the Study of Natural Philosophy*, from both of which he had derived such a zeal to travel and study natural history that he copied out long passages from Humboldt and seriously contemplated making a journey to Tenerife, inquired about ships, and learnt Spanish. At home at Shrewsbury he practised making observations with a clinometer on tables that he had tilted at different angles in his room, and was soon 'working like a tiger' at geological maps and going out with clinometer and hammer to pursue his studies in the field. 'As yet I have only indulged in hypotheses, but they are such powerful ones that I suppose, if they were put into action for one day, the World would come to an end,' from which it appears that Darwin was then a catastrophist.

In the summer of 1831 Darwin accompanied Sedgwick on a geological excursion in North Wales, when an incident occurred that made a deep impression on him. Darwin had learnt that a shell of the tropical mollusc *Voluta* had been found in a gravel-pit near Shrewsbury, and he expected that Sedgwick would be delighted at 'so wonderful a fact as a tropical shell being found near the surface in England'. To Darwin's astonishment Sedgwick said that if the shell really had been embedded in the gravel-pit, 'it would be the greatest misfortune to geology, as it would overthrow all that we know about the superficial deposits of the midland counties' of England. The gravel-pit was a glacial deposit, and nothing before had made Darwin realize that 'science consists in grouping facts so that general laws or conclusions may be drawn from them', a lesson that he put to good use.

On 29 August 1831 Darwin returned to Shrewsbury and found letters from Henslow and Professor George Peacock telling him that Captain FitzRoy wanted to invite a young man to sail round the world with him in H.M.S. *Beagle* as naturalist, without pay. The post was offered to Darwin because Henslow himself and after him Leonard Jenyns had not felt able to accept it. Passages from Henslow's letter are worth quoting because they show what a competent judge's opinion of Darwin's merits was, at a time before he had had any opportunity of proving himself:

I have stated that I consider you to be the best qualified person I know of who is likely to undertake such a situation. I state this not in the supposition of your being a *finished* naturalist, but as amply qualified for collecting, observing, and noting, anything worthy to be noted in Natural History. . . . Captain FitzRoy wants a man (I understand) more as a companion than a mere collector and would not take anyone, however good a naturalist, who was not recommended to him likewise as a gentleman. . . . Don't put any modest doubts or fears about your disqualifications, for I assure you I think you are the very man they are in search of.

Darwin would have loved to accept this offer straight away, but his father had grave objections to his going, because if he sailed in the *Beagle* it would, he feared, be disreputable to his career as a clergyman; it was a wild, useless scheme certain to involve great discomfort in a bad ship, it was yet another change of plan in his career, and he would never settle down afterwards to a steady life. Accordingly on 30 August Darwin wrote to Henslow refusing the offer, and on the following day he went to stay with his uncle Josiah Wedgwood at Maer Hall to be in readiness for his beloved shooting on 1 September. Josiah Wedgwood took a different view from Darwin's father, and felt about it strongly enough to call Darwin back from his shooting and to return with him to Shrewsbury where he soon convinced Dr Darwin that his objections could and should be overcome: 'the pursuit of natural history, though certainly not professional is very suitable to a clergyman'. Dr Darwin gave his consent and Darwin wrote immediately to Professor Peacock and to Captain Beaufort reversing his letter of refusal to Henslow and accepting the offer.

On the following day, 2 September, he went to Cambridge to discuss details with Henslow. Whether or not he was to sail in the *Beagle* was a question that still hung perilously in the balance. While in Cambridge he learnt of a letter that a Mr Wood had received from FitzRoy, who was so much against Darwin's sailing that he and Henslow abandoned the scheme altogether. The reason for FitzRoy's opposition was apparently that he had already invited a Mr Chester to sail with him and share his cabin; but in London on 5 September Darwin met FitzRoy who took a better view of the matter because Chester could not come and there would be room in the *Beagle* for Darwin. FitzRoy advised him not to make up his mind yet, for all unknown to Darwin, there was yet another hurdle to be crossed—FitzRoy believed in Lavater's principles of physiognomy as a means of assessing character and had misgivings that the shape of Darwin's nose was not compatible with the energy and determination that he required in his naturalist to withstand the hardships that lay ahead. On 11 September FitzRoy and Darwin sailed from London to Plymouth to inspect the *Beagle*, during which journey FitzRoy must have been satisfied about the significance of Darwin's nose, because a few days later the anxious and uncomfortable days of uncertainty came to an end, and it was decided that Darwin would sail.

The next few weeks were occupied in preparations for the voyage. FitzRoy looked into every detail in the equipment for the expedition himself. The *Beagle* had been found to be in such bad condition after her last voyage that much woodwork had to be replaced. The upper deck was raised, which increased her safety in bad weather and raised her tonnage to 242. She was rigged as a barque, and Harris's new copper lightning conductors were fitted to her masts and yards. She carried twenty-six chronometers to effect the work of determining longitude, and the stores included anti-scorbutics for the crew, thousands of tins of preserved meats, vegetables, and soups, and an assortment of household articles including wine-glasses, tea-trays, mahogany sideboards, beaver hats, white linen, wash-basins, and chamber-pots with which to set up the Fuegians when they were landed on their native shore; such was the faith of England in the power of missionary work in the days of William IV. Darwin himself took a hand-lens, simple microscope, blowpipe and equipment for chemical analysis, clinometer, contact goniometer, mountain barometer, pocket compass, magnet, and a small library of books. This included the first volume of Lyell's *Principles of Geology* that Henslow advised him to take with him, but on no account to believe.

On 24 October 1831 Darwin joined the ship, but the date of departure was constantly delayed. 'These two months at Plymouth were the most miserable which I ever spent, though I exerted myself in various ways. I was out of spirits at the thought of leaving all my family and friends for so long a time, and the weather seemed to me inexpressibly gloomy. I was also troubled with palpitations about the heart, and like many a young ignorant man, specially one with a smattering of medical knowledge, was convinced that I had heart-disease. I did not consult any doctor as I fully expected to hear the verdict that I was not fit for the voyage, and I was resolved to go at all hazards.' On 10 December the ship put to sea in heavy weather but on the following day had to put back to Plymouth again. The same happened on 21 December when the *Beagle* struck a gale off the Lizard and again had to turn back. At last, on 27 December 1831, the *Beagle* made her way out to sea and a new chapter in the history of science began.

Chapter 3

The Voyage of the 'Beagle'

'Nobody who has only been to sea for 24 hours has a right to say that sea-sickness is even uncomfortable. The real misery only begins when you are so exhausted that a little exertion makes a feeling of faintness come on.' For ten days after leaving Plymouth, as the little *Beagle* pounded her way through heavy seas in the Bay of Biscay, Darwin was initiated into the way of life that was to be his for nearly five years and to carry him over forty thousand miles. For sea-sickness his only relief was to lie in his hammock, and as Poop-cabin which he shared with two other officers measured only fifteen feet by ten, and contained a chart-table ten feet by six, chart-lockers, bookshelves, and the drawers in which Darwin kept his clothes, instruments, and materials, he was able to say with truth, 'I have just room to turn round and that is all.' Being tall, he could only get the extra length that he needed to sling his hammock by taking out the uppermost drawer where he kept his clothes so as to fasten the foot-clews to the wall of the cabin behind it. During this trying period Captain FitzRoy showed what a good commander he was in the solicitude that he showed for his landlubber companion by coming to Darwin's cabin and arranging his hammock with his own hands. Darwin was 22, FitzRoy 26 years old.

On 6 January 1832, Darwin for the first time felt moderately recovered as the ship sailed into Santa Cruz harbour in Tenerife, and he looked forward eagerly to the

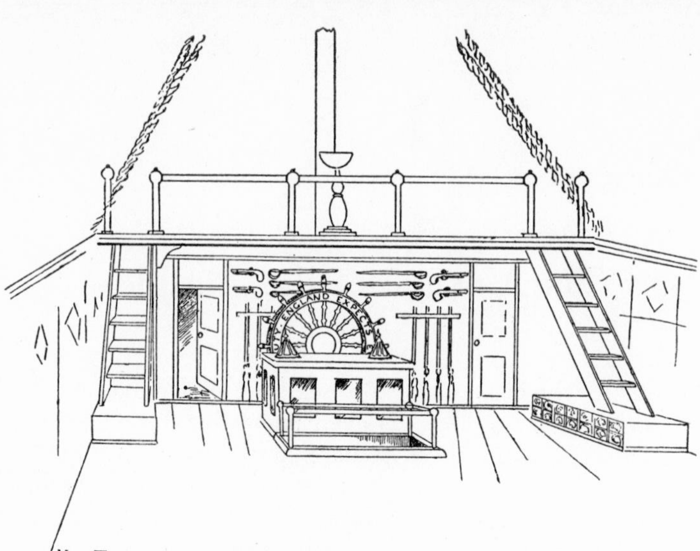

Note. The circle in centre of wheel was a drawing by Earle, the artist, of Neptune with his trident

H. M. S. Beagle's Quarter-deck

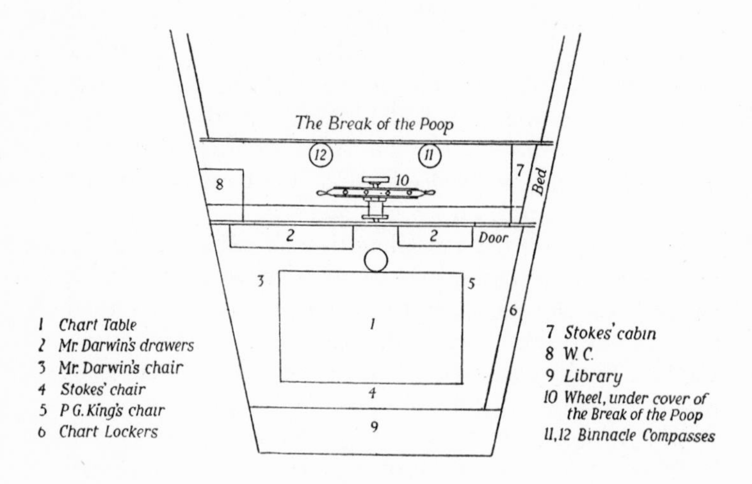

Poop Cabin

Fig. 1 These drawings of the Quarter-deck of H.M.S. *Beagle*, the plan of Poop Cabin, and the side elevation of the ship shown in Fig. 2, were made by Philip Gidley King, Darwin's shipmate.

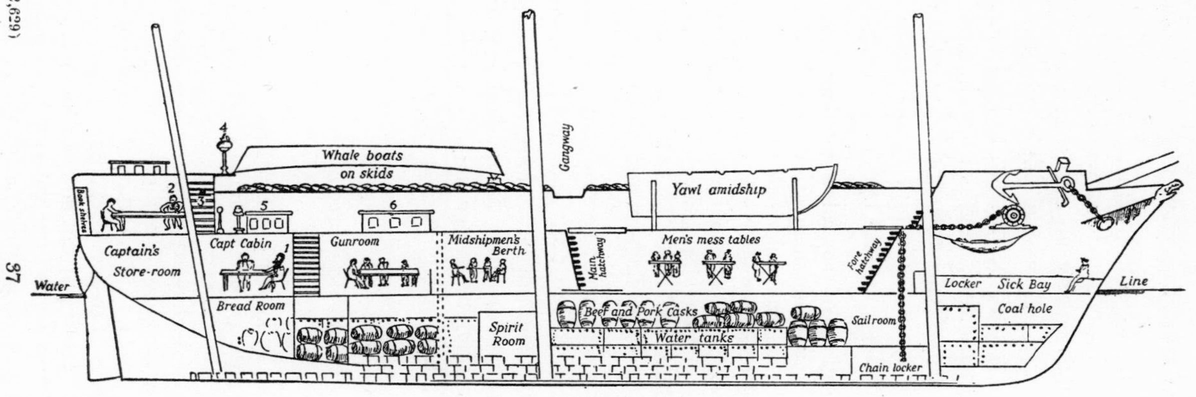

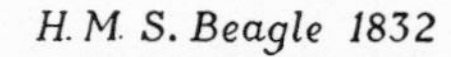

H. M. S. Beagle 1832

1 Mr. Darwin's seat in Captain's Cabin 2 Mr Darwin's seat in Poop Cabin 3 Mr. Darwin's drawers in Poop Cabin
4 Azimuth Compass 5 Captain's skylight 6 Gunroom skylight

Fig. 2 Side elevation of H.M.S. *Beagle.*

fulfilment of one of his fondest dreams, for Humboldt had described the Canary Islands and Darwin himself had only recently contemplated making an expedition to them on his own. Consternation fell on the ship's company when the local authorities refused permission to land unless the crew underwent quarantine, and disappointment was general. After a deathly silence the captain gave the order, 'Up jib', but ten days later compensation came when Darwin landed on S. Iago in the Cape Verde Islands.

Here I first saw the glory of tropical vegetation: Tamarinds, Bananas, and Palms were flourishing at my feet. I expected a good deal, for I had read Humboldt's descriptions, and I was afraid of disappointments: how utterly vain such fear is, none can tell but those who have experienced what I have today. . . . It has been for me a glorious day, like giving to a blind man eyes, he is overwhelmed with what he sees and cannot justly comprehend it. Such are my feelings, and such may they remain.

They did. It was not only what he saw that gave him this thrill that lasted for the rest of his life; he started to collect natural-history specimens, no longer as an amateur furtively wasting the time that his headmaster or his father considered should be better spent on some more worthy occupation, but openly as a publicly recognized duty.

From S. Iago the *Beagle* sped across the Atlantic to St Paul's Rocks and Fernando Noronha, where he enjoyed landing, before reaching Bahia.

I have been wandering by myself in a Brazilian forest: amongst the multitude it is hard to say what set of objects is most striking; the general luxuriance of the vegetation bears the victory, the elegance of the grasses, the novelty of the parasitical plants, the beauty of the flowers, the glossy green of the foliage, all tends to this end. A most paradoxical mixture of sound and silence pervades the shady parts of the wood: the noise from the insects is so loud that in the evening it can be heard even in a vessel anchored several hundred yards from the shore: yet within the recesses of the forest a universal stillness appears to reign.

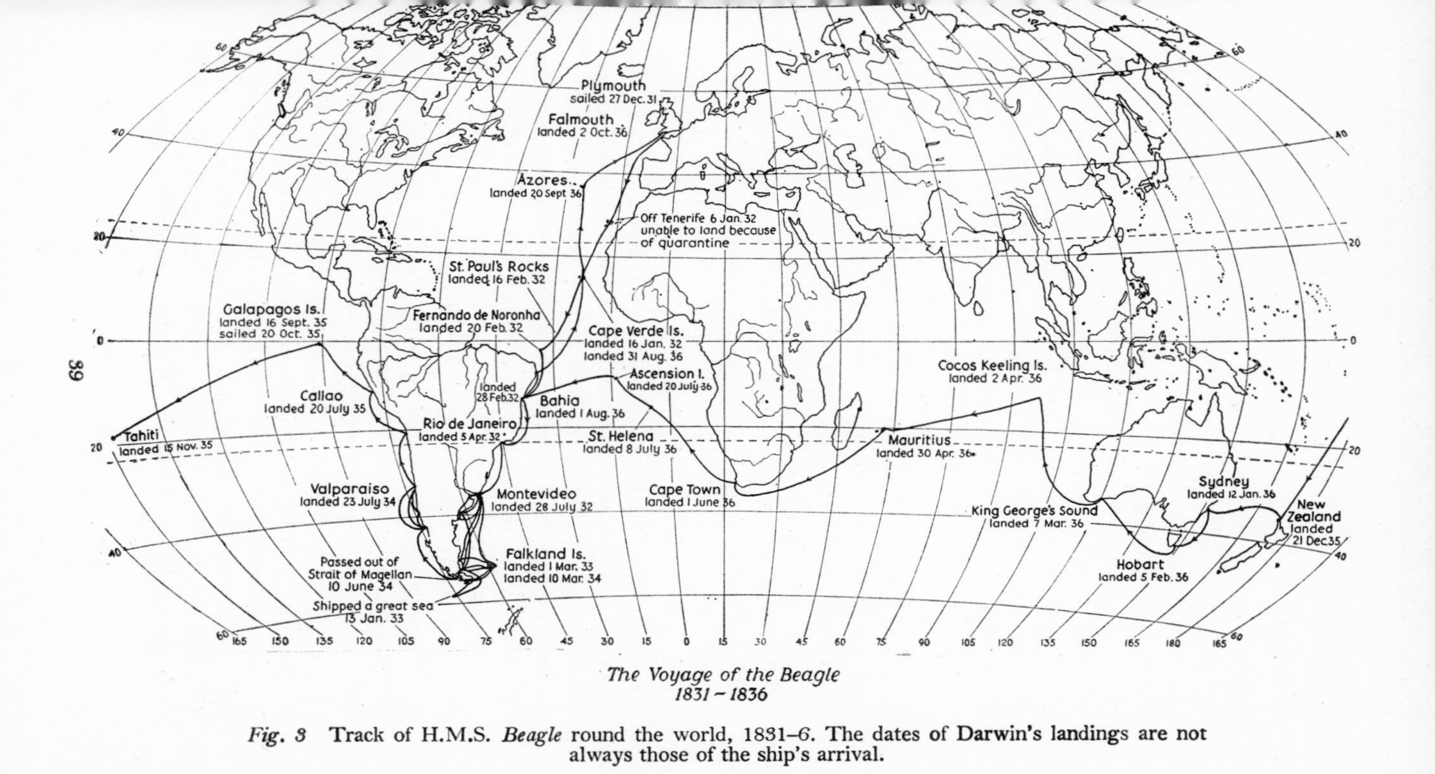

The Voyage of the Beagle
1831 – 1836

Fig. 3 Track of H.M.S. *Beagle* round the world, 1831–6. The dates of Darwin's landings are not always those of the ship's arrival.

In another place he wrote, 'it is nearly impossible to give an adequate idea of the higher feelings which are excited; wonder, astonishment and sublime devotion, fill and elevate the mind.' In his mind's eye he could see his future parsonage through a vista of palm-trees.

This paradise of natural history was, however, not without a price that took the form of hazards to health from the bites of insects and general conditions of sepsis. On one occasion Darwin pricked his knee, which became so swollen that he was unable to move for ten days. After riding through miles of forest on another occasion he caught fever. Shortly afterwards, three of his shipmates who had made an excursion up the bay caught fever and died. A little later again, Darwin was laid up with a swollen and inflamed arm. The science of tropical medicine had not yet been founded. Another hazard was accident. While landing on the beach at Botofogo near Rio de Janeiro, 'I suffered on a small scale, sufficient, however, to paint some of the horrors of shipwreck. Two or three heavy seas swamped the boat, and before my affrighted eyes were floating books, instruments and gun cases and everything which was most useful to me. Nothing was lost and nothing completely spoiled, but most of them injured.'

Any doubts that FitzRoy might have had about the fitness of his naturalist for the work that he had to do were quickly dispelled. After a few weeks at sea FitzRoy wrote to Captain Beaufort, the Hydrographer, 'Darwin is a very sensible, hard-working man, and a very pleasant mess-mate. I never saw a "shore-going fellow" come into the ways of a ship so soon and so thoroughly as Darwin.' Of all the ship's company Darwin alone had the privilege of messing with the captain in his cabin, and the awe with which the captain of a ship was respected, together with FitzRoy's own temperament, sometimes made matters difficult, for he and Darwin had fundamentally opposed outlooks on life. One of the deepest impressions made on

Darwin by his experiences in Brazil was the horror of slavery as he there saw it practised. Regarding the story of an old negro woman who had thrown herself off a high rock to avoid being recaptured, Darwin pointed out that if she had been a Roman matron her act would have been regarded as noble patriotism, but because she was a slave it was considered to be brutish obstinacy. FitzRoy, on the other hand, accepted slavery as part of the established order and defended it, adding that he had heard slaves say in the presence of their master that they were happy and did not want to be free. When Darwin asked him how much credence he gave to evidence of this kind, FitzRoy became furious and retorted that as Darwin doubted his word they could no longer live together. Darwin thought that he might be obliged to leave the ship, and the other officers invited him to mess with them; but after FitzRoy had sent for the first lieutenant and assuaged his anger by abusing Darwin to him, he sent an officer to Darwin with an apology and a request that he would continue to mess with him. Some months later he wrote to Beaufort, 'Darwin is a regular Trump.'

An important date in the voyage was 26 October 1832, for at Monte Video on that day Darwin received mail from England, and this included the second volume of Lyell's *Principles of Geology*, then recently published, in which Lyell described Lamarck's theory of transmutation of species and, as already mentioned (p. 10), rejected it.

The *Beagle* spent three and a half years in South American waters and Darwin's life began to conform to a pattern. When the ship sailed for distant destinations or cruised up and down the coast, he generally sailed with her, but between times he made numerous long excursions inland on horseback, always with a volume of Milton's poems in his pocket. Among these excursions were journeys from Rio de Janeiro up the Rio Macae, and from Maldonado up the Rio Polanca. On another occasion he went from Monte Video to the river Uruguay and returned by Mercedes. One of his most interesting expeditions was a traverse from Patagones near the mouth of the Rio Negro to Bahia Blanca, where he met General Rosas. He then went on to Buenos Ayres through districts infested with hostile Indians who had recently overwhelmed frontier posts and massacred the garrisons.

On the way he passed near a range of mountains, the Sierra de la Ventana, and it was characteristic of Darwin on his journeys that when he saw a mountain he always tried to climb it.

In these wild countries it gives much delight to gain the summit of any mountain. There is an indefinite expectation of seeing something very strange, which, however often it may be balked, never failed with me to recur on each successive attempt. Every one must know the feeling of triumph and pride which a grand view from a height communicates to the mind. In these little frequented countries there is also joined to it some vanity, that you perhaps are the first man who ever stood on this pinnacle or admired this view.

On this occasion, after sleeping out, when the dew at nightfall wetted the saddle-cloths on which he and his gaucho companions slept and the cloths were frozen in the morning, he approached the peaks and started climbing up rocks so rough and indented 'that what was gained in one five minutes was often lost in the next.' He reached a ridge and found to his disappointment that a valley with precipitous sides separated him from the peaks that were his goal. He descended into the valley and suddenly saw two horses grazing. Immediately he hid in the long grass, for the horses must have riders and these might be Indians. As there were no signs of them he went on and reached the summit of one of the peaks with bad cramp in both legs brought on from the change in muscular action from hard riding to still harder climbing. After this little exploit, which combined the true mountaineer's passion to

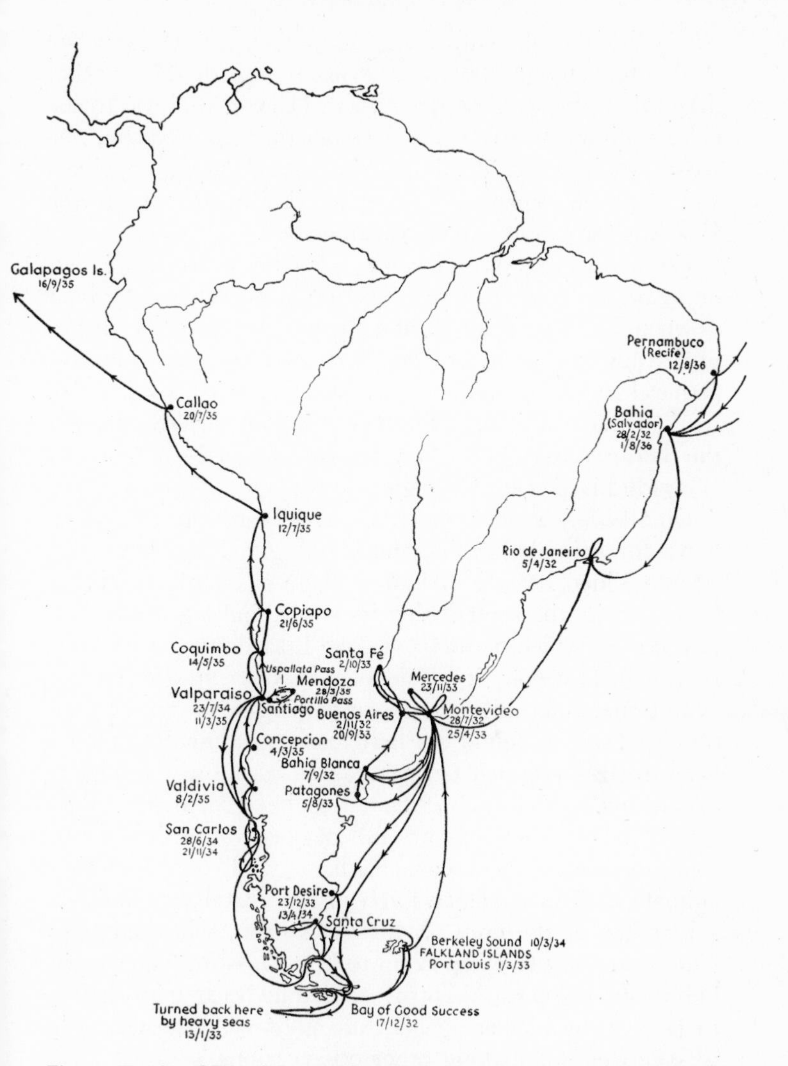

Fig. 4 Tracks of Darwin's more important journeys by sea and by land in South America.

climb virgin peaks with the geologist's insatiable appetite for inquiry and specimens, whetted by a little danger that 'like salt to meat, gave it a relish', Darwin went on to the next military post. 'I am become quite a Gaucho,' he wrote to his sister, 'drink my Mattee and smoke my cigar, and then lie down and sleep as comfortably with the Heavens for canopy, as in a feather bed.'

From Buenos Ayres Darwin went on to Santa Fé, but he again suffered from an infection and returned by boat down the Parana river to find Buenos Ayres in the throes of revolution. There had been fourteen in twelve months. General Rosas's passport and his civilities to Darwin worked like magic, and Darwin was able to pass through the belligerents' lines, but he had to bribe a man to smuggle his servant through.

On all his journeys, Darwin's eyes were like those of a hawk for animals, fossils, and plants. On Rat Island near Monte Video he saw a skink or legless lizard, which led him to make the remark that its small hind legs mark 'the passage by which Nature joins the Lizards to the Snakes', to which, however, it would be a mistake to ascribe any evolutionary significance. Near Bahia Blanca on 23 September 1832 he found his first fossil; nothing less than a head of *Megatherium*. On passage at sea he saw luminous organisms, probably *Noctiluca*, that he studied in a glass tumbler. His notebooks are full of observations on rheas, condors, pumas, tucotucos, capybaras, and countless other animals, as well as plants. Early in 1833 FitzRoy appointed a member of the crew, Syms Covington, who had been fiddler and boy to Poop-cabin to help Darwin, who taught him to shoot and to skin birds, so that he became invaluable to Darwin by increasing his collections while he was able to save time for making other observations.

Natural History, however, was not always Darwin's sole interest when on shore. At Monte Video he wrote to his sister, 'our chief amusement was riding about and admiring the Spanish ladies. After watching one of these angels gliding down the streets, involuntarily we groaned out, "How foolish English women are, they can neither walk nor dress." And then how ugly Miss sounds after Señorita. I am sorry for you all. It would do the whole tribe of you a great deal of good to come to Buenos Ayres.'

Twice the *Beagle* visited Tierra del Fuego. On the first occasion they rounded Cape Horn and tried to beat to westward. After battling with heavy storms for a fortnight, on 13 January 1833 'a great sea struck us and came on board; the after tackle of the quarter boat gave way and an axe being obtained they were instantly obliged to cut away one of the beautiful whale boats; the same sea filled our decks so deep, that if another had followed it is not difficult to guess the result.' They ran for shelter and anchored behind False Cape Horn before starting on an expedition in the ship's boats up Beagle Channel to land the three Fuegians that FitzRoy had taken to England on his previous voyage, and the missionary Matthews who was to stay with them and continue the good work of instilling Christianity into the savages. Jemmy Button's tribe was found, wigwams were built on shore, gardens were dug and planted, and the household goods, wine-glasses, tea-trays, mahogany sideboards, beaver hats, white linen, and complete sets of toilet crockery were landed to set them up in hearth and home.

FitzRoy and his men, with Darwin, then sailed on to explore the western arm of Beagle Channel. The scenery was very grand: lofty mountains covered with snow, and glaciers that stretched down to the water where they became detached and floated away as icebergs. The boats were drawn up on shore when

> One of these glaciers placed us for a minute in most imminent peril. Whilst dining in a little bay about half a mile from one and admiring the beautiful colour of its vertical and overhanging face, a large mass fell roaring into the water. Our boats were on

the beach; we saw a great wave rushing onwards, and instantly it was evident how great was the chance of their being dashed to pieces. One of the seamen just got hold of the boat as the curling breaker reached it: he was knocked over and over but not hurt and most fortunately our boat received no damage. If they had been washed away, how dangerous would our lot have been, surrounded on all sides by hostile savages and deprived of all provisions.

FitzRoy's account of this incident was slightly different: 'there was scarcely time for the most active of our party to run and seize the boats before they were tossed along the beach like empty calabashes. . . . Had not Mr Darwin, and two or three of the men run to them instantly, they would have been swept away from us irrecoverably.' To the stretch of water that they were then entering FitzRoy gave the name of Darwin Sound, and the peak to the north of it became Mount Darwin.

After a few days they turned back to the settlement where they had landed the 'civilized' Fuegians and the missionary. Everything had been plundered from them by the savages, and the missionary had been ominously threatened. It was fortunate that the treatment was no worse, for the savages were cannibals. The missionary was taken back on board the *Beagle*, but the 'civilized' Fuegians were left in their native land. One of them, Jemmy Button, had quite forgotten his own language and tried to talk to his brother in English and Spanish. 'Three years has been sufficient to change savages into as far as habits go, complete and voluntary Europeans.' A year later, when the *Beagle* called again, they could not recognize Jemmy who came out in a canoe to meet the ship. When he was landed a year previously, he was 'so particular about his clothes, that he was always afraid of even dirtying his shoes; scarcely ever without gloves and his hair neatly cut.' Now he was naked, his hair hanging over his shoulders, and ashamed. 'I never saw so complete and grievous a change,' lamented Darwin. Jemmy brought them presents like the nice man that he was, but he had not the least wish to return to England. FitzRoy's fond hopes of the results of successful missionary work were dashed to pieces, but Jemmy Button lived on in the minds of FitzRoy and Darwin as evidence that even a savage can be improved.

Another feat of endurance by Darwin took place near Port St Julian, when he, FitzRoy, and four armed men set out in a boat. The wind came on to blow hard and the boat was run on shore so that they all had to continue on foot. They were greatly troubled by thirst, and as what appeared to be a lake was seen in the distance, Darwin and one of the men volunteered to walk there, only to find that it was not water but snow-white salt that they had seen. By the evening two of the party including FitzRoy were unable to walk any further, and all were excessively tired; Darwin and the other three men left their arms with the exhausted two and returned to the boat. Fresh men were sent back with water, a signal fire was lighted, and before midnight all had been collected and returned on board the *Beagle*. Darwin spent the following two days very feverish in bed.

On the first occasion when the *Beagle* arrived in the Falkland Islands on 1 March 1833, the whole ship's company were flabbergasted to find the Union Jack flying and to learn that Great Britain had taken possession of the islands a month before their arrival. The inhabitants numbered one Englishman and twenty Spaniards. On the *Beagle*'s next visit, 10 March 1834, they found that nearly everyone had been murdered. During the survey of unknown waters off the coast of Patagonia the *Beagle* had struck on a rock, and FitzRoy decided to lay her on shore to inspect her bottom. This was done at the mouth of the river Santa Cruz, where she was careened and it was found that several feet length of her false keel had been knocked off. She was repaired during one tide and refloated safely, after which FitzRoy led a party in three boats up the river Santa Cruz to explore it as far as they could. The current was too strong for rowing or sailing, and the boats were tied astern of each other and towed by a line to which all the members of the party on the bank were harnessed for an hour and a half at a time. After twelve days they saw the summits of the Andes in front of them; guanacos were plentiful on the banks and condors wheeled overhead. Eventually, when about twenty miles from the mountains and twice as near the inlets of the Pacific Ocean as they were from the shores of the Atlantic whence they had come, shortage of provisions forced them to retreat. They had reached a point that must have been only a very few miles distant from Lake Argentino, which was subsequently discovered thirty-three years later. The expedition had enabled Darwin to see a complete cross-section of the geological structure of Patagonia.

Shortly afterwards the *Beagle* entered the Straits of Magellan and left them by the Magdalen Channel, which had only recently been discovered and was very seldom used. They passed out into the Pacific Ocean between the East and West Furies. 'The sight of such a coast is enough to make a landsman dream for a week about death, peril and shipwreck.' Darwin's experiences on the west coast of South America conformed to the same pattern as on the east coast: surveying cruises in the *Beagle*, periods ashore, and arduous expeditions. Among the places visited in the ship were the island of Chiloe and the Chonos Archipelago. On the return from one of these cruises at Valdivia he experienced an earthquake. A fortnight later the shock of an earthquake was felt on board, and on the following day Darwin was able to inspect the devastation caused in the harbour and town of Concepcion, where every house was in ruins, and to study the upraising of the land that had taken place.

From Valparaiso on 14 August 1834 Darwin started on a geological expedition to the base of the Andes. He reached the summit of Mount Camapana, visited the copper mines of Jajuel, stayed five days at the Baths of Cayquenes, made an excursion to Cachapual, where he 'scrambled up one very high peaked mountain', visited the gold mines of Yaquil and then, on 20 September, felt very unwell. He managed to drag himself back to Valparaiso, where in the house of his friend Mr Corfield he remained in bed until the end of October, suffering from a disease the nature of which has never been determined. Darwin was inclined to think that the ill health from which he suffered after his return to England was to some extent due to this attack.

On 14 March 1835 he started from Valparaiso on his expedition across the Andes to Mendoza. It lasted twenty-our days and he travelled with uncommon comfort as he took a bed with him. After passing Santiago he crossed the Puquenes ridge, 12,000 feet high, and then the Portillo Pass, for the Cordillera of the Andes here consisted of two ridges. 'My flannel waistcoat appeared in the dark when rubbed as if washed with Phosphorus; every hair on a dog's back crackled, the sheets and leather gear of the saddle in handling all sent out sparks.' At the eastern foot of the Andes in the town of Luxan near Mendoza he spent the night on 26 March 1835, and there he experienced 'an attack, and it deserves no less a name, of the Benchuca, the great black bug of the Pampas. It is most disgusting to feel soft wingless insects, about an inch long, crawling over one's body; before sucking they are quite thin, but afterwards round and bloated with blood, and in this state they are easily squashed.' The probable significance for Darwin's subsequent health of this experience of the bug, which he must also have met on many other occasions in South America, will be described in due course (p. 115). From Mendoza he returned to Chile by crossing the Uspallata Pass, near which he found the fossilized remains of a forest of coniferous trees and ruined, deserted houses at a very high altitude, once inhabited by Indians. Both these observations provided him with important evidence of the uplifting which the whole continent had undergone. At Santiago, after such an expedition, not surprisingly he felt unwell.

Darwin's last expedition in South America took him from Valparaiso northwards to Copiapo where the *Beagle* was to call for him. He covered over five hundred miles with one guide, four horses, and two mules, cooking their own meals and usually sleeping in the open. At Panincillo he visited the copper mines that an Englishman had bought for £3 8s 0d, the inhabitants having abandoned them because they did not know how to reduce copper pyrites. At Arqueros he visited the silver mine and made a special note that the house where he spent the night was exceptional in not having fleas. Eventually, after riding across a desert, he reached Copiapo and embarked in the *Beagle*. The ship called at Callao, but since its declaration of independence ten years previously, Peru was in such a state of anarchy that Darwin could not with safety leave the precincts of Callao or Lima where he spent a few days. The safest place to walk securely was the island of San Lorenzo covering Callao harbour, where Darwin found embedded together some shells of recent molluscs and remains of human habitation raised eighty-five feet above sea level. On 7 September 1835 the *Beagle* left the west coast of South America.

The Galapagos Islands played a part of such importance in the formation of Darwin's ideas that it is worth while to trace his steps in that archipelago. On 16 September he landed on Chatham Island and started to observe the tortoises and lizards and to collect shells, insects, birds, and plants. He climbed the crater of a volcano which he was able to see had been submarine from the limestone strata mixed with volcanic dust that dipped away on all sides. This proved that the island had emerged from the sea. He revelled in a veritable Phlegrean Field of black lava studded with volcanic cones, the sight of which reminded him of the iron furnaces near Wolverhampton. On 23 September he crossed over to Charles Island where the acting Governor, an Englishman, mentioned to Darwin that he was able to tell at sight from which island any tortoise came.

During the ensuing days Darwin collected 'all the animals, plants, insects and reptiles from this Island. It will be very interesting to find from future comparison to what district or "centre of creation" the organized beings of this archipelago must be attached.' On 1 October he landed on Albemarle Island and observed the doves, finches, and iguanas. On 8 October it was the turn of James Island where he rode on a tortoise and noted its speed as 360 yards an hour, and spent the following days collecting specimens of every kind. The *Beagle* then sailed to Abingdon Island to pick up an officer who had been sent to survey there, and next made for Wenman and Culpepper Islands, which lie a hundred miles north of the main group, before setting course on 20 October 1835 for the passage of 3,200 miles across the Pacific Ocean to Tahiti. On the way they sailed through the archipelago of the Low Islands, so called because they consist of coral atolls barely rising more than a few feet above the level of the sea. Darwin had given much thought to possible ways by which they might have been formed when he was on the west coast of South America.

Tahiti came into view on 15 November, and crowds of natives on Point Venus welcomed the arrival of the ship. Three days later Darwin started on an expedition inland which, as usual, included the ascent of a mountain. FitzRoy had a diplomatic mission to perform, because an English ship had been plundered by the inhabitants of an

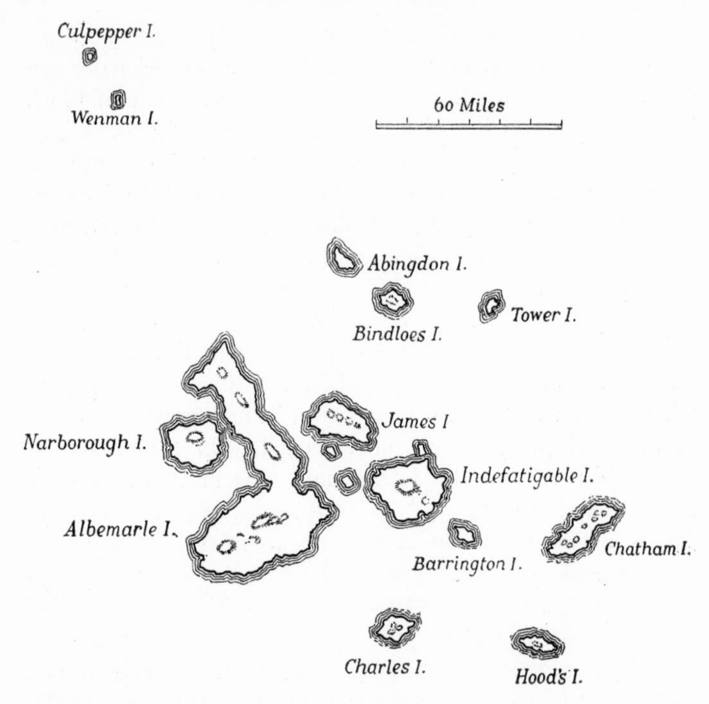

Fig. 5 The Galapagos Archipelago showing the English names of the islands. From Darwin: *Geological Observations on Volcanic Islands,* 1844.

island in the Low Archipelago under the sovereignty of the Queen of Tahiti, and FitzRoy was charged with the duty of collecting compensation in a sum of 3,000 dollars. The Queen convened a parliament and the chiefs immediately subscribed the money. Darwin had nothing but praise for the loyalty and happiness of the Tahitians, and for the successful efforts of the missionaries who had greatly improved the morals of the inhabitants since the island was visited by Captain Cook. Darwin also held an opinion that was later to be shared by Gauguin: 'it requires little habit to make a dark skin more pleasing and natural to the eye of a European than his own colour.'

Plate 4 (left) Robert Fitzroy, captain of the *Beagle*, oil painting by Francis Lane, from a photograph. *Royal Naval College, Greenwich; Greenwich Hospital Collection.*

Plate 5 (right) Syms Covington, Darwin's assistant on the *Beagle*.

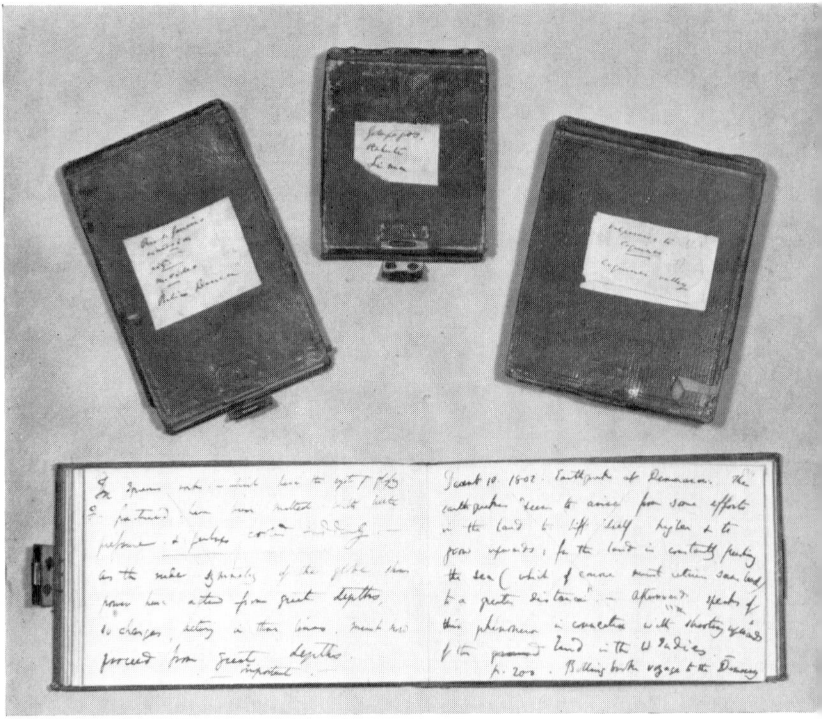

Plate 6 The notebooks kept by Darwin during the voyage of the *Beagle*, from which the Diary was prepared.

The *Beagle*'s next landfall was the Bay of Islands, New Zealand where Darwin landed, but he was not favourably impressed either by the natives or the Englishmen and was glad to leave for Sydney. His first impression as he walked through the town was one of pride and satisfaction: 'Here in a less promising country, scores of years have effected many times more than centuries in South America.' After an excursion to Bathurst, in the course of which he saw kangaroos and platypus, met a party of aborigines, and visited Govett's Leap, he wrote to his sister, 'This is really a wonderful Colony; ancient Rome, in her Imperial grandeur, would not have been ashamed of such offspring.' He was deeply impressed by the fact that seven-eighths of an acre of land at Bathurst had been sold by auction for £12,000. As time went on, however, he found grounds for criticism and less satisfaction in the social picture and moral condition of Australia, for which he blamed the policy of the home government and the behaviour of the convicts. As an example of the way in which he had already begun to appreciate commercial values, he argued that as the country was unfit for building canals, there was a limit beyond which the land carriage of wool would not repay the expense of sheep-rearing; agriculture he thought would not succeed on an extended scale, and therefore Australia's future depended on her becoming the southern commercial centre of the world, 'a great princess in the South' that he had no doubt she would become, but he did not like her.

A visit to Tasmania included the ascent of Mount Wellington and a brief mention of the Tasmanian aborigines and their wonderful powers of concealment on almost bare ground. From an estimated population of twenty thousand, they had by 1835 been reduced to two hundred and ten who were concentrated on Gun Carriage Island in Bass Strait. It was unfortunate that Darwin never had an opportunity to see these living fossil specimens of a people in an Old Stone Age state of culture, with a skull-capacity of only 1,200 cubic centimetres. The last survivor died in 1877.

At Cocos Keeling Island Darwin had his first chance to examine a coral atoll at close quarters and to test the theories on which he had been working to account for the geological formation of those curious structures. He was particularly interested in the evidence for subsidence that the island showed, and also in the different objects, including seeds, that are drifted across the sea for long distances from Java and Sumatra and also from Australia and thrown up on the beach, the hardier seeds retaining their power of germination in spite of their immersion in salt water. The *Beagle*'s next landfall was Mauritius, where he ascended the mountain of La Pouce and studied some raised coral reefs on the beach. On 31 May 1836 the *Beagle* anchored in Simon's Bay and Darwin procured a gig in which he drove to Cape Town where he soon found that the Dutch 'thoroughly dislike our whole nation'. With a young Hottentot guide and a couple of horses he made an expedition to Paarl and then crossed the French Hoeck Pass, returning over Lowry Cole's Pass to Cape Town where he met the astronomers Sir John Herschel and Sir Thomas Maclear, and Dr Andrew Knight who had just returned from one of his expeditions inland, from whom Darwin obtained much information of natural-history interest.

On 18 June 1836 the *Beagle* put to sea and arrived off St Helena on 8 July. The geology of the island filled him with interest as did its natural history: very few birds or insects, 52 species of indigenous plants but 424 imported species mostly from England, which gave the countryside an English appearance. Many of these English plants flourished there better than in their native country, a fact that was to have important consequences in Darwin's chains of thought.

On again the *Beagle* sailed and anchored off Ascension Island on 19 July. There Darwin found a letter from his sisters who wrote that Adam Sedgwick had called on his father and told him that Darwin would take a place among the leading scientific men, on the strength of the letters and specimens that he had sent home to Henslow. 'After reading this letter I clambered over the mountains of Ascension with a bounding step and made the volcanic rocks resound under my geological hammer.'

Four days later the *Beagle* put to sea again but the ship's company were dismayed to see that her head was directed west-southwest. To complete the chain of chronometrical stations that he had taken round the world FitzRoy wanted to check his readings with those that he had taken on the outward journey, and on 1 August the ship reached Bahia, where Darwin took several long walks. 'I was glad to find my enjoyment in tropical scenery had not decreased from the want of novelty, even in the slightest degree.' Another call at S. Iago in the Cape Verde Islands, a visit to Terceira in the Azores, where Darwin rode to an active crater and saw jets of steam issuing from fissures, and a passing call at S. Miguel where a boat was sent ashore to collect letters, were the only remaining events of the voyage of the *Beagle*. Anchor was dropped at Falmouth on 2 October 1836; Darwin disembarked and caught the mail-coach for Shrewsbury. In the joyful bosom of his family he did not forget to write to his uncle Josiah Wedgwood to thank him again for his good offices five years before, by which it had been possible for him to sail in the *Beagle*.

Darwin had no doubt that the voyage of the *Beagle* was by far the most important event in his life and determined his whole career. The reason why this was so forms the subject of all the remaining chapters of this book.

Chapter 4

Geological Results of the Voyage of the 'Beagle'

In later years Darwin used to say that nobody was less qualified than he to fill the post of naturalist on the *Beagle*, and, considering the amount of academic training that he had received in scientific subjects before he embarked, his statement might have been justified on paper, however mistaken it afterwards turned out to be in fact. The brilliance of his work on evolution and natural selection, and the world-shattering effect that it produced in changing the basis of human thought, has had the result of eclipsing his contributions to pure geology, which is unfortunate because they were fundamental and numerous, and the near-oblivion into which they have fallen is all the more regrettable. The first edition of his *Journal of Researches*, written in 1837 and published in 1839, specified in its title that these researches were into the Geology and Natural History of the various countries visited by H.M.S. *Beagle*, and this order of subjects was not reversed until the second edition was published in 1845.

Darwin himself claimed that the voyage led him to attend closely to several branches of natural history which improved his powers of observation, but that 'the investigation of geology of all the places visited was far more important, as reasoning here comes into play'. Everything that Darwin did followed naturally and simply from what he had done before, and his geological observations on volcanic islands, the structure of South America, and coral-reefs form a perfect sequence, the results of which were basic for many aspects of his argument on evolution, such as proof of geographical and climatic changes in the past, elevation and subsidence of land, oceanic islands and the permanence of ocean basins, conditions requisite for preservation of organisms as fossils, and the imperfection of the geological record. His geological work resulting from the voyage of the *Beagle* will therefore be briefly described in this chapter, before passing on to his biological work in the next.

Darwin's first opportunity to test his powers as a geologist came on S. Iago in the Cape Verde Islands. S. Iago also convinced him immediately of 'the wonderful superiority of Lyell's manner of treating geology, compared with that of any other author, whose works I had with me or ever afterwards read.' As a direct result of studying Lyell's *Principles of Geology* during the time between the *Beagle*'s departure from Plymouth and arrival at S. Iago, Darwin was able to write: 'On first examining a new district nothing can appear more hopeless than the chaos of rocks; but by recording the stratification and nature of the rocks and fossils at many points, always reasoning and predicting what will be found elsewhere, light soon begins to dawn on the district, and the structure of the whole becomes more or less intelligible.'

Darwin quickly saw from the exposure of the rocks on the coast of S. Iago that the lowest rocks were crystalline and of ancient volcanic origin. This layer was overlain by a bright white layer of limestone, 60 feet above the sea, 20 feet thick, containing shells of marine organisms of late Tertiary date. This showed him that the limestone had been deposited under water in a shallow sea, and that as these beds were now 60 feet above sea-level, the whole island had been up-raised. Above the limestone was a layer of more recent basaltic lava of volcanic origin, the heat of which had altered the uppermost part of the underlying limestone and baked it into a hard, compact, fine-grained rock to a depth of about one foot below the line of junction. A perfect gradation was visible from loosely aggregated remains of shells into a crystalline rock without a trace of these. This introduced him to the effects of metamorphism at first hand.

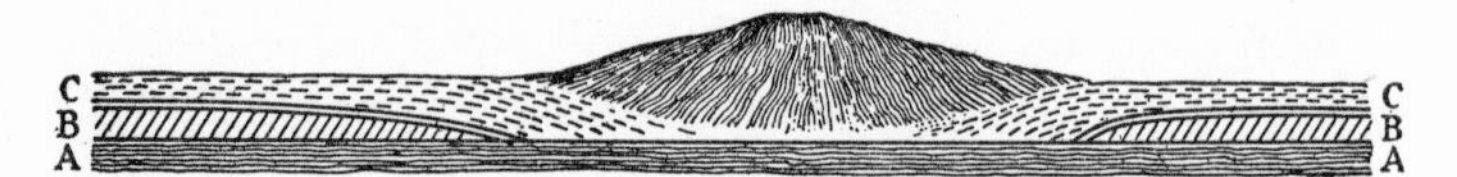

Fig. 6 Darwin's diagram of the geological structure of the coast of St Iago, Cape Verde Islands. A, substratum of ancient volcanic rocks. B, bright white layer of limestone, originally deposited below the sea but now raised. C, recent basaltic lava. Near the extinct volcano shown, the limestone and overlying basaltic layers dip beneath the sea, evidence of local subsidence. From *Geological Observations on Volcanic Islands*, 1844.

In general the limestone layer continued horizontally for miles at the same height of 60 feet above the sea; in some places it dropped to about 40 feet and in others rose to 80 feet, and Darwin attributed these variations to the uneven surface of the old sea-bottom on which the limestone had been deposited. In another place, however, near an extinct volcanic hill, the basal volcanic rock, the limestone stratum overlying it, and the basaltic lava overlying that, all dipped beneath the sea, and Darwin saw that this was the result of local subsidence. As he afterwards wrote, these observations 'revealed to me a new and important fact, namely that there had been afterwards subsidence round the craters, which had since been in action, and had poured forth lava. It then first dawned on me that I might perhaps write a book on the geology of the various countries visited, and this made me thrill with delight.' It was thus in the capacity of a geologist that Darwin first fancied himself as an author.

His study of S. Iago enabled Darwin to draw further original conclusions of importance. That island, like those of Mauritius and St Helena that he afterwards visited, is bounded by a ring of mountains composed of basalt. To explain their formation, the accepted theory then was that they were the result of what were called 'craters of elevation', supposed to originate in gigantic blisters on the earth's crust subsequently opened out at the top. Darwin showed how much more probable it was that the central hollow between the mountains was not formed by the arching of the surface but by the central region having been elevated to a lesser extent than its surroundings.

The next landfall, St Paul's Rocks, provided scope for observations of equally great significance, for this tiny island is not volcanic, and, with the Seychelles, enjoys the exceptional rarity of being an oceanic island of neither volcanic nor coralline origin. The fact that all other oceanic islands are either volcanic or coralline was to be of cardinal importance later when Darwin turned his attention to the geographical distribution and origin of the flora and fauna of such islands. Meanwhile, the visit to St Paul's Rocks gives an opportunity for a glimpse of Darwin at work:

> Extensive portions of these rocks are coated by a layer of a glossy polished substance, with a pearly lustre and of a greyish white colour; it follows all the inequalities of the surface, to which it is firmly attached. When examined with a lens, it is found to consist of numerous exceedingly thin layers, their aggregate thickness being about the tenth of an inch. It is considerably harder than calcareous spar, but can be scratched with a knife; under the blowpipe it scales off, decrepitates, slightly blackens, emits a fetid odour, and becomes strongly alkaline; it does not effervesce in acids. I presume this substance has been deposited by water draining from the birds' dung, with which the rocks are covered.

Darwin's proficiency as a petrologist also emerges from his comparison of lavas of undoubted volcanic origin with the plutonic rocks of the Andes, which convinced him that they were closely related. He studied the minerals found in granites and those that occur in lavas and found them in all respects similar, and he was able to show a completely graded series between crystalline granites and glass-like lavas. By noting with his compass and clinometer the direction of the strike and the angle of dip, he observed that the planes of cleavage in slates and the planes of foliation in schists and gneisses remained constant over wide areas, whereas their planes of inclination might vary greatly. Cleavage-planes and planes of foliation were closely parallel to the direction of the great axes along which elevation of land had taken place, and generally parallel with the coast-line. In Tierra del Fuego he satisfied himself that the planes of cleavage were quite independent of the planes of stratification and he concluded, directly contrary to the then prevailing and long-accepted view of authorities such as Sedgwick and Lyell, that cleavage and foliation were not original phenomena dependent on the deposition of the strata, but had been subsequently superimposed by pressure, resulting, in the case of foliation, in recrystallization. This was the origin of the 'deformation' theory of metamorphic rocks. At the Cape of Good Hope Darwin observed clay-slate passing into gneiss as it approached granite, which showed that foliation could originate by metamorphosis of homogeneous rocks.

South America provided Darwin with magnificent opportunities for making observations of far-reaching geological importance. The effects of the earthquake of Concepcion in 1835 which he saw at first hand immediately after the event, and those of the earthquake of 1829 in the Chonos Archipelago showed that they had resulted in an elevation of the land by about 10 feet. In addition to this connection between earthquakes and elevation, he was able to make out a connection between elevation and volcanic activity, for at the same time that the country around Concepcion

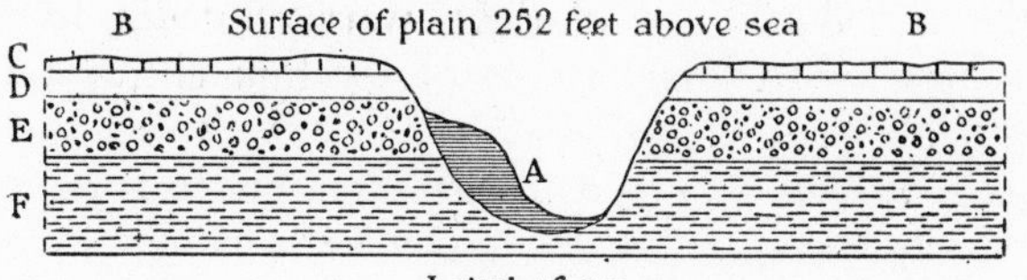

Fig. 7 Darwin's diagram of the structure of the Plain of Coquimbo, Chile. A, stratified sand in a ravine containing shells of different recent species of molluscs in the same proportions as those found on the beach. B, surface of the Plain covered with scattered shells of recent species in nearly the same proportions as on the beach. C, upper and D, lower beds of limestone containing recent shells, not in the same proportions as on the beach. E, upper and F, lower old Tertiary strata containing shells of species nearly all extinct. The presence of scattered recent shells on the Plain is evidence of elevation of at least 252 feet within the life-period of living species of shells. From *Geological Observations on South America*, 1846.

was elevated, a number of volcanoes in the Andes renewed their activity and a new submarine volcano erupted near the island of Juan Fernandez.

It was by careful study of shell-bearing deposits that Darwin was able to make the most striking discoveries regarding elevation of land that South America has undergone. On the east coast between the estuary of the River Plate and the south of Patagonia he was able to identify beds containing shells of species still living in the adjacent Atlantic Ocean, that had been elevated to a height of a few feet near Monte Video, 60 feet near Bahia Blanca, 100 feet at San José, and 330 feet at Port Desire. Some of the shells still retained their colour and contained sufficient organic matter to smell bad when burnt. This was clear evidence of elevation that had taken place sufficiently recently to be within the life-span of existing species, over an extent of coast-line more than 1,000 miles long. On the west coast, similar beds containing shells were raised 350 feet on the island of Chiloe, from 400 to 1,000 feet in the Bay of Concepcion, and up to 1,300 feet near Valparaiso. That the shells in these beds were truly fossil and not the remains of man's search for food was shown by the fact that some of them were exceedingly small, corresponding to young stages of development, and by the remarkable observation that in these beds the shells of different species occurred in the same proportions as did their living representatives in the adjacent waters of the Pacific Ocean.

Near the Uspallata Pass, at a height of 7,000 feet above sea-level he found in a broken escarpment a clump of fossilized conifer trees projecting two to seven feet perpendicularly from the stratum (itself inclined 25°) in which they were embedded, which proved that they had grown *in situ* and had not been drifted from elsewhere. The beds containing the trees were covered by thousands of feet of alternating sedimentary deposits and volcanic lavas, showing that the trees had been buried thousands of feet under the level of the Atlantic Ocean which then extended 700 miles westwards from its present shores to bathe the feet of the Andes. They have since been raised 7,000 feet above that level.

An indication of the speed at which elevation had taken place was found near Callao, where remains of human activity, represented by plaited rushes and cotton string, were embedded with the shells and raised to a height of 85 feet above sea-level, which proved that the elevation had taken place since the time when Indians first inhabited Peru. Coming to more recent times, the rise in level of the land at Valparaiso between 1817 and 1834 could be estimated at 10 feet. Darwin was therefore able to demonstrate a zone over 2,000 miles long over which elevation had taken place, and to make an objective, quantitative estimate of the rate at which it had occurred.

Great as was the importance of these up-raised shell-bearing beds, it was equalled by the fact that such beds were very restricted in size and nowhere approached the extensive deposits found elsewhere in the world. This needed explanation, and Darwin found that it was due to the fact that elevation itself exposed the elevated strata to increased erosion and destruction through the action of water and other agencies. He was thereby led to consider what the conditions must be for the formation of deposits thousands of feet thick containing fossils such as are found elsewhere. He concluded that it could only have been when a slow subsidence constantly depressed the bottom of a shallow sea near a tract of land from which material was eroded to become deposited as sediment, maintaining the same depth of sea-bottom as the underlying layers sank lower. He found the proof of this theory at Navidad, 60 miles south of Valparaiso. There he saw beds of early Tertiary rocks 800 feet thick containing fossil shells. When alive, the animals to which these shells belonged must have lived in shallow water at a depth of between 6 and 60 feet. It follows that when their contained shells were alive, the lowest beds of these deposits must have lain nearly 700 feet higher than tney now are, and that they have sunk at the same rate as the overlying 700 feet of deposits were laid down. In the valley of Copiapo a bed of early Tertiary shells is covered by deposits of sandstone 6,000 feet thick, and this shows by the same token that these beds have undergone subsidence to the extent of nearly 6,000 feet since the shells now contained in them were alive, and have since been raised.

From these observations, Darwin was able to define the conditions under which the preservation of fossils might be expected. There must be a long-continued supply of sediment derived from the erosion of neighbouring land, a sea of shallow depth, and continued subsidence at the same place and at a rate commensurate with that of deposition. For all these conditions to be met at the same place must have been rare in the history of the earth, and as in their absence and particularly under conditions of elevation fossiliferous deposits are destroyed, fossilization must have been rare and discontinuous. This was the evidence on which he based his demonstration that the fossil record must inevitably be incomplete.

From the composite picture that he was able to build up of the elevation and subsidence that had taken place here and there and to different extents in different places, Darwin was led to draw further conclusions. In the first place his observations meant that geological formations were not universal but local phenomena, and the same was true of changes in the nature of the deposits and changes of climate. As he said, 'The causes which gave to the older Tertiary productions of the quite temperate zones of Europe a tropical character, were of a local character and did not affect the whole globe.' Darwin then compared the ranges of latitude within which fossil and living representatives were found with a view to obtaining an estimate of past climatic conditions. He concluded that during the Tertiary period the climate of Chile and of Patagonia was not hotter than would be expected from the latitudes of those areas, which was contrary to the then generally held view that early geological periods were characterized by a high temperature all over the globe. During the recent Ice Age in Europe and North America, the climate was colder than at the present day, and this provided evidence of change of conditions.

Further proof of a recent change of conditions was provided by the deserted houses, abandoned by Indians in high valleys of the Andes up to the snow-line in regions now quite uninhabitable because there is no water and the land produces absolutely nothing.

I have convincing proof that this part of the continent of South America has been elevated near the coast at least from 400 to 500, and in some parts from 1,000 to 1,300 feet, since the epoch of existing shells; and further inland the rise may have been greater. As the peculiarly arid character of the climate is evidently a consequence of the height of the Cordillera, we may feel almost sure that before the later elevations, the atmosphere could not have been so completely drained of its moisture as it now is; and as the rise has been gradual, so would have been the change in climate.

The realization that the classification of geological periods based on the deposits in regions where they were first studied cannot be extended all over the globe because local conditions varied so greatly, led in turn to a generalization of great significance regarding geological time. The length of time required for the deposition of a sedimentary formation, before the discovery of methods of measurement based on the rate of decay of radio-active elements, could be estimated only from the thickness of the deposits and from the rate of deposition. But formations are not continuous; each is full of gaps, and between formations there are gaps of immense and unknown duration, not measurable from the thickness of extant strata, gaps during which erosion was taking place removing the evidence of the time involved in the deposition of now vanished sediments. 'Moreover,' Darwin pointed out, 'how often has it not been found that between two conformable and apparently immediately successive deposits a vast pile of water-worn matter is interpolated in an adjoining district.' The result of these considerations was to lengthen enormously the estimated age of the earth.

The experience that Darwin gained in finding evidence of elevation and subsidence and in studying volcanoes enabled him to tackle the problem of coral-reefs even before he had ever seen one. While he was still on the west coast of South America, he turned his attention to the problem of atolls or lagoon-islands. These are characterized by the fact that their highest points of land do not rise more than about 30 feet above sea-level, and that they consist of reefs showing a margin of flat, solid surface sometimes uncovered at low tide, enclosing a shallow

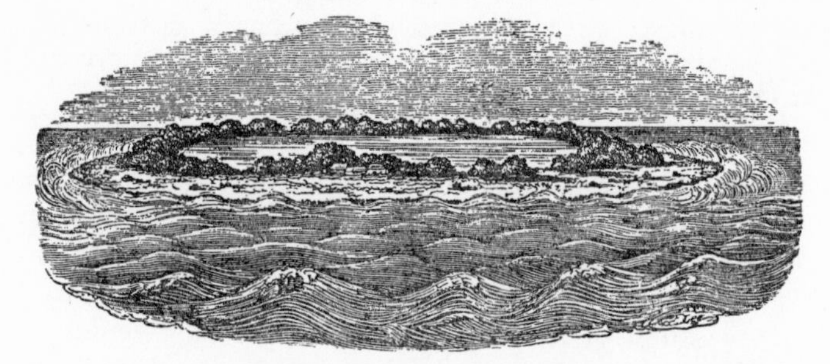

Fig. 8 View of Whitsunday Island, South Pacific Ocean, showing the circular atoll of coral-reefs enclosing a lagoon. From Darwin: *Structure and Distribution of Coral Reefs*, 1842.

lagoon seldom more than 200 feet deep within an irregular, more or less circular outline. One other fact concerning coral-reefs is relevant, namely that coral-polyps can flourish and build a reef only if they live at a depth of not more than 120 feet below the surface in sea water free from mud and from fresh water, at a temperature not lower than 20° C. They are killed by exposure to air and sunshine. Coral growth is most vigorous on the side of a reef exposed to the roughest sea which brings oxygen and food-particles to the polyps. It is estimated that a reef may rise in height by one foot in a hundred years.

The prevailing view regarding the formation of coral-reefs at that time was Lyell's, which claimed that atolls represented reefs built on the rims of submerged volcanic craters. Darwin was able to show that for a number of reasons this view could not be held. In the first place, no volcanic crater could have been five times as long as it was broad, which is the case with Bow atoll, nor could a volcanic crater have been 60 miles long which is the length of Menchikov Island, or narrow and crooked as Rimsky-Korsakov Island is. Next, considering the maximum depth at which coral-polyps can live and flourish, it is impossible to believe that all these submarine volcanoes raised the rims of their craters to the same height, within

120 feet of the surface of the sea, over vast stretches of ocean. Further, the volcanic-crater theory will not account at all for the formation of barrier-reefs, which resemble atolls in their low height above sea-level and in enclosing a narrow arm of the sea up to 180 feet deep between the reef and the adjoining land. The barrier-reef of New Caledonia is 400 miles long and the Great Barrier Reef of Australia over 1,200 miles long; no submarine volcanic crater could account for the formation of features of this magnitude.

Darwin's argument was beautifully simple, based on the maximum permissible depth at which corals will live and on the uniformity of the heights of atolls and barrier-reefs above sea-level. A foundation for the corals must have been provided at a depth not exceeding 120 feet. It is impossible to believe that submerged rocky mountains existed originally with their tops all at approximately the same height; therefore the platforms must have been brought to the required height. It is equally impossible to believe that the platforms were formed by elevation from greater depths, because it is inconceivable that they all stopped rising at almost exactly the same level without a single one emerging above the surface of the sea. If it should be thought that the uniformity of the height of atolls might be due to erosion by the sea of the tops of rising foundations, the answer is that the result of such a process would be flat, disk-shaped pieces of land, not circular reefs enclosing lagoons in hollow basins. The only possibility remaining is that the platforms for the corals to build on were brought into position by subsidence.

Having reached this point in his argument, Darwin was in a position to test his theory when the *Beagle* visited coral-reefs. As he said, it is difficult to obtain 'demonstrative proofs of a movement, which invariably tends to conceal its own evidence,' but he was able to find some. For instance, on Pouynipete in the Caroline Islands, there

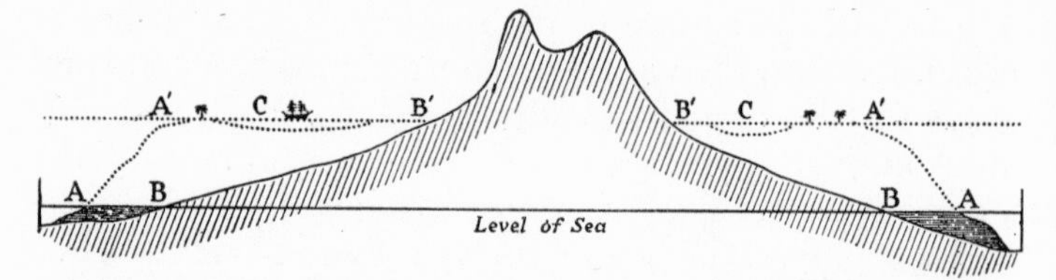

Fig. 9 Darwin's diagram showing the formation of an atoll as a result of subsidence. The vertical section is taken through an island (shown shaded) bordered by a coral-reef (shown dark) the outer edges of which are at AA, while the shores of the island are at BB. If the land be imagined as sinking, the relative level of the sea will rise and the shores of the island will then be at B′B′. The coral-reef will have grown upwards, keeping pace with the relative rise in sea-level, and its outer edges will be at A′A′, bordering a narrow strip of dry reef bearing trees, separated from the shores of the island by a shallow circular lagoon-channel CC, on which a ship is shown. From *Structure and Distribution of Coral Reefs*, 1842.

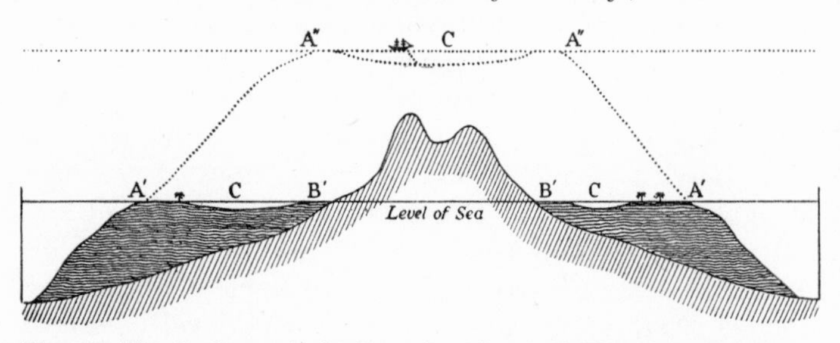

Fig. 10 The final stage in the formation of an atoll. The edges of the coral-reef at A′A′, the shores of the island at B′B′, and the lagoon-channel CC, are as in Fig. 9. If subsidence continues and the relative level of the sea rises still further, the island will be completely submerged and the coral-reef will grow upwards and form a circular ring of dry land at A″A″, enclosing a circular shallow lagoon at C on which a ship is shown. From *Structure and Distribution of Coral Reefs*, 1842.

are ruins of a town now only accessible by means of boats, as the waves reach the steps of the houses, from which it follows that subsidence has continued since the houses were built. Furthermore, there are submerged and 'drowned' atolls more than 120 feet below sea-level, consisting of dead coral-rock. It is now known that the Great Barrier Reef rests on the edge of the down-faulted coastal plane of northeast Australia, which is further evidence of subsidence. Darwin's work on atolls and barrier-reefs was thus a continuation of his investigations into the conditions of deposition of thick fossiliferous strata in South America: 'It was easy to replace in imagination the continued deposition of sediment by the upward growth of coral. To do this was to form my theory of the formation of barrier-reefs and atolls.'

There is, however, a third category of reefs called fringing reefs or shore-reefs that skirt an island or part of a continent and to this extent resemble barrier-reefs, but differ from them in being narrower and having only a small boat-channel between them and the island or continent as the case may be. Fringing reefs may be raised above sea-level and form masses of dead coral-rock. They differ from atolls in that they enclose high land, not a lagoon. Fringing reefs have therefore developed on the sloping shore of land that is either stationary in height or undergoing elevation. They may of course have given rise to atolls or barrier-reefs if the land that they fringe subsequently underwent subsidence.

If now the geographical distribution of atolls, barrier-reefs, and fringing reefs be plotted on a map of the world, it is seen that vast areas of ocean contain reefs that conform to one or other of these types. Atolls and barrier-reefs are found, and subsidence has taken place, in the Low Archipelago, Society, Fiji, Ellice, Gilbert, Marshall, and Caroline Islands, New Caledonia, the northeast coast of Australia, Cocos Keeling, Laccadive and Maldive Islands, and the Chagos Archipelago, to mention only the chief examples. Fringing reefs are found in areas that lie largely parallel to those of atolls and barrier-reefs, such as the Hawaiian group, Friendly, Marianna, Navigator, and Solomon Islands, New Hebrides, and the string of islands extending from Nicobar along the south side of Sumatra to the islands of the Banda Arc, Halmahera, Philippines, and Loo Choo, Mauritius, Madagascar and parts of the east coast of Africa, and the West Indies. On a map marked in this way, Darwin entered the positions of active volcanoes and found that none was associated with the areas containing atolls and barrier-reefs, and that all lay in or close to areas containing fringing reefs. This was another link with the work that he had been doing in South America.

Darwin summed up his studies of coral-reefs in the following generalization:

> When the two great types of structure, namely barrier-reefs and atolls on the one hand, and fringing reefs on the other, are laid down on a map, they offer a grand and harmonious picture of the movements which the crust of the earth has undergone within a late period. We see there vast areas rising, with volcanic matter every now and then bursting forth. We see other wide spaces sinking without any volcanic outbursts; and we may feel sure that the movement has been so slow as to have allowed the corals to grow up to the surface, and so widely extended as to have buried over the broad face of the ocean every one of those mountains, above which the atolls now stand like monuments, marking the place of their burial.

It is remarkable how broad a brush he was able to use on how large a canvas from such simple deductions and observations. *The Structure and Distribution of Coral Reefs* was first published in 1842.

Darwin's theory explains not only how the various types of reef occur where they do, but also why they do not occur in many places where they might have been expected. There are no coral-reefs round the islands of Juan Fernandez, the Galapagos, St Helena, Ascension Island, or the islands in the Gulf of Guinea, presumably because of the cold ocean currents that keep down the temperature of the water in those places. There are no atolls in the West Indies because they are in an area of elevation. The only coral-reefs in the Atlantic Ocean are round Bermuda. Why there should be no reefs round such islands as the Cape Verde group or St Paul's Rocks is obscure; Darwin suggested that the particular ecological niche in nature's economy occupied elsewhere by corals might there be occupied by other organisms.

Darwin's views on the methods of formation of coral-reefs were explained to Lyell soon after Darwin's return to England, and an account of this meeting between the two men has been preserved by J. W. Judd. Darwin told Judd that he had never fully realized the importance of his theory till he had had an opportunity of discussing it with Lyell. 'Lyell, on receiving from the lips of its author a sketch of the new theory, was so overcome with delight that he danced about and threw himself into the wildest contortions, as was his manner when excessively pleased.' Indeed, Darwin's demonstration made such an impression on Lyell that on 24 May 1837 Lyell wrote to Sir John Herschel saying, 'I am very full of Darwin's new theory of Coral Islands, and I have urged Whewell [then President of the Geological Society] to make him read it at our next meeting. I must give up my volcanic crater theory for ever, though it costs me a pang at first, for it accounted for so much.'

Lyell had been longing for Darwin's return to England ever since he had learnt of Darwin's geological observations in South America, described in letters to Henslow, and when Lyell and Darwin met, a great friendship was started which was to have profound effects in the history of science. At the very beginning of their friendship, the pupil had instructed his master, and it speaks very highly for the characters of the two men that this reversal of the normal relationship between teacher and student served to cement their attachment to each other.

Meanwhile, Darwin's views on the methods of formation of coral-reefs had also rapidly gained the support of the American naturalist J. D. Dana of the United States Exploring Expedition in 1839, and of J. B. Jukes who

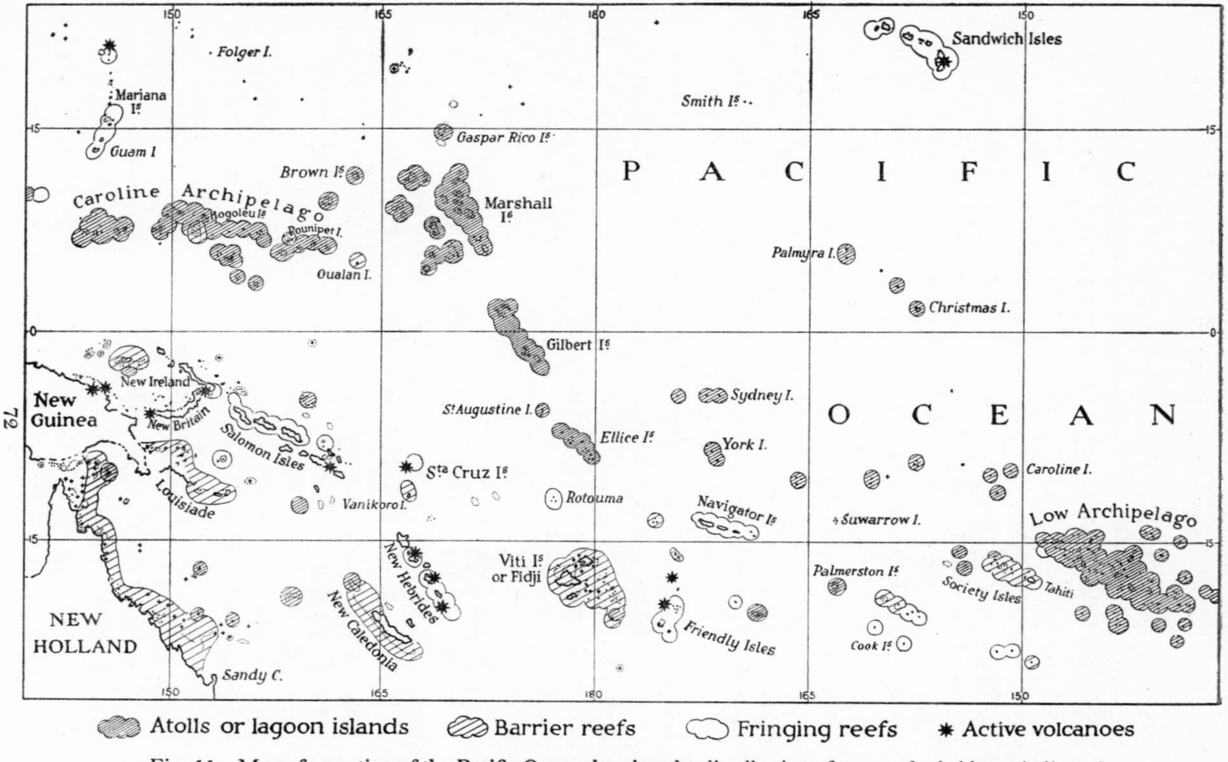

Fig. 11 Map of a portion of the Pacific Ocean showing the distribution of zones of subsidence indicated

sailed as naturalist in H.M.S. *Fly* in the survey of the Great Barrier Reef in 1842. Lyell, as already mentioned, rallied to Darwin's side as soon as he had studied his observations and arguments, but there were not wanting men who tried to pick holes in them and to find exceptions to the general picture of the association of atolls and barrier-reefs with subsidence and fringing reefs with stationary conditions or elevation. In particular, John Murray as a result of his observations during the voyage of H.M.S. *Challenger* in 1880 made a case for the formation of atolls as a result of elevation, by supposing that the platforms on which atolls rest were raised to the necessary height by deposition of sediment, and that the marginal corals, growing most vigorously, expanded the atoll-ring outwards over the debris on the slopes of the platforms.

The only way to test the difference of opinion between Darwin and Murray lay in further observation and study of the composition of the deposits on the sea bottom and, if possible, the foundations deep beneath atolls. Darwin had been deeply interested in the observations made by G. C. Wallich who sailed as naturalist in H.M.S. *Bulldog* in 1860 and reported the results of borings in the ocean bottom that revealed varying thicknesses of foraminiferous deposits, and sometimes bare rock. As Darwin said, 'it bears on the decay of the exuviae of organisms at the bottom of the sea,' which was a point on which he was still collecting information. At about the same date Darwin suggested the use of echo-sounding methods for measuring the depth of the sea. Within a year of his death, Darwin wrote to Alexander Agassiz on 5 May 1881 saying, 'If I am wrong, the sooner I am knocked on the head and annihilated so much the better. It still seems to me a marvellous thing that there should not have been much, and long-continued, subsidence in the beds of the great oceans. I wish some doubly rich millionaire would take it into his head to have borings made in some of the Pacific and Indian atolls, and bring home cores for slicing from a depth of 500 or 600 feet.'

Under the aegis of the Royal Society of London, a boring was made on the atoll of Funafuti in the Ellice Islands. After a number of difficulties had been overcome, it was reported in 1904 that the bore had reached a depth of 1,114 feet and that the core contained remains of recent corals throughout its length. This showed that there were remains of corals 1,000 feet below the level at which they could live, which supported Darwin's theory of subsidence; but it was objected that the bore might have passed through the submarine scree of coral debris that litter the slopes of atolls and not through its foundation. With the borings made to depths of 4,222 feet (1,407 metres) and 4,630 feet (1,540 metres), at Eniwetok atoll near Bikini in the Marshall Islands, greater precision was obtained in 1953. Down to 200 metres the core showed corals and foraminifera extending through the Pliocene period, to 333 metres through the Miocene period, to 933 metres through the Oligocene period, and down to 1,540 metres through the Eocene period to the foundation of basaltic rock. The whole series of sediments were deposited by living organisms over a period of some 60 million years, and the fossils, even in the lowest Eocene layers of the core, were clearly recognized as shallow-water forms, which confirms Darwin's theory of subsidence and provides evidence of subsidence of a magnitude of 1,500 metres.

The progress of scientific research has, however, enabled a further development to take place, from an unexpected quarter, as a result of the researches of R. A. Daly during the present century. During the Ice Age, such a large quantity of water was immobilized in the polar ice-caps that the level of the oceans dropped, perhaps by as much as 150 feet. The atolls then in existence would have had their corals killed and been cut down by wave-action to that level. When the ocean level rose again after the melting of some of the polar ice-caps, the old truncated atolls would have provided platforms for new coral-reefs to be built on them. This is the 'glacial-control' theory, which accounts satisfactorily for the fairly uniform shallow depth of the lagoons enclosed within the atoll-rings, difficult to account for if subsidence had continued uninterruptedly for a long time. Subsidence in accordance with Darwin's theory is required for the formation of the old atolls before the Ice Age and the glacial control theory accounts for the new atolls as they are at present. Between them, Darwin's and Daly's theories provide a satisfactory solution of the whole problem of the origin of coral-reefs. With his keen interest in general concepts of world-wide application, nobody would have welcomed the outcome of these researches more than Darwin himself.

The observations that Darwin made during the voyage of the *Beagle* led, as has been seen, to original contributions of fundamental importance for geology, most of which have stood the test of time triumphantly and become incorporated in standard teaching. In two cases only did his observations subsequently lead him astray, in each because of the reliance that he placed on the possibilities of recent elevation and subsidence, of which he had seen such good evidence in South America and in coral-reefs all over the world.

While Darwin was in the *Beagle*, Jean de Charpentier, as a result of his extensive and long-continued observations on the spot, was laying an irrefutable foundation for the theory of transport of erratic blocks by glaciers over distances of 100 miles from the Alps to the Jura mountains. In so doing he provided confirmation of the deductions that James Hutton and John Playfair had made some years previously but which remained ignored. The earlier and more fanciful speculations of Louis Agassiz on this subject would not deserve mention, except for the fact that Darwin showed that they were mostly unacceptable, for they involved the refrigeration of Europe before the Alps were uplifted, after which event Agassiz suggested that the erratic blocks slid down the inclined planes of ice to their present destination. In place of this, Darwin invoked subsidence of central Europe to allow for the possibility that 'an arm of the sea extended between the Jura and the Alps,' across which he suggested that icebergs detached from the alpine glaciers transported erratic blocks to their present resting-places on the slopes of the Jura, and he also attributed the striations on glaciated rocks to the action of grounded icebergs. He had had experience of icebergs in South America, and the fall of one of these from its parent-glacier into the sea had narrowly missed causing disaster to Darwin and his shipmates (p. 45). He had also seen icebergs carrying rocks. But Charpentier's theory accounts for all the facts so perfectly, down to minute details, that glaciers, not icebergs, are recognized as the agents responsible for the transport of erratic blocks from the Alps to the Jura.

The second case in which Darwin was led astray related to the so-called Parallel Roads of Glen Roy, which, as it turned out, also involved glacial phenomena. These Roads are three sets of raised beaches on the slopes of Glen Roy and neighbouring valleys at 1,150 feet, 1,065 feet, and 857 feet above sea-level. To account for them, Darwin wrote, 'Having been deeply impressed with what I had seen of the elevation of the land in S. America, I attributed the parallel lines to the action of the sea.' He imagined that they were the result of the action of marine waves when the land was submerged to those depths below its present level. The correct explanation is that during the Ice Age, a glacier from Ben Nevis blocked the exits of the valleys of Glen Roy and Glen Gloy, thereby damming back the waters of a high-level lake, the beaches of which formed the highest Road. As outlets occurred at lower levels when the ice had withdrawn, the level of the water in the lake sank and the other beaches were formed. When confronted with the results of T. F. Jamieson's researches, Darwin showed himself a good loser: 'Your arguments,' he wrote, 'seem to me conclusive. I give up the ghost. My paper is one long gigantic blunder. . . . How rash it is in science to argue because any case is not one thing, it must be some second thing which happens to be known to the writer.' Never again did Darwin trust to the principle of exclusion in science, a lesson which all scientists would do well to take to heart.

Chapter 5

Biological Results of the Voyage of the 'Beagle'

'During the voyage of the Beagle I had been deeply impressed by discovering in the Pampean formation great fossil animals covered with armour like that on the existing armadillos; secondly by the manner in which closely allied animals replace one another in proceeding southwards over the Continent; and thirdly by the South American character of most of the productions of the Galapagos archipelago, and more especially by the manner in which they differ slightly on each island of the group.' In this famous passage Darwin enumerated the four lines of evidence which led him to question and eventually to reject the belief in fixity of species with which he had started on the voyage of the *Beagle*. Once engaged on this road, there was no turning back, but there were three stages in the progress of Darwin's ideas which may be enumerated here, to serve as a guide and help the reader to follow the thread. The first stage was his theory of evolution and natural selection as hammered out by the end of the year 1838, which forms the subject of this chapter. Next came the stage when he wrote out a full account of his theory in his Essay of 1844, described in Chapter 6. Lastly, there was the composition of the *Origin of Species* which forms the subject of Chapter 7.

We begin to trace this development by considering his experiences derived from the voyage of the *Beagle*. The first line of evidence alluded to above concerns the principle known as 'the succession of types'. All that this meant was that in some areas species had become extinct, as could be proved by their fossil remains, and that other, but similar, species were alive. It implied nothing about the way in which the types succeeded each other, which might have been by special creation for all that anyone then knew. Darwin found his first fossil *Megatherium* on 23 September 1832 near Bahia Blanca in Argentina, and on 24 November he wrote to Henslow, 'I have been very lucky with fossil bones. . . . I found a large surface of the osseous polygonal plates. . . . Immediately I saw them I thought they must belong to an enormous armadillo, living species of which genus are so abundant here.' Later on he wrote, 'the most important result of this discovery, is the confirmation of the law that existing animals have a close relation in form with extinct species.' Although Darwin discovered these facts for himself in 1832, he claimed no priority for them because he subsequently found that analogous observations had been published in 1831 by E. W. Brayley on fossil mammals found at Eschscholtz Bay in northwest Alaska, while others had been made by William Clift on fossil marsupials in Australia in the same year.

Presently Darwin found many more fossil remains of large mammals including rodents, giant sloths, *Toxodon*, *Mastodon*, horses, and the curious *Macrauchenia*, a camel-like creature with claws, which he discovered near Port St Julian in southern Patagonia, embedded together with the remains of shells belonging to living species. The occurrence of remains of horses and of *Mastodon* in South America was clear evidence of extinction, for there were no living mammals anything like them in South America. But why, Darwin asked himself, were the giant, extinct armadillos built on the same plan as living armadillos, the giant extinct sloths on the same plan as living sloths, the fossil rodents on the same plan as the living tucotuco and capybara?

The second line of evidence concerned the principle known as 'representative species', by which is meant that adjacent areas of a continent are inhabited by different but similar species which take each other's place. In spite of the importance that geological observations occupied in Darwin's attention, his notes show that throughout the time that he spent in South America he searched diligently for the differences between species in the light of changes of habitat and of the existence of physical barriers between the geographical ranges of species occupying adjacent areas.

One piece of evidence in this field was borne in on him dramatically. He had seen large numbers of the common species of rhea (*Rhea americana*) in Argentina and Uruguay, and when he was in northern Patagonia he heard the gauchos speak of another, rarer species of rhea, dark and mottled, with shorter legs feathered lower down, called by them the Avestruz Petise. At Port Desire in southern Patagonia in December 1833, the *Beagle's* artist Conrad Martens shot a rhea which Darwin considered was an immature specimen of the common species. It was cooked and served for dinner, after which Darwin realized that he had eaten the representative species. The head, neck, legs, wings, large feathers, and parts of the skin were preserved, to become the type-specimen of *Rhea darwinii*. It was probably the absence of a marked geographical barrier such as a range of mountains, a desert, or a sea between the two species of rhea that dulled his alertness on this occasion, but it gave all the more point to the question: why is the petise built on the same plan as the common rhea and not on that of an African ostrich or an Australian emu? Why are the agoutis and vizcachas on the savannas of La Plata built on the plan of the peculiar South American type of rodents and not on that of the North American or Old World hares and rabbits? Why are the aquatic coypus and capybaras built on the plan of South American rodents and not on that of the North American beaver or the ubiquitous musk-rat?

The third line of evidence concerns the resemblance of the inhabitants of oceanic islands to those of the nearest continental mainland. When in the Falkland Islands in March 1834, eighteen months before he visited the Galapagos Islands, Darwin was already asking himself whether there were rats, mice, and foxes on 'small islands of Georgia' by which he meant the arc of islands extending east of the Falkland Islands from South Georgia to the South Orkneys and Shetlands. This shows that he was already contemplating the problem of island populations. His pocket-book under the date 18 September 1835, within two days of his first landing in the Galapagos Islands, carries the entry, 'I certainly recognize South America in ornithology'; the Galapagos finches were unmistakably South American in character. Why was this?

Nor was this all. The inhabitants of other oceanic islands supplied Darwin with even more perplexing questions. The volcanic nature and physical conditions of the Galapagos Islands resemble those of the Cape Verde Islands, yet the Galapagos birds all differ from the Cape Verde birds, which means that the physical conditions of the environment do not determine the character of the inhabitants. Instead, the Cape Verde Island birds resemble the African birds. Why is this? The island of Tristan da Cunha in southern mid-Atlantic was not visited by the *Beagle*, but Darwin knew that some of its plants were South American in character and others South African. Why was this, if it was not a bad joke on the part of the Creator to deceive naturalists?

The fourth line of evidence concerns the differences between the inhabitants of the different islands in the Galapagos Archipelago. The physical conditions of these islands are identical, and if the character of the organisms was determined by these conditions, by environment, climate, and natural surroundings, the species on each of the islands should have been identical. To his utter astonishment Darwin found that they were not.

Unfortunately I was not aware of these facts till my collection was nearly completed: it never occurred to me, that the productions of islands only a few miles apart, and placed under the same physical conditions, would be dissimilar. . . . In the case of the mocking-bird, I ascertained that one species (*Orpheus trifasciatus*) is exclusively found on Charles Island; a second (*O. parvulus*) on Albemarle Island; and a third (*O. melanotus*) common to James and Chatham Islands. The last two species are closely allied, but the first would be considered by every naturalist as quite distinct. . . . I have stated, that in the thirteen species of ground-finches, a nearly perfect gradation may be traced, from a beak extraordinarily thick, to one so fine, that it may be compared to that of a warbler.

Why was this?

Not only birds but tortoises led Darwin to ask the same question, and towards the end of the voyage he wrote:

When I recollect the fact, that from the form of the body, shape of scale, and general size, the Spaniards can at once pronounce from which Island any tortoise may have been brought: when I see these Islands in sight of each other and possessed of but a scanty stock of animals, tenanted by these birds but slightly differing in structure and filling the same place in Nature, I must suspect they are only varieties. The only fact of a similar kind of which I am aware is the constant asserted difference between the wolf-like Fox of East and West Falkland Islands. If there is the slightest foundation for these remarks, the Zoology of Archipelagoes will be well worth examining; for such facts would undermine the stability of species.

It was in this condition of doubt about the fixity of species that Darwin returned to England, where he soon met Lyell. Darwin told Henslow, 'Mr Lyell has entered in the *most* good-natured manner, and almost without being

Fig. 12 Heads of some of the Galapagos species of ground-finches showing the variation in structure of the beak correlated with different feeding habits. 1, *Geospiza magnirostris* (feeds on large seeds). 2, *G. fortis* (smaller seeds). 3, *Camarhynchus parvulus* (feeds on insects). 4, *Certhidea olivacea* (small insects). 'Seeing this gradation and diversity of structure in one small, intimately related group of birds, one might really fancy that, from an original paucity of birds in this archipelago, one species had been taken and modified for different ends.' Darwin: *Journal of Researches*, 1845.

asked, into all my plans.' It would be no exaggeration to say that Lyell's friendship was the most important influence in Darwin's career, and a debt that he felt that he could never discharge sufficiently. 'I have long wished,' Darwin wrote to Lyell in 1845, 'not so much for your sake as for my own feelings of honesty, to acknowledge more plainly than by mere reference, how much I geologically owe you.'

After spending a few weeks in Cambridge, Darwin settled in on 13 March 1837 at 36 Great Marlborough Street in London, with Syms Covington, his seaman-assistant in the *Beagle*, as his amanuensis. His first scientific activities when he returned were to sort out his collections, in which task he was helped by Richard Owen who was then Hunterian Professor at the Royal College of Surgeons. Had it not been for the fact that Darwin was carried round the world in a King's ship, he would have preferred to send his collections to the Muséum National d'Histoire Naturelle in Paris because, as he said, 'their value would be so much more in that collection than in the British Museum. I ought to make up my mind to give my own set to Paris, but I confess I should be grieved to lose my trophies. I should feel like a knight who has lost his armorial bearings.' Darwin's preference for the Paris Museum may have been due to the fact that Owen had worked there under Cuvier and that its collections had been made deliberately in accordance with the plans of Buffon's and Daubenton's great work on Natural History, while the collections in the British Museum had been inherited, given, bought, or made as and when specimens became available. Faujas de Saint-Fond described it as 'rather an immense magazine, in which things seem to have been thrown together at random, than a scientific collection'. Until 1807 the Natural History Department included all the Antiquities, Coins, and Medals; after that date it included 'Modern Curiosities', and a register of accessions was started in the 'Zoological Branch' in 1837, the year in which Darwin was considering how to dispose of his collections. It would be of interest to know whether he in fact visited the Paris Museum in 1827. In the event, some of Darwin's specimens went to the British Museum in 1837, others to the Zoological Society's Museum, and others again to the Museum of the Royal College of Surgeons. Both the two last collections eventually came to the British Museum.

Next Darwin arranged for specialists in various fields to describe his collections for publication in the *Zoology of the Voyage of the Beagle* under his editorship. His authors included Richard Owen on fossil mammals, G. R. Waterhouse on recent mammals, John Gould on birds, Leonard Jenyns on fishes, and Thomas Bell on reptiles. The Government made a grant of £1,000 towards the cost of this publication.

Darwin himself spent from January to June 1837 in

writing his *Journal of Researches*, which, however, did not appear until 1839 because FitzRoy's volumes on the oceanographical work of the voyage were not ready until then. Darwin's book, one of the finest works of travel ever written, was not thought worthy of publication by Dr Holland. Fortunately wiser counsel prevailed. The book is almost entirely descriptive and does not betray the turmoil that was going on in Darwin's mind, except in one place where, with the help of hindsight, the modern reader can detect a delicate formulation of the problem. When dealing with the differences between the flora and fauna on the eastern and western sides of the Andes, Darwin wrote, 'unless we suppose the same species to have been created in two different countries, we ought not to expect any closer similarity between the organic beings on opposite sides of the Andes, than on shores separated by a broad strait of the sea,' to which he added a footnote, 'The whole reasoning, of course, is founded on the assumption of the immutability of species. Otherwise the changes might be considered as superinduced by different circumstances in the two regions during a length of time.' Here was his first veiled but public admission of the possibility that species might be mutable.

In view of the part that Humboldt played in stimulating Darwin's interest in travel and natural history, it is interesting to read Humboldt's opinion of Darwin's book, expressed in a letter to Mrs Austin written on 7 June 1844: 'Alas! you have got some one in England whom you do not read—young Darwin, who went with the expedition to the Straits of Magellan. He has succeeded far better than myself with the subject I took up. There are admirable descriptions of tropical nature in his Journal, which you do not read because the author is a zoologist, which you imagine to be synonymous with bore. Mr Darwin has another merit, a very rare one in your country—he has praised me.'

The private diary or journal that Darwin kept contains an important entry in 1837: 'In July opened first note book on "Transmutation of Species"—had been greatly struck from about Month of previous March on character of S. American fossils—and species on Galapagos Archipelago. These facts origin (especially latter) of all my views.' The First Notebook shows how much thought he had already put into the problem by July 1837. It begins with an unexpected reference to a passage in Erasmus Darwin's *Zoönomia* that has nothing at all to do with Erasmus's belief in transmutation of species, but concerns the difference between the products of cuttings and of seeds in plants. The passage reads, 'This paternal offspring of vegetables, I mean their buds and bulbs, is attended with a very curious circumstance: and that is that they exactly resemble their parents, as is observable in grafting fruit-trees, and the propagating flower-roots; whereas the seminal offspring of plants, being supplied with nutrient by the mother, is liable to perpetual variation.'

Under this false attribution of gender to the two methods of reproduction, asexual and sexual, lurks an important truth that Darwin noticed: sexual reproduction, involving two parents, pollination and fertilization, 'is liable to perpetual variation,' because, as we now know, it enables segregation and recombination of genes to take place. On the other hand, asexual reproduction by cuttings, layers, or grafts, produces scions whose genetic make-up is identical with that of the stock from which they have been budded-off or cut. In their production, the genes neither segregate nor recombine but remain the same, and this is why they 'exactly resemble their parents'. Without the benefit of any of this modern knowledge, Darwin had put his finger on the importance of variation and the fact that it results from sexual reproduction. Variation takes place between one generation and the next, for, as he wrote in the vivid telegraphic style of his Notebooks, 'there may be unknown difficulty with *full grown* individual with fixed organization thus being modified'. On the other hand, 'we see the young of living beings become permanently changed or subject to variety, according to circumstance—seeds of plants sown in rich soil, many kinds are produced, though new individuals produced by buds are constant.' These observations enabled Darwin to conclude, 'hence we see generation,' by which he meant sexual reproduction, 'seems a means to vary or adaptation'.

Darwin's next step was to show that variation must be heritable to be significant for his purpose, and it has been shown by Sydney Smith that he took this step, from the critical marginal notes that he entered in his copy of Lyell's *Principles of Geology*, fifth edition (1837). Opposite Lyell's statement that 'peculiarities of form, structure, and instinct, are transmissible to the offspring,' Darwin added the comment, 'with no tendency to go back'. As, in Darwin's day, nothing whatever was known of the facts of heredity, he had great difficulty in distinguishing between variations that were heritable and those that were not, but he had already recognized 'two kinds of varieties. One approaching to nature of monster, hereditary, other adaptation.' The former were 'sports', now called mutations, and Darwin knew that their characters were inherited; the latter were modifications which Darwin distinguished because they adapted the organism to the environment. He inclined to the view that they, also, might be inherited, but he could not make out how they were caused. 'Examine ptarmigan, hare becoming white in winter of Arctic countries; few will say it is direct effect, according to physical laws, as sulphuric acid disorganizes wood [shades of the shed at Shrewsbury where he helped his brother Erasmus in his chemical experiments], but adaptation.' In some remarkable passages he drew attention to the close relation between 'monsters' and the results of 'adaptation', by showing that an albino is a monster, 'yet albino may so far be considered as adaptation, as best attempt of nature, colouring matter being absent'. Similarly 'a dwarf plant grown from seed in the lowlands is a "monster"' but in alpine districts it is an adaptation. Again, if a puppy is born in a temperate climate with a thick coat it is a 'monstrosity', but if a puppy with a normal coat born in a temperate climate is taken into a cold country and there develops a thick coat, it is an 'adaptation'. This is an anticipation by over a century of what are now known as 'genocopies' and 'phenocopies' (see p. 189). Baffled in his attempts to explain 'the wonderful power of adaptation', Darwin was forced to conclude 'this really perhaps greatest difficulty'.

Having satisfied himself that variation could be heritable, Darwin next showed that it must be unlimited in extent. This also is known from his comments in the margins of Lyell's *Principles of Geology*. Opposite Lyell's assertion of 'indefinite divergence [from the common type], either in the way of improvement or deterioration being prevented,' which was Malthus's view, Darwin commented, 'if this were true *adios* theory,' which shows not only that he had recognized the fact that no limit could be ascribed to the possibilities of variation, but also that he had a theory. What this was will soon become apparent.

Unlimited heritable variation requires one more qualification: it must be fortuitous, or random. Fortuitousness had already been recognized in biology by Linnaeus when he stated that hybridization between species had taken place 'accidentally,' and by Maupertuis, who attributed the production of six-fingered men and black races to accidental variation, although it is certain that at this time Darwin did not know of their views. He came across the notion of fortuitousness in an article on domestication of mammals by Cuvier's brother Frédéric, who wrote, 'we could only produce domestic individuals and not races, without the occurrence of one of the most general laws of life—the transmission of a fortuitous modification into a durable form.'

Now, with his knowledge that sexual reproduction gives rise to fortuitous, unlimited, heritable variation, Darwin turned the problem of transmutation of species on its head and asked himself the question, if this is the case, 'why are species all constant over whole country?' He answered this question immediately in the only manner possible in the then-prevailing ignorance of the facts of inheritance: because of the results of 'inter-marriages partaking of characters of both parents.' In other words, Darwin was driven to rely on the principle of so-called blending inheritance, which held that the characters of offspring struck an average between those of the two parents, and that therefore any variation in a population would be 'swamped' and cancelled out in a small number of generations.

This plausible but pernicious error, which had to wait for Mendel to explode it with the results of his experimental studies in genetics, presented Darwin with the greatest difficulty that he had to struggle with for the rest of his life, unnecessarily as is now but was not then known, because although interbreeding keeps the members of a population in the same species, it does not quash variation but conserves and spreads it, and is one of the methods by which species change. In 1837, however, Darwin had nothing to go on but blending inheritance, and he got round the difficulty of its supposed effect of quashing variation in an ingenious way, by appealing to isolation. 'Separate a pair and place them on fresh island, it is very doubtful if they would remain constant,' he wrote and went on, 'Isolate species, especially with some change [of environmental conditions], probably vary quicker.' In other words, isolation of a small number of pairs of organisms will protect any variations that they may show from being obliterated through interbreeding with the whole population, and their offspring will differ from that population and give rise to a variety. These passages read like a summing up of his notes on species inhabiting the two sides of the Andes Cordillera, and Darwin found these views confirmed, first in Humboldt's *Narrative of Travels* where he read 'the exclusion of all foreign mixtures contributes to perpetuate varieties, or the aberrations from a common standard,' and then in Leopold von Buch's *Description of the Canary Islands*: 'Von Buch distinctly states that permanent varieties become species, not being crossed with others'.

Armed with these ingredients, by July 1837 Darwin was in a position to build what he called 'my theory'. Its foundation was, 'We *know* world subject to cycle of change, temperature and all circumstances . . . Absolute knowledge that species die and others replace them—Two hypotheses: fresh creations is mere assumption, it explains nothing further; points gained if any facts are connected.' As will shortly be seen, transmutation of species explains many connected facts. He therefore adopted the hypothesis that transmutation of species has occurred and proceeded to test it in the light of his observations in South America and the Galapagos Islands. 'As we thus believe species vary,' he wrote, 'in changing climate we ought to find representative species: this we do in South America.' These representative species are similar because they were descended from a common ancestor, and they are different because they have varied and become adapted to different local conditions. *This* was why the petise was built on the same plan as the rhea, and the other South American animals adhered to the South American type. With regard to the succession of types, he continued, descent of species by variation from other species 'explains why modern animals same type as extinct. . . . according to my view, in South America parent of all armadilloes might be brother to *Megatherium*, uncle now dead.' They are of the same type because they had a common ancestor from which one line of descendants has become extinct while the other still lives.

On the resemblance of inhabitants of oceanic islands to those of the nearest continental mainland he notes, 'If species 1 may be derived from form 2 etc.,' then (remembering Lyell's arguments of transportal) 'island near continents might have some species same as nearest land, which were late arrivals, others old ones (of which none of same kind had in interval arrived) might have grown altered. Hence the type would be of the continent, though species all different. Two cases as at Galapagos and Juan Fernandez.' This was why the Galapagos birds were South American in type and the Cape Verde Island birds African.

Finally, on the differences between the inhabitants of islands of the same archipelago, 'According to this view, animals on separate islands ought to become different if kept long enough apart, with slightly different circumstances. Now Galapagos tortoises, mocking-birds, Falkland fox, Chiloe fox, English and Irish hare.'

'My theory' had successfully answered the questions that confronted him during his travels, and he soon found that it answered a great many more. Descent with modification from a common ancestor meant that 'Organized beings represent a tree, irregularly branched—hence genera—As many terminal buds dying, as new ones generated.' A few lines later on, with obvious reference to his work on coral reefs which are dead below a certain depth, Darwin corrected himself saying, 'The tree of life should perhaps be called the coral of life, base of branches dead so that passages cannot be seen.' As some of the 'terminal buds' die, gaps are left between them, and therefore 'my theory agrees with unequal distances between species, some fine and some wide which is strange if Creator had so created them.'

'We can see why structure is common in certain coun-

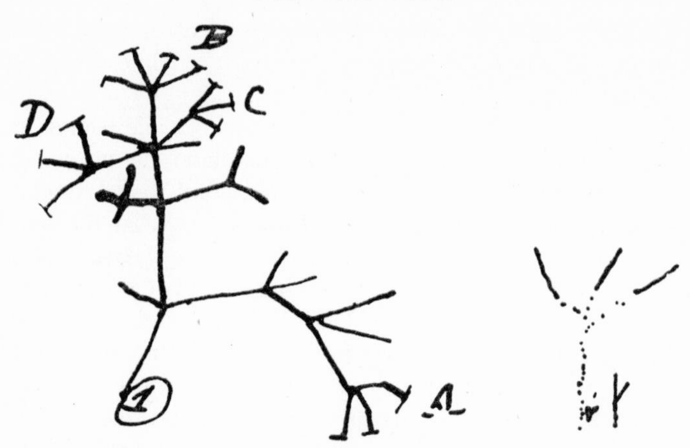

Fig. 13 (left) Darwin's first diagram of an evolutionary tree. The original ancestral species is shown at 1 ; of the subsequent branches those that have become extinct are shown ending simply; those that have given rise to surviving species are shown ending with a cross-line. The latter fall into four groups, A, B, C, and D, each of which then constitutes a genus. The amount of extinction that has taken place is responsible for the width of the gap between A and B, while B is closely related to C, and fairly closely related to D. From 'First Notebook on Transmutation of Species', 1837.

Fig. 14 (right) Darwin's diagram to illustrate his metaphor of 'The coral of life', showing three descendant groups whose common ancestor is extinct and represented by dotted lines. The stem of a tree is alive below the level of the branches that it gives off, whereas the polyps of coral-reefs are dead below a depth of 120 feet below sea-level, whence the metaphor. From 'First Notebook on Transmutation of Species', 1837.

tries when we can hardly believe necessary, but if it was necessary to one forefather, the result would be as it is. Hence antilopes at Cape of Good Hope and Marsupials at Australia.' Darwin had discovered why marsupials are the dominant animals in Australia, and, as W. F. Cannon has pointed out, he realized that the conditions of existence of an organism include the conditions of existence of all its ancestors as well. Darwin also discovered why marsupials are so different from other mammals: 'Countries longest separated—greatest differences,—if separated from immense age, possibly two distinct types, but each having its representatives—as in Australia. . . . In Marsupial division do we not see—splitting in orders carnivora, rodents, etc. just commencing.' This shows that he appreciated that the adaptive radiation of marsupials in Australia was parallel to and independent of that of other mammals elsewhere, occupying comparable ecological niches in each area. He extended this ecological concept when he wrote, 'I cannot for a moment doubt but what Cetacea and Phocea now replace Saurians of Secondary epoch', which is a neat way of saying that whales and seals now occupy the niches formerly occupied by plesiosaurs and ichthyosaurs, niches that would not have become available to them if the latter had not become extinct and vacated them.

These passages show that Darwin was one of the founding fathers of the science of ecology. One of his most important contributions was the realization that niches might exist corresponding to a level of organization below that of the organisms that ultimately filled them. He started with the generalization that 'the enormous number of [species of] animals in the world depends on their varied structure and complexity, hence as the forms became complicated, they opened fresh means of adding to their complexity'; in other words they stimulated each other to a sort of biological arms race. However, 'there is no necessary tendency in the simplest animals to become complicated. . . . I doubt not if the simplest animals could be destroyed, the more highly organized would soon be disorganized to fill their places.' A marginal comment in his copy of Lyell's *Principles of Geology* is relevant here: 'Because there were localities fitter for simplest animals as well as the most complex, therefore some remained simple if not created.' This was Darwin's repudiation of Lamarck's assumption of an innate tendency to perfection in organisms which could only account for the existence of simple organisms on the supposition that they had recently been created by spontaneous generation (p. 6).

At the end of the year 1837 Darwin felt able to draw up a summary of what 'my theory' would do.

With belief of transmutation and geographical grouping we are led to endeavour to discover *causes* of changes,—the manner of adaptation. . . . instinct and structure becomes full of speculation and line of observation. . . . My theory would give zest to recent and fossil comparative anatomy; it would lead to study of instincts, heredity and mind heredity, . . . It would lead to closest examination of hybridity,—to what circumstances favour crossing and what prevent it; and generation [sexual reproduction] causes of change in order to know what we have come from and to what we tend, this and direct examination of direct passages of structure in species might lead to laws of change, which would then be main object of study, to guide our speculations with respect to past and future.

To this manifesto and programme of research he added a few words more that show how he intended his views to apply to all living beings without exception: 'If we choose to let conjecture run wild, then animals—our fellow brethren in pain, disease, death, suffering and famine, our slaves in the most laborious works, our companions in our amusements,—they may partake from our common origin in one ancestor, we may be all netted together.'

This was how Darwin collected, marshalled, and tested his ideas on transmutation of species in the construction of 'my theory'. He also explained his method of working, which is worth mentioning because of the manner in which it was afterwards impugned. 'The line of argument often pursued throughout my theory is to establish a point as a probability by induction and to apply it as hypotheses to other points and see whether it will solve them.' He started from what he believed to be a fact, spun a hypothesis from it by induction, and then by deduction thought of consequences that could be tested for refutation or confirmation. It is also to be noticed that 'my theory' was not a static description of evolution as a series of historic events but an attempt at a dynamic explanation of how it had occurred.

At this stage Darwin claimed no originality for 'my theory'. The idea of descent of species from a common ancestor had been the subject of speculation by Diderot, Erasmus Darwin, and Lamarck. There was also the analogy provided by the history of languages. In 1786, Sir William Jones had shown that a comparison between Sanskrit, Greek, and Latin revealed similarities that could only be explained on the assumption that these three languages had emanated from some common source which now, perhaps, was a dead language. This concept of a family of related languages, descended from a common ancestral language, was extended in 1816 by Franz Bopp who introduced the term Indoeuropean to include Sanskrit, Persian, Greek, Latin, German, and most of the languages spoken in Europe. Although a poor linguist himself, Darwin was aware of the significance of comparative philology for his own problem. 'Scarcely any novelty in my theory,' said Darwin, 'only slight differences, the opinion of many people in conversation.' Early in September 1838 he wrote, 'Seeing what Von Buch, Humboldt, G. St-Hilaire, and Lamarck have written I pretend to no originality of ideas (though I arrived at them quite independently and have used them since), the line of proof and reducing facts to law only merit if merit there be in following work.' And yet, 'my theory' was already definitively and distinctively Darwin's; it was not indebted in any way to Erasmus Darwin in whose works he 'was much disappointed, the proportion of speculation being so large to the facts given'; nor did it owe anything to Lamarck's *Philosophie zoologique*, on Darwin's copy of which he wrote, 'very poor book'. By 1838 nobody but Darwin had integrated limitless, heritable, fortuitous variation, isolation of geographical races, representative species, succession of types, adaptation, and extinction, into a theory of transmutation and provided evidence in support of it.

It was to this stage in the progress of his ideas that Darwin afterwards referred in his *Autobiography* when, after giving the points that had most impressed him during the voyage of the *Beagle* (mentioned on p. 78), he added:

> It was evident that such facts as these, as well as many others, could be explained on the supposition that species gradually became modified; and the subject haunted me. But it was equally evident that neither the action of the surrounding conditions, nor the will of the organisms (especially in the case of plants), could account for the innumerable cases in which organisms of every kind are beautifully adapted to their habits of life,—for instance a woodpecker or tree-frog to climb trees, or a seed for dispersal by hooks or plumes. I had always been much struck by such adaptations, and until these could be explained it seemed to me almost useless to endeavour to prove by indirect evidence that species have been modified.

In other words, he was looking for the 'causes of change' to which he had referred in his summary of what 'my theory' would achieve, and for an explanation of the origin of adaptations. Of these, he had a useful catalogue ready to hand in the works of Paley, to which he had paid so much careful attention (pp. 17, 29, Plate 9).

In his *Autobiography* Darwin continued, 'I soon perceived that selection was the keystone of man's success in making useful races of plants and animals. But how selection could be applied to organisms living in a state of nature remained for some time a mystery to me.' Taking only entries in his Notebooks on Transmutation of Species written before 3 October 1838, a date the importance of which will shortly be apparent, we find the following points made. A necessary step in the argument was of course to show that the amount of variation found between different varieties of domestic animals produced by artificial selection by man can reach the same order of magnitude as variations existing between two species. Darwin showed it and wrote, 'I was struck looking at the Indian cattle with Bump, together with Bison of some resemblance as if the variation in one was analogous to specific character of other species in genus.' In other words, the amount of difference between the domestic breeds of cattle is comparable to the difference between the two species of cattle and bison.

As regards selection operating in nature, the following remarks are fundamental: 'with respect to extinction we can easy see that variety of ostrich Petise may not be well adapted, and thus perish out, or on the other hand like Orpheus being favourable, many might be produced. This requires principle that the permanent varieties, produced by confined breeding and changing circumstances are continued and produce according to the adaptation of such circumstances, and therefore that death of species is a consequence . . . of non-adaptation of circumstances.' This is a clear recognition of the fact that varieties not well adapted to their environment tend to perish while those that are well adapted flourish and multiply. The penalties of inadequate adaptation are specifically related to changes in the environment in the following passage: 'The constitution being hereditary and fixed certain physical changes [in the environment] at last become unfit [for the organism] the animal cannot change quick enough and perishes.' It is interesting that Darwin applies the terms 'fit' and 'unfit' to the environment instead of to the organism.

Towards the end of September 1838 he wrote, 'if the circumstances which must be external which induce change are always of one nature species is formed, if not—the changes oscillate backwards and forwards and are individual differences. . . . All this agrees well with my view of those forms slightly favoured getting the upper hand and forming species.' This is a clear recognition of the fact that selection in nature of fortuitous variants that happen to be better adapted to their environment than their unsuccessful rivals results in the automatic improvement of adaptations without the intervention of any design or final cause, and, eventually, to the formation of new species. Two points should be noticed here. The first is that improvement of adaptation does not necessarily imply any increase in complexity of the organisms concerned; it may involve a decrease of organization. The second point is that the production of adaptive structures that are useful to their owners does not imply purposive design in their production.

At the beginning of the Notebook containing the entry last mentioned, Darwin afterwards wrote (in 1856), 'Towards close I first thought of selection owing to struggle.' He had discovered for himself that in nature, selection of variants that happened to be favourably adapted to their environments would produce change and ultimately new species. It is therefore somewhat surprising to find the following statement in his *Autobiography* written in 1876: 'In October 1838, that is fifteen months after I had begun my systematic enquiry, I happened to read for amusement Malthus on *Population*, and being well prepared to appreciate the struggle for existence that everywhere goes on from long-continued observation of the habits of animals and plants, it at once struck me that under these circumstances favourable variations would tend to be preserved and unfavourable ones to be destroyed. The result of this would be the formation of new species. Here, then, I had at last got a theory by which to work.' This famous sentence has usually been taken to mean that Darwin obtained the idea of natural selection of variations from Malthus, but as may be seen from the quotations from his Notebooks written before he read Malthus's book, this is not the case. The question must therefore be asked what it was in Malthus's book that made so deep an impression on him.

In his Notebook under the date of 28 September 1838, Darwin made a note which enables the relevant passage in Malthus's work to be identified; it runs: 'It may safely be pronounced, therefore, that population, when unchecked, goes on doubling itself every twenty-five years, or increases in a geometrical ratio.' This is an increase beyond the increase in the means of subsistence, and a substantial rate of mortality is therefore inevitable. As Darwin had already grasped the importance both of variation and of selection, the effect of this passage in Malthus's book was to suggest to him the inexorable pressure exerted by selection in favour of the better adapted and against the less well adapted. Furthermore, as he had also grasped the principle of ecological niches, he concluded, 'one may say there is a force like a hundred thousand wedges trying to force every kind of structure into the gaps in the oeconomy of nature, or rather forming gaps by thrusting out weaker ones.' This was how he came to recognize the action of the pressure exerted by this force which resulted in sorting out variations and producing adaptation: the key to evolution.

It seems that Darwin began to read Malthus's book on 28 September. Owing to his curious habit of cutting pages out of his Notebooks when he wanted to use them for writing his later works, and the loss of these pages, the full sequence of development of his thought cannot be followed in detail, but it seems that he finished reading Malthus on 3 October 1838, after which he entered a quotation from the book in his Notebook. Darwin's disagreement with many of Malthus's remarks is plain to see from his underlining certain words and his marks of exclamation. Darwin quoted:

It accords with the most *liberal!* spirit of philosophy to believe that no stone can fall, or plant rise, without the immediate agency of the deity [Malthus had written 'divine power']. But we know from *experience!* that these operations of what we call nature, have been conducted *almost!* invariably according to fixed laws: and since the world began, the causes of population and depopulation have been probably as constant as any of the laws of nature with which we are acquainted. This [continued Darwin] applies to one species—I would apply it not only to population and depopulation but extermination and production of new forms.

Darwin also made a special note of the necessity to dissociate himself from Malthus's view that the possibilities of variation were strictly limited.

It is therefore clear that Darwin did not owe Malthus anything on the score of variation or natural selection, but only the realization that the high rate of mortality exacted by nature resulted in pressure, and while Malthus argued that this pressure was exerted against the poor members of the human race, Darwin applied the principle to plants and animals and argued that the pressure was exerted against the less well adapted. That this is the correct interpretation of events follows from Darwin's letter to Wallace in 1858 in which he wrote, 'I came to the conclusion that selection was the principle of change from the study of domesticated productions; and then, reading Malthus, I saw at once how to apply this principle.' He had already arrived at the principle of natural selection and had seen how, given variation, it would lead to unlimited change away from the ancestral type, improvement of adaptation, and eventually the production of new species. Malthus enabled him to see how inexorably nature enforced this principle. The view that Darwin was led to the idea of natural selection by the social and economic conditions of Victorian England is devoid of foundation.

There is irony in the fact that Malthus's aim was to prove that man was socially unimprovable, while Darwin used one point in his argument to show that all species can improve their adaptations. The irony is all the greater because in man Malthus's principle has not been objectively demonstrated, since no deliberate and concerted

Plate 7 Sir Charles Lyell, drawing by George Richmond.

Plate 8 Sir Joseph Hooker, 1881, portrait by John Collier.

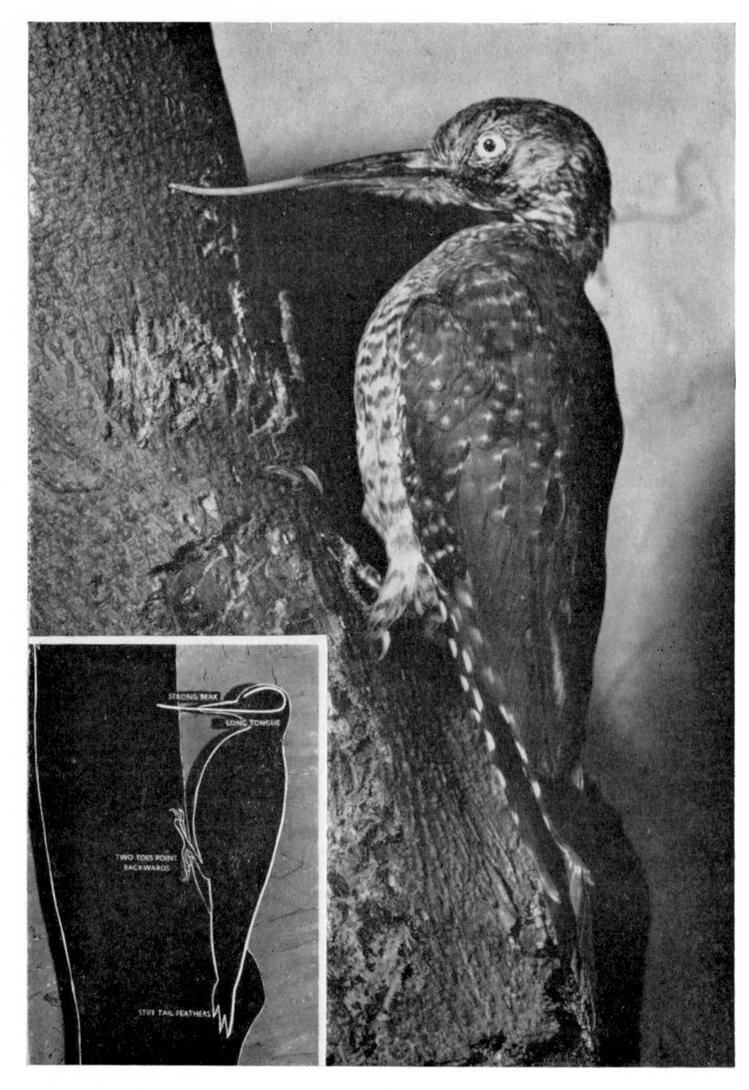

Plate 9 An example of adaptation. The woodpecker has two toes on each foot pointing backwards, enabling it to get a firm foothold on the bark of trees, stiff tail-feathers serving to prop it securely against the tree, a long stout beak with which it chisels holes in the bark, and a very long tongue with which it reaches and takes the grubs at the bottoms of the holes. As other birds lack these structures and functions which adapt the woodpecker to its conditions of life, these adaptations must have arisen during the evolution of the woodpecker, and Darwin's great problem, and contribution, was to discover how adaptations arise and are improved.

attempt has been made to discover by how much the production of food for human consumption could be increased by scientific methods. While Malthus was concerned to show that the checks to increase of population in man consisted of inadequate available means of subsistence, epidemics, and conscious prudential restraint in procreation, Darwin generalized the means by which natural selection acts on plants and animals in nature by showing that they include besides starvation such factors as predation, reproductive competition, and accidents of physical environment.

The episode of Darwin's reading of Malthus's book shows something of the slow and methodical nature of Darwin's mental processes. Brilliant, clever, and quick-witted men skipped over and missed the minute and obscure indications that Darwin patiently and systematically picked up and built into a system, without the use of any complicated apparatus or new instruments, simply from scrupulous adherence to the results of observations interpreted logically in the light of a key of such simplicity that only a genius could have found it. It is worth while to consider what Darwin had done by the end of 1838, and how the clever men missed what he had found. Basic to the concept of natural selection was the struggle for existence. This was common property; it was realized by Diderot, Erasmus Darwin, Lamarck, and Lyell; De Candolle had elevated it to the status of the war of nature. It pierces rather ashamedly through the pious lucubrations of Paley, and Darwin had observed it for himself. Selection by man in breeding-pen and garden had been practised ever since the Neolithic period. The idea of selection had actually been applied to conditions in nature by Lyell, who used it only to explain the extinction of species: 'A faint image of the certain doom of a species less fitted to struggle with some new condition in a region which it had previously inhabited, and where it has to contend with a more vigorous species, is presented by the extirpation of savage tribes of man by the advancing colony of some civilized nation.' As Lyell then firmly denied the possibility of transmutation, selection had no part to play in his thinking on that score.

Edward Blyth had given a description of the results of variation in species preyed on by sharp-eyed predators. If the behaviour or colour of the variants departed ever so little from the type of the species, either by failing in vigilance or in matching the natural background, or in straying away from it, such variants would fall victims to the predators by the natural interplay of causes which 'remove all that deviate from their normal or healthy condition, or which occur away from their proper or suitable locality,' and thereby 'tend to limit the geographical range of species, and to maintain their pristine characters without blemish or decay to their remotest posterity.' There is a paradox here, for Blyth's reason for rejecting the possibility of transmutation was because he thought that if it had occurred species would merge into each other, and 'we should seek in vain for those constant and invariable distinctions which are found to obtain'. In other words, Blyth rejected the possibility of transmutation of species because he rightly rejected the very reason for which Lamarck accepted it.

There is a second paradox because Blyth used the principle of natural selection to prove that species were immutable and had been specially created in the ranges allotted to them, and that evolution was impossible. Although Blyth had been playing with the very tools that Darwin so successfully used, it is difficult to see that Darwin was indebted to him, for his conclusions were the exact negation of what Darwin was trying to prove. Besides, Darwin had no difficulty in showing from his own observations that Blyth's view of species being allotted particular areas was not in accordance with fact, for he had seen in South America that woodpeckers, which are birds conspicuously well adapted to live and get their food on trees, also live in the Pampas, to which they have extended their range, where there are no trees at all so that they make their nests in holes in banks. As for the argument that selection had for all time kept a species true to type, this would mean that species must by now be perfectly adapted to the environments in which they live, as Paley believed they were; but again from his personal experience, Darwin knew of numerous cases where organisms showed imperfect adaptation to their environments; even a deformity could be regarded as 'the best attempt of nature under very unfavoured conditions as an adaptation'. He also knew of other cases in which intruders or introduced species had overrun and beaten the indigenous inhabitants. In other words, species have not all reached a steady state of perfection from which no improvement could be possible. It is only because improvement is possible that evolution can happen at all.

So the incongruous situation had arisen that some men —Diderot, Erasmus Darwin, Lamarck—had suggested that evolution had occurred but were unable to prove it because they could not provide the evidence, nor could they explain it because they relied only on speculative appeals to effects of volition, tendencies to perfection, fulfilment of needs, inheritance of acquired characters, or direct effects of the environment, and knew nothing of how natural selection produces adaptation. Lyell and Blyth who knew of the action of natural selection used it to prove that evolution could not occur. Paley provided examples of adaptations of plants and animals to their environments in order to show evidence of purposive design. Darwin used the same examples of adaptations to show that they originated by natural selection without purposive design. Malthus had put forward his system to prove that man was unimprovable. Darwin used Malthus's argument to show that mortality in the struggle for existence was the method by which nature enforced natural selection, which improved adaptation. Lyell used the principle of uniformitarianism to prove that evolution was impossible because evolution involved progressionism and progressionism involved catastrophism and catastrophism must be rejected. Darwin used uniformitarianism to show that simple, existing causes produced and directed evolution, and that there was no link between catastrophism and progressionism, which latter was more in accordance with the evidence. Alternatively it might be said that by cutting down the sizes of the catastrophists' catastrophes to minute dimensions, so that they formed finely graded events in time as well as in space, Darwin made the catastrophists' position acceptable because their principle of progressionism, provided that it simply meant change without implying obligatory increase of complexity, was in accordance with the evidence of the history of the earth, which the eternal stability of uniformitarianism was not.

The supreme paradox was, therefore, that Darwin used Lyell's methods to show that Lyell's views on biology were wrong and that his opponent Sedgwick's were more nearly correct. Above all, Darwin fulfilled the prophecy of John Herschel who had written to Lyell from Cape Town on 20 February 1836, not many weeks before Darwin called on him there, saying that 'the origination of fresh species, could it ever come under our cognizance, would be found to be a natural in contradistinction to a miraculous process—although we perceive no indications of any process actually in progress which is likely to issue in such a result.' This letter was printed in Charles Babbage's *Ninth Bridgewater Treatise* in 1837. Darwin read it on 2 December 1838 and wrote in his Notebook, 'Herschel calls the appearance of new species the mystery of mysteries and has grand passage upon the problem. Hurrah—"intermediate causes".'

Darwin had found the process actually in progress which issued in the origination of fresh species, and he had also found one thing more that transcended the limits of biology and raised the strongest opposition to his views when, ultimately, they were published. He had found that the natural selection of fortuitous variations without design resulted in what Paley had regarded as the strongest argument in favour of purposive design and constant supernatural supervision by beneficent divine guidance in the production of adaptations. The whole object of the Bridgewater Treatises was to support this view. Darwin had shown that species evolve, just as planets revolve, not by the direct volition of the Creator but as a result of natural laws: 'intermediate causes'. There were probably many sources from which Darwin could have derived this idea, but it is possible that one was Étienne Geoffroy-Saint-Hilaire on whose work Darwin noted 'grand idea God giving laws and leaving all to follow consequences'. It was in line with such views that Darwin had already written, 'Astronomers might formerly have said God ordered each planet to move in its particular destiny. In same manner God orders each animal created with certain form in certain country, but how much more simple and sublime power—let attraction act according to certain law, such are inevitable consequences—let animal be created, then by the fixed laws of generation, such will be their successors.'

It was something remarkable to have undermined the entire basis for natural theology as Paley conceived it; it was something even more to have shown that adaptations that serve a purpose did not imply purposive final causes in their production. This was an extension of Hume's argument that the existence of order and adaptation cannot justify the inference that they are the work of a designer. Darwin had now shown that the existence of order and adaptation are not ultimate facts at all, but the result of intermediate causes, variation and natural selection, the product of which could be imperfect adaptation. Adaptation means that the organism possesses structures or functions that enable it to adjust itself sufficiently successfully to the conditions of its environment. These structures and functions fulfil a purpose: teeth bite and wings fly. But it was not because they would bite after they had arisen that teeth were destined to arise. It was because they served to bite after they had fortuitously arisen from something else (protective scales) that teeth were retained and enlarged, or lost if no longer used. There was no designed programme or fulfilment of a predetermined aim such as would result from final causes. Adaptation is purposive but not teleological, and Pittendrigh's term 'teleonomic' renders the service of recognizing that adaptations are directed to an end without implying that they were designed to serve that end. Paley's divine watchmaker was unemployed, because the wonderful property of organisms is that they make and mar themselves. This was the real significance of the revolution in thought that Darwin had sprung on the world.

By the end of the year 1838, then, Darwin had discovered the most important principle in biology, comparable in scope to Newton's discovery of gravitation. But Darwin kept it to himself; he had grown shy of repeating the discomfiture that he had brought upon himself when he rushed eagerly to communicate his discoveries to Grant and to Henslow. 'I was so anxious to avoid prejudice,' he wrote, 'that I determined not for some time to write the briefest sketch of it,' referring to his discovery. One of the chief reasons for this reticence is that the biological results of the voyage of the *Beagle* were not confined to the theory of evolution by natural selection, formulated two years from the date when Darwin landed back in England; they also included the evolution of Darwin's own mind. When he sailed in 1831 he was an ordinary, orthodox candidate for holy orders who quoted the Bible at the *Beagle's* officers. He collaborated in a paper with FitzRoy on the moral state of Tahiti and the good work that missionaries were doing. In New South Wales in January 1836, reflecting on the strange character of Australian animals, he wrote in his diary, 'An unbeliever in every thing beyond his reason might exclaim, "Surely two distinct Creators must have been at work".' Then he observed the conical pitfall of an ant-lion and saw how it shot jets of sand at its prey, exactly as in the Old World. 'Would any two workmen ever hit on so beautiful, so simple, and yet so artificial a contrivance? It cannot be thought so—The one hand has surely worked throughout the universe.' Here it is not difficult to recognize Paley's words that 'we never come into the province of a different Creator'.

When Darwin returned to England he was a man of science, impervious to arguments by analogy and other undisciplined lines of thinking, insistent on objective evidence insofar as he could get it for every step in induction and deduction by which he built up his theory. It would be interesting to know exactly how this change was effected, and it is probable that a contributory factor was his realization that the Scriptural account of the Creation could not be reconciled with his geological observations. FitzRoy made a remark that was probably significant when he wrote that walking with a friend over vast plains composed of rolled stones embedded in diluvial detritus hundreds of feet thick he said, 'this could never have been effected in a forty days' flood,' for which impiety on his own part FitzRoy excused himself by saying that he had been 'led away by sceptical ideas,' no doubt, Darwin's. FitzRoy was running more truly to form when he attributed the extinction of large mammals to their having been shut out of the Ark.

Whatever the reason for Darwin's changed outlook,

within a few months of his return to England he was filling his Notebooks with entries that he would never have made before he sailed in the Beagle, and that would have made his friends' hair stand on end had they read them, as the following examples will show: 'Why is thought being a secretion of brain more wonderful than gravity a property of matter?' 'Free will is to mind what chance is to matter; it is our arrogance, our admiration of ourselves.' 'Chance governs the descent of a farthing, free will determines our throwing it up.' 'It may be doubted whether a man intentionally can wag his finger from real caprice, it is chance which way it will be, but yet it is settled by reason.' 'It is an argument for materialism, that cold water brings on suddenly in head a frame of mind analogous to those feelings which may be considered as truly spiritual.' 'A train of thought action &c. will arise from physical action on the brain.' 'Love of the deity effect of organization, oh you materialist!' 'Now that I have a taste of hardness of thought. . . .' Darwin had indeed become the hardest-headed biologist of his time; and this was one of the most important results of the voyage of the *Beagle*.

Chapter 6

Marriage, Down, and the Essay on Species

The formulation of the theory of evolution by natural selection did not exhaust Darwin's interests or activities in the year 1838. He was constantly engaged in work on his Notebooks on Transmutation of Species and preparing his books on *Coral Reefs*, *Volcanic Islands*, and the *Geology of South America.* On 16 February 1838 he was appointed Secretary of the Geological Society of London, and in July of that year he started a new series of Notebooks on Metaphysics, morals, and speculation on expression. With astonishing speed the various parts of the *Zoology of the Voyage of the Beagle* were published one by one under his editorship, and he started working on the Parallel Roads of Glen Roy.

Meanwhile his fancies had turned, not lightly, but ponderously, to thoughts of love. He drew up what can only be called a balance-sheet of advantages and disadvantages of the married state, like a judge's summing-up of the evidence, and few documents reveal the man himself so well as this one. If he did not marry he might travel, exclusively for geology, or if he did not travel he might work at transmutation of species; if he did marry, with limited means, he would feel it his duty to work for money; life in London was nothing but society; he might think of a professorship at Cambridge in geology or zoology; he could not take a country house and do nothing. If he did not marry he might live in London, 'for where alse possible —in small house near Regent's Park—keep horses'; but if he did marry could he act thus 'with children and poor—? No.' It would be better to live in the country near London, 'but great obstacles to science and poverty.' Cambridge would be better, 'but fish out of water, not being Professor and poverty.' He might live in the outskirts of London, but 'I have so much more pleasure in direct observation, that I could not go on as Lyell does, correcting and adding up new information to old train.'

In this way he approached nearer and nearer to THE Question: MARRY: children—constant companion, (friend in old age)—charms of music and female chit-chat, good for one's health; but forced to visit and receive relations *terrible loss of time*: NOT MARRY choice of society *and little of it*, conversation of clever men at clubs, not forced to visit relatives, no expense or anxiety of children, perhaps quarrelling, 'if many children forced to gain one's bread. —(But then it is very bad for one's health to work too much).' Then comes the climax of the debate: 'My God, it is intolerable to think of spending one's whole life, like a neuter bee, working, working, and nothing after all.— No, no, won't do.—Imagine living all one's day solitarily in smoky dirty London House.—Only picture to yourself a nice soft wife on a sofa with good fire, and books and music perhaps . . . Marry—Marry—Marry Q.E.D.'

Having come to this conclusion he still had some misgivings; if he had to go every day walking with his wife he would never know French or see the Continent or America or go up in a balloon; 'poor slave, you will be worse than a negro . . . Never mind my boy—Cheer up. . . . There is many a happy slave.' Acting on this decision he left London on 9 November 1838 for a short visit to Maer Hall where, two days later, he proposed marriage to his cousin Emma Wedgwood and was accepted. 'The day of days,' he wrote in his Journal. Seldom can an engagement have given so much unreserved pleasure to the entire families of both parties.

Back in London one week later he plunged straight into his Notebooks again and started house hunting. He looked at 8 Albany Place, Regent's Park, houses in Albany Street, Montague Place, Keppel Street, 1 Bernard Street, Russell Square, 20 Woburn Square ('rather nice house'), Tavistock Square. On 29 December he wrote to Emma to say that he had taken 12 Upper Gower Street (afterwards renumbered 110 Gower Street and destroyed by the German Air Force in spring 1941) into which, with the help of Syms Covington, he moved on 1 January 1839, papers and all, and continued working. On 20 January he wrote to Emma, 'I take so much pleasure in the house, I declare I am just like a great overgrown child with a new toy; but then, not like a real child, I long to have a co-partner and possessor.' A great overgrown child he remained all his life. On 24 January 1839 he was elected a Fellow of the Royal Society and on 29 January his wedding took place at Maer, after which the happy couple immediately returned to London and took up residence in their new home. On his wedding-day the bridegroom entered in his Notebook on Transmutation of Species, 'Uncle John [Hensleigh Allen] says he feels sure, that the reason people send for their seeds to London is that people in the southern Counties have whole fields, some for cauliflower &c.—Uncle John believes one single turnip in a garden is sufficient to spoil a bed of Cauliflowers,' from which it may be deduced that conversation at the wedding breakfast touched on the subject of plant hybridization.

Four days after arrival in London, Emma wrote to her sister, 'Charles and I did some shopping, which he professes rather to like and I bought my morning gown. . . . And then we went shopping through the melted snow to Broadwood's, where we tried the pianoforte . . . yesterday we trudged out again and half-ruined ourselves at the plate shop, and in the evening we actually went to the play, which Charles thinks will look very well in the eyes of the world.' As for Darwin himself, 'I have been riding very regularly for the last fortnight,' he wrote in April, 'and it has done me a wonderful deal of good.'

In the spring of that same year, 1839, Darwin happened to meet in Trafalgar Square an officer who had been a shipmate in the *Beagle* walking with Joseph Dalton Hooker, whom he introduced to Darwin, so beginning another of the greatest friendships ever knitted between two men. The son of Sir William Hooker, the Director of the Royal Botanic Gardens at Kew, Hooker was about to embark on Sir James Ross's expedition to the Antarctic in the *Erebus*, which sailed in company with the *Terror*. Hooker had had some difficulty with Ross over his appointment as naturalist to the expedition, because Ross had appointed Robert McCormick to be the zoologist. When Hooker asked if he could be the naturalist, Ross answered that 'such a person as a Naturalist must be perfectly well acquainted with every branch of Natural History, and must be well known in the world, *such a person as Mr Darwin*; here,' continued Hooker, 'I interrupted him with "What was Mr Darwin before he went out?" ' Matters were smoothed out, and Hooker was appointed assistant surgeon to the *Erebus* and Ross recognized him as botanist to the expedition. Not the least interesting part of this episode is that it shows the reputation that Darwin had already acquired even before his *Journal of Researches* describing the voyage of the *Beagle* was published, for that happened in August 1839 whereas Ross's remark to Hooker was made in April of that year.

Darwin's *Journal of Researches* figures again in that intricate web of human associations between kindred spirits that had already caught him, Lyell, and Hooker up in its meshes. An old friend of the Hooker family, Charles Lyell of Kinnordy, father of Darwin's great friend, had sent to Hooker the proof-sheets of the *Journal of Researches* while

Hooker was preparing to take his M.D. examination, on which his appointment to the *Erebus* depended. His time-table was so full that he slept with the proofs under his pillow and read them before getting up in the morning. Before the *Erebus* sailed at the end of September 1839, Mr Lyell sent Hooker a published copy of the book, and Hooker eventually acknowledged it, saying, 'Your kind present is indeed now a well-thumbed book, for all the officers send to me for it.' From Tierra del Fuego, Hooker wrote to his mother, 'Clouds and fogs, rain and snow justified all Darwin's accurate descriptions of a dreary Fuegian summer. Indeed all Darwin's remarks are so true and so graphic wherever we go that Mr Lyell's kind present is not only indispensable but a delightful companion and guide.' This encomium of Darwin's book is confirmed by a letter later sent to Hooker by a shipmate, J. E. Davis, second master of the *Terror*: 'I like Darwin's Journal much: he has accomplished what old Johnson said of Goldsmith when he heard he was going to write a Natural History: "He will make it as interesting as a Persian tale".'

Hooker described Darwin as 'a rather tall and rather broad-shouldered man, with a slight stoop, and agreeable and animated expression when talking, beetle brows, and a hollow but mellow voice.' Another person whom Darwin met, introduced by his brother Erasmus, was Harriet Martineau 'who has been as frisky lately as the rhinoceros.' His circle of friends also included the great botanist Robert Brown, who had sailed to Australia with Matthew Flinders in H.M.S. *Investigator*, Sydney Smith, Macaulay, Lord Stanhope, Charles Babbage, John Motley, George Grote, Monckton Milnes, Roderick Murchison, Sir John Herschel, Dean Milman, and Thomas Carlyle. He also met Alexander von Humboldt. Although launched in society, he managed to restrict his circle to people of real value.

On 27 December 1839 his first son, William Erasmus, was born and immediately became the object not only of great affection but meticulous observation.

> During the first seven days various reflex actions, namely sneezing, hickuping, yawning, stretching, and of course sucking and screaming, were well performed by my infant. On the seventh day I touched the naked sole of his foot with a bit of paper, and he jerked it away, curling at the same time his toes, like a much older child when tickled. The perfection of these reflex movements shows that the extreme imperfection of the voluntary ones is not due to the state of the muscles or of the coordinating centres, but to that of the seat of the will.

Darwin's insatiable thirst for observation and explanation in this field was later to form the subject of one of his books, the *Expression of the Emotions*.

In the autumn of 1839 Darwin had felt obliged to give up going to parties because they tired him too much. Between the time when he returned from the voyage of the *Beagle* and the year 1842 when he left London, he was ill over a dozen times, which introduces the whole question of Darwin's illness. His symptoms included great lassitude, gastro-intestinal discomfort and pain often resulting in nausea with prolonged periods of vomiting, and sleeplessness. As his doctors were unable to discover any organic cause for his ailments they were hard put to diagnose his trouble and prescribe for it. Not a few of his contemporaries ascribed it to hypochondria, and this view has been echoed by recent commentators who have attempted to account for Darwin's state of health on the assumption that he had a 'poor nervous heredity on both sides', that he was troubled by 'depressive obsessional anxiety and hysterical symptoms' due to a 'distorted expression of the aggression, hate, and resentment, felt at an unconscious level by Darwin towards his tyrannical father,' that he suffered from 'prolonged struggles to sublimate affective needs,' and that his whole medical history reads like that of a neurotic subject, especially his acquiescence in the excessive care that his wife bestowed on him, and the advantage that he took of his semi-invalidism to avoid the strains of a social life which interfered with his scientific work. It has been suggested that Darwin's theories of evolution and natural selection killed the Heavenly Father, and that Darwin suffered the remorse of Oedipus.

It must remain a matter of opinion whether this is a sufficient explanation of the reduction to semi-invalidism of a man with the physical stamina, courage, fortitude, healthy mind, and good judgment that Darwin showed during the voyage of the *Beagle*, when for five years he cheerfully endured the hardships of life at sea in the little ship and ashore, when he roughed it with gauchos, ate coarse food and enjoyed it, climbed mountains, made numerous, lengthy, arduous, and dangerous journeys on foot and on horseback, slept out, caught venomous snakes, shot, fished, admired Spanish ladies, cracked jokes, and took everything in his stride. Darwin himself knew that in some quarters his ailments were ascribed to hypochondria and he resented this deeply. As he wrote to Hooker, 'every one tells me that I look quite blooming and beautiful; and most people think I am shamming, but you have never been one of those.'

Recently it has been shown that there is evidence on which a diagnosis of Darwin's disease may perhaps be objectively based. It will be remembered that on 26 March 1835, at Luxan, (p. 49) he 'experienced an attack (for it deserves no less a name) of the Benchuca, the great black bug of the Pampas.' This bug, now known as *Triatoma infestans*, is the most important carrier of *Trypanosoma cruzi*, the causative agent of Chagas's disease. It has been shown that seventy per cent of these insects are infected with the trypanosome, and they occur widely in South America. Darwin himself tells us how 'one which I caught at Iquique [Peru] was very empty; being placed on the table and though surrounded by people, if a finger was presented, its sucker was withdrawn, and the bold insect began to draw blood. It was curious to watch the change in the size of the insect's body in less than ten minutes. There was no pain felt. This one meal kept the insect fat for four months; in a fortnight, however, it was ready, if allowed to suck more blood.'

The conclusion of the specialists on Chagas's disease is that Darwin, could not, in view of the evidence, have avoided becoming infected by the trypanosome. It has been shown by Saul Adler that the symptoms caused by Chagas's disease can be matched, detail for detail, with Darwin's medical history from the time when he landed in England from the *Beagle* until his death. Trypanosomes can be recovered from the blood of patients many years after infection, and there are long periods of latency. The trypanosome invades the muscle of the heart in over eighty per cent of Chagas's-disease patients, which makes them very tired; it invades the ganglion cells of Auerbach's nerve plexus in the wall of the intestine, damage to which upsets normal movement and causes great distress; and it invades the auricular-ventricular bundle of the heart which controls the timing of the beats if auricle and ventricle, interference with which may result in heart-block. The lassitude, gastro-intestinal discomfort, and heart trouble from which he suffered an attack in 1873 and died in 1882, all receive a simple and objective explanation if he was infected with the trypanosome when he was massively bitten by the bug on 26 March 1835.

As *Trypanosoma cruzi* was not identified until 1909, it is not surprising that Darwin's doctors were unable to find any evidence of organic disease if he was suffering from Chagas's. Whether he also suffered from neurotic tendencies is a question that must be left unanswered, except to suggest that if he was suffering from a disease

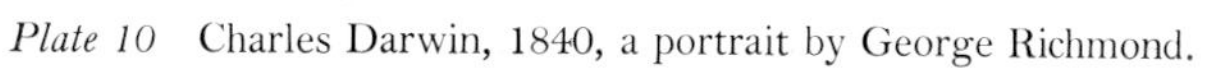

Plate 10 Charles Darwin, 1840, a portrait by George Richmond.

Plate 11 Emma Darwin, 1840, a portrait by George Richmond.

like Chagas's, which his doctors were unable to diagnose or treat, it would not be surprising if he shunned society and sheltered under the care of his wife. It has, however, been claimed that he suffered from some of the symptoms that later distressed him before he ever reached South America. In November 1831, at Plymouth during the anxious time of waiting for the *Beagle* to sail, when he was sadly out of spirits at the prospect of leaving his family and his friends for so long a time, he felt palpitations and pain about the heart; but this is no evidence against his subsequently having contracted Chagas's disease, nor need it be evidence of disease at all. However this may be, and it will never be definitively proved one way or the other, the fact remains that the rest of Darwin's work was done against a background of poor health that amounted to semi-invalidism.

On 19 February 1841 he resigned from the secretaryship of the Geological Society, and in the following year he made his last geological excursion to examine the evidence of former glacial action in North Wales. It must have been a bitter blow to him to feel obliged by poor health to abandon a pleasure that was so dear to him. With his wife he then set about finding a house in the country. After fruitless searches in Surrey and elsewhere, the possibilities of living at Down House in Kent were broached in April 1842, for on the 27th of that month Darwin wrote to his sister Susan to express gratitude for their father's and her interest in the project of taking Down House. On 22 July 1842 Darwin offered £2,200 for it, which his father paid, and on 14 September Darwin and his wife moved in, only just in time because Emma gave birth nine days later to a child that unfortunately lived for only three weeks.

Down House, in the village of Downe, is situated off the road to Sevenoaks in rolling country to the north of the chalk scarp that rises from the Weald. Darwin described it as 'a good, very ugly house with 18 acres, situated on a chalk flat, 560 feet above sea. There are peeps of far distant country and the scenery is moderately pretty: its chief merit is its extreme rurality. I think I was never in a more perfectly quiet country.' Such was the place, with its garden, shrubberies, and orchards, beautiful trees and pleasant footpaths, where Darwin gradually settled down into a routine that filled each ordinary day with four hours' work while taking snuff, 'the chief solace of life,' walks in the garden with visits to the greenhouse, a constitutional walk in the neighbourhood and along the 'sand-walk', occasionally a ride on a horse, periods of rest on a sofa when a book was read to him or he himself read a novel, smoking a cigarette, a game of backgammon after dinner followed by reading and listening to the piano. His son has related that it was his custom and pleasure to rise early, and, except when at his worst, he started the day well, but exhausted his energy sooner or later, which is why he preferred to travel by the earliest possible train and to call on his friends by ten in the morning. This supports the view that his ailments were of an organic nature, for it is more usual in cases where there is no organic disease to find that the morning begins with poor health and spirits which improve as the day goes on.

A description of a visit to Down in the early days of its occupancy was given by Hooker.

A more hospitable and more attractive home under every point of view could not be imagined—of society there was most often Dr Falconer, Edward Forbes, Professor Bell, and Mr Waterhouse—there were long walks, romps with the children on hands and knees, music that haunts me still. Darwin's own hearty manner, hollow laugh, and thorough enjoyment of home life with friends; strolls with him all together, and interviews with him one by one in his study, to discuss questions in any branch of biological or physical knowledge that we had followed; and which I at any rate always left with the feeling that I had imparted nothing and carried away more than I could stagger under.

Another face that was soon to become familiar at Down was that of Thomas Henry Huxley. Like Darwin and Hooker, Huxley had been 'well salted in early life' when he sailed in H.M.S. *Rattlesnake* on a voyage of surveying and exploration in Australian and New Guinea waters from 1847 to 1850. Shortly after Huxley's return, Darwin made his acquaintance and this fast turned into firm friendship. In these congenial surroundings Darwin was as happy as could be, in spite of his poor health and anxiety about the health of his children when they were seriously ill, which was frequently the case. Apart from this, his chief worries arose from the discovery of Californian and Australian gold with its threat of 'beggaring me by making my money on mortgage worthless; the French coming by the Westerham and Sevenoaks roads, and therefore enclosing Down; and thirdly, professions for my boys.'

It will be remembered that after finding in 1838 the key to evolution by means of natural selection, Darwin refused even to commit himself on paper for some time. He wrote in his *Autobiography*: 'In June 1842 I first allowed myself the satisfaction of writing a very brief abstract of my theory in pencil in 35 pages; and this was enlarged during the summer of 1844 into one of 230 pages.' It is to this Essay of 1844 that attention may now be turned, as it was the first round-up and statement of his theory, written out in full. It represents the second stage in Darwin's progress along the path of evolution. Quotations may also be made from his Sketch of 1842 because of its apt terseness. In his Notebooks on Transmutation of Species in February 1838, Darwin had made a note for his own future guidance, 'The only cause of similarity in individuals we know of is relationship, children of one parent, races of animals—argue opening thus.' In fact, he opened his case quite differently, beginning with Variation under Domestication and Principles of Selection.

Of the hereditary tendency Darwin could say only that it existed, of variation that it resulted from sexual reproduction, and of the causes of variation that they were unknown but that some variations were heritable without environmental agency, particularly 'when we see in the same litter, produced by the same act of conception, animals considerably different.' Other variations were due 'to the direct effect of known or unknown agencies acting for one or more generations on the parents,' or, in other words, to effects of environmental factors that he, like all his contemporaries, believed could be heritable. When he was writing his Essay in 1844, science still had thirty-one years to wait before Oskar Hertwig showed that in fertilization one sperm nucleus unites with one egg nucleus. Darwin therefore had no reason to doubt that 'when the dam of one species has borne offspring to the male of another species, her succeeding offspring are sometimes stained (as in Lord Morton's mare by the quagga, wonderful as the fact is) by this first cross,' an unfounded folk-belief that has led to lawsuits even in the twentieth century.

Selection as practised by man has made one breed of horses to race and another to pull, sheep with fleeces good for carpets and others good for broadcloth, dogs to find game and dogs to fetch game, cattle with fat mixed with the meat for the butcher and cattle with fat accumulated in the bowels for the tallow-chandler. The same results can be shown in plants as in the case of cabbages and cauliflowers, plants grown for leaves and plants grown for fruit, and the different varieties of *Dahlia* produced since 1804, when they were first cultivated in England.

Next in the Essay came a section on variation in a wild state and on the natural means of selection. 'Considering how many animals and plants, taken by mankind from different quarters of the world for the most diverse purposes, have varied under domestication in every country and in every age, I think we may safely conclude that all organic beings with few exceptions, if capable of being domesticated and bred for long periods, would vary.' As already explained, on the erroneous view of blending inheritance to which there was at that time no alternative, Darwin thought that variation was liable to be obliterated by interbreeding within the population, but this he considered could be avoided if small portions of a population were isolated. He was concerned to show not only that organisms vary, and that the amount of variation possible is unlimited, but that in the struggle for existence if there should happen to be in an individual 'any minute variation in structure, habits, or instincts, adapting that individual better to the new conditions . . . it would have a better *chance* to survive.' If a dog preyed chiefly on rabbits but sometimes on hares, and rabbits decreased in numbers while hares increased, the dogs would be driven to catch more hares, and dogs 'with the lightest forms, longest limbs, and best eyesight . . . would be slightly favoured, let the difference be ever so small, and would tend to live longer and to survive during that time of the year when food was shortest; they would also rear more young, which young would tend to inherit these slight peculiarities. The less fleet ones would be rigidly destroyed.' Improved adaptation would be the result, and this automatic selection of those individuals that would be most prolific in their offspring would explain how some plants might have pollen that was more attractive to insects and so bring about cross-pollination, and might have berries that were more attractive to birds that frequented trees, so that the berries, with their contained seeds, were dropped with the birds' droppings on the branches of trees where they germinated resulting in plants like mistletoe. Descendants would be gradually modified away from the original type, and if this modification in structure and in habits continued long enough, the result would be that the descendants would no longer breed with individuals of the original type and would constitute a new species. In other words, the origination of new species is a result, a by-product, of improvement of adaptations in different directions.

The principles of natural selection may most easily be expressed in the form of a table of seven steps, involving four inductions and three deductions, as follows:

1. Organisms have a potential rate of reproduction that is higher than the rate of increase of their food-supply.
2. The number of individuals in a species remains more or less constant.
3. Therefore there must be a high rate of mortality—many more young produced than ever reach maturity.
4. Individuals in a species are not identical but show variation.
5. Therefore some variants will succeed better and others less well in the competition for survival in their environments, and the parents of each successive generation will be naturally selected from among those individuals that are most prolific in offspring because they show variation in the direction of more effective adaptation to the conditions of their environment.
6. Hereditary resemblance between parents and offspring is a fact.
7. Therefore the offspring of each generation will include individuals that maintain and improve on the degree of adaptation realized by their parents, and ultimately depart further and further from the original type until the new forms are no longer fertile with the old and then constitute a new species.

It is important to note that Darwin's principle of selection is based on the increased survival that effective adaptation confers on those individuals that therefore leave a greater number of offspring. On this point confusion has arisen in some quarters where it has been contended that Darwin's principle of selection only concerned longevity, while 'reproductive' selection was thought to be something different that he had not envisaged. This is quite erroneous; he always kept reproductive capacity in mind.

Variation does not produce new species straight away but varieties, and Darwin's next step was to show that the difference between varieties and species is a difference not of kind but only of degree. It was and is usual to define this difference by saying that varieties when crossed are fertile, but that species, when they can be made to cross, are infertile. Numerous examples of species can, however, be found that when crossed produce hybrid offspring, and these hybrids may themselves be fertile. There is therefore no reason to draw any hard and fast line between species and varieties, and no reason why species may not have originated as varieties.

Variation in instincts is the next topic in the Essay, and here Darwin was able to show that the study of comparative behaviour provides evidence that related animals may show similarities in their instincts, such as shamming death in insects and building nests in birds. Here he invoked the principle of gradation to show that there is a perfect series of insects from those that momentarily stand still to others that remain immovable for long periods o time, and of birds from those that lay their eggs on the ground to those that build nests of increasing degrees of complexity.

At this point Darwin introduced a section on the difficulties in the way of regarding complex structures and instincts as having arisen by natural selection of fortuitous variations. Examples are the comb-building capacities of the hive-bee, the habits of seed-eating birds like sparrows of feeding their young with the caterpillars that they catch, or the formation of the eye or the ear in vertebrate animals. Here again, Darwin's method was to invoke the principle of gradation and to claim that 'if selection can produce the smallest change, and if such a series exists, then it is clear . . . that it may *possibly* have been acquired by gradual selection of slight, but in each case useful deviations.'

After he had thus introduced the mechanism that he advocated as the means by which evolution had taken place, Darwin next proceeded to consider the evidence that it has taken place. This curious reversal of the normal order of presentation of the problem was the result of his determination not to put forward his conclusions about the fact of evolution before he was able to explain the origin of adaptations. Foremost among the witnesses to the fact of evolution was the geological record, but Darwin had to show not only that fossil forms intermediate between existing living forms were not to be expected, but also that of the fossil, ancestral forms that were to be expected only very few would be available because of the imperfection of the geological record. This was where his extensive observations on the geology of South America came in so useful to him, for he was able to provide direct evidence that unless there had been long-continued deposition of sediment in an area together with progressive subsidence, no series of fossils could be expected to have been preserved. This was the reason for the 'fewness of preserved organisms compared to what have lived in the world.'

The sudden appearance of a profusion of fossil organisms in the lowest-known fossiliferous deposits presented him with a special difficulty; for 'If the Palaeozoic system is really contemporaneous with the first appearance of life, my theory must be abandoned,' because these fossils already show high degrees of organization, such as trilobites, molluscs, echinoderms, and other forms which must be supposed to have already had a long evolutionary history behind them. Darwin pointed to the fact that 'the lowest formations known to us are only those which have escaped being metamorphosed' and their contained fossils protected from destruction. 'If the several known formations are at all nearly consecutive in time, and preserve a fair record of the organisms which have existed,' he continued, 'my theory must be abandoned.' Here he was able to bring to bear not only his observations that areas of land subjected to elevation tended to have their fossil contents destroyed by erosion, but also his conclusion that the gaps between geological formations might represent stretches of time far longer than the times required for the deposition of the formations themselves (p. 65).

Although groups of species might appear to come in abruptly, all together at the start of some formation or other, and to become extinct equally abruptly at the end, this was only the picture presented by a local phenomenon. 'The slow and gradual appearance of new forms follows from our theory, for to form a new species, an old one must not only be plastic in its organization, . . . but a place in the natural economy of the district must come to exist for the selection of some new modification of its structure, better fitted to the surrounding conditions than are the other individuals of the same or other species.' Here was Darwin's recognition of the fundamental importance of ecology in providing niches that evolving organisms could fill if they varied and the variants better adapted to fill such niches were selected.

Extinction of species was a fact for which Darwin had discovered first-hand evidence himself in the disappearance of the horse and *Mastodon* in South America, but it was still difficult for contemporary opinion to accept a conclusion that implied such abandonment on the part of the Creator. 'To marvel at the extermination of a species appears to me to be the same thing as to know that illness is the road to death—to look at illness as an ordinary event, nevertheless to conclude, when the sick man dies, that his death has been caused by some unknown and violent agency.'

The facts of geographical distribution of plants and animals provided Darwin with one of those long chains of close argument based on evidence, in which he delighted. If, as he contended, species originated by descent from other species, a new species must have arisen in a single region of the earth and once only. Taking the distribution of land mammals, whose powers of migration are largely restricted to land connections and impeded by wide stretches of sea, Darwin showed that Eurasia and North America could be considered as a single area because of the possibilities of easy crossing of the Bering Strait, and that the other distinguishable areas were Africa, South America, and Australia. Each area has its characteristic forms and 'the amount of difference in the organisms bears a certain, but not invariable relation to the amount of physical difficulty to transit' between them. In other words, the distribution of mammals on earth is such as would be expected if they had evolved in one area and had migrated thence to their present habitats, but it would be inexplicable if they had been specially and separately created where they now live.

It is frequently found that high mountainous areas are inhabited by identical species of plants that are not found in intervening lowland regions. It was important for Darwin to provide an explanation of this fact, which might otherwise be used as an argument in favour of the view that species could come into existence in more than one place and more than once by special creation. He found the explanation in the effects of climatic changes during the Ice Age. As the temperature fell, plants adapted to temperate climates were driven away from the poles and towards the equator, while arctic species took their places in formerly temperate latitudes. Later, when the Ice Age waned, the arctic plants migrated not only towards the poles but also up mountains to higher altitudes, while the temperate climate plants returned to the lowlands. The isolation of identical species, or closely related species, on different and widely separated mountains is therefore in no way opposed to the origination of each species in one area only and once only.

Geographical distribution is also concerned with the different numbers of species found in different regions, and with the reasons for this. New Zealand, stretching over seven hundred miles of latitude with forests, marshes, plains, and mountains, has far more diversified habitats and ecological niches than an equal area at the Cape of Good Hope; yet there are far more different species in the latter than in the former. On the theory of special creation there is no better explanation of this fact than there is of why in the Galapagos Islands the 'creative power' had been so prodigal in multiplying species. On the theory that species originated from other species by transmutation in particular areas and migrated away from them, the facts of geographical distribution of organisms in New Zealand and in South Africa, with their differences in accessibility, would be expected to be as they are.

Next comes the problem of the affinities and classification of living and fossil organisms. They are classified according to the characters that they possess in common and are placed in one or other of a not very large number of major groups, such as ferns or conifers, molluscs or mammals. Within each of these groups there is subdivision into smaller groups, mammals being thus subdivided into ungulates, carnivores, rodents, and primates, to mention only a few. Within these again is a further subdivision into lower categories such as families, genera, and species. This arrangement, so different from a single file climbing up a ladder, or from an arbitrary assortment like the stars in imaginary constellations, or from a fortuitous collection of pebbles on a beach, would be the natural result of the divergence of a species into related species forming a genus, similarly formed genera giving rise to a family, and so on with orders, classes, and the highest categories of biological classification. Organisms fall into groups that are contained in larger groups, and these in still larger groups. The affinities of organisms expressed in the form of a natural classification would therefore represent the results of their evolution and descent from common ancestors.

Organisms are classified by their structure, and in each large group there is a uniformity of plan. 'What, for instance,' asked Darwin, 'is more wonderful than that the hand to clasp, the foot or hoof to walk, the bat's wing to fly, the porpoise's fin to swim, should all be built on the same plan? and that the bones in their position and number should be so similar that they can all be classed and called by the same names?' These correspondences, unaffected by the different functions that they perform, are what is meant by saying that such structures are homologous. Such structures, Darwin went on, 'can by the creationist be viewed only as ultimate facts and incapable of explanation; whilst on our theory of descent these facts all necessarily follow: for by this theory all the beings of one class, say of the mammalia, are supposed to be descended from one parent-stock, and to have been altered by such slight steps as man effects by the selection of chance domestic variations.'

Uniformity of plan also extends to embryonic development: 'Thus, for instance, at one period of the embryo, the wings of the bat, the hand, hoof or foot of the quadruped, and the fin of the porpoise do not differ. At a still earlier period the embryo of the fish, bird, reptile and mammal all strikingly resemble each other.' These resemblances which provide evidence of affinity are not merely superficial and external, but extend throughout the structure of the embryos and apply to their internal organ-systems. Darwin was the first to draw attention to the significance of embryology for evolution, and his explanation of the similarities between young stages of development of related animals was that the natural selection of variations that adapted the organisms to their environment when adult affected mostly late stages of development, leaving the early stages mostly unchanged in the relatively constant environment of egg-membrane or womb. Consequently, 'there will be less tendency to modify the young: and hence we might expect to find at this period similarities preserved between different groups of species which have been obscured and quite lost in the full-grown animals.' The embryos remain similar to the embryos of the ancestors; the adults of the descendants have diverged.

Abortive organs are also explained by embryology and uniformity of plan of structure. They are vestiges of organs that performed adaptive functions in the ancestors but now either perform no functions at all or have been modified to perform different functions. Examples are the teeth of whalebone whales, limbs of snakes, wings of ostrich and penguin, and flowers of the feather-hyacinth. 'On the ordinary view of individual creations, I think that scarcely any class of facts in natural history are more wonderful or less capable of receiving explanation.' On the theory of evolution they are easily understood.

Very briefly summarized, these were the main lines of argument that Darwin wove into his Essay of 1844, ending with a memorable demonstration of the absurdity of the alternative explanation of the origin of living beings.

Shall we then allow that the three distinct species of *Rhinoceros* which separately inhabit Java and Sumatra and the neighbouring mainland of Malacca were created, male and female, out of the inorganic materials of these countries? Without any adequate cause, as far as our reason serves, shall we say that they were merely, from living near each other, created very like each other, so as to form a genus dissimilar from the African section [of rhinoceros], some of the species of which sections inhabit very similar and some very dissimilar stations? Shall we say that without any apparent cause they were created on the same generic type with the ancient woolly rhinoceros of Siberia and of the other species which formerly inhabited the same main division of the world: that they were created, less and less closely related, but still with interbranching affinities, with all the other living and extinct mammalia? That without any apparent adequate cause their short necks should contain the same number of vertebrae with the giraffe; that their thick legs should be built on the same plan with those of the antelope, of the mouse, of the hand of the monkey, of the wing of the bat, and of the fin of the porpoise. . . . that in the jaws of each when dissected young there should exist small teeth which never come to the surface. That in possessing these useless abortive teeth, and in other characters, these three rhinoceroses in their embryonic state should much more closely resemble other mammalia than they do when mature. And lastly, that in a still earlier period of life, their arteries should run and branch as in a fish, to carry the blood to gills which do not exist. . . . I repeat, shall we then say that a pair, or a gravid female, of each of these three species of rhinoceros, were separately created with deceptive appearances of true relationship, with the stamp of inutility on some parts, and of conversion in other parts, out of the inorganic elements of Java, Sumatra and Malacca? or have they descended, like our domestic races, from the same parent-stock? For my own part I could no more admit the former proposition than I could admit that the planets move in their courses, and that a stone falls to the ground, not through the intervention of the secondary and appointed law of gravity, but from the direct volition of the Creator.

This Essay was written at a time when information on the subject was exceedingly scanty, much was unreliable, and some definitely erroneous. The notion of blending inheritance, in the total absence of any experimental evidence on hereditary transmission, was all there was to go on. Fertilization of an egg by a sperm had not been observed, let alone chromosomes. Mimicry had not been discovered. The uniformity of plan of body-cavity, kidneys, and genital ducts had not been worked out. The affinities of king-crabs and scorpions to spiders, and the relations of the hinge-bones of the jaws of reptiles to the ear-ossicles of mammals had not been shown. The similarity between the feeding mechanisms of the lancelet and of larval lampreys and the conversion of the structure in question in the latter into the thyroid gland was unknown. The similarities between the larval forms of echinoderms and of the most lowly chordates had not been discovered, nor had the vestiges of the egg-tooth in marsupials which, although viviparous, preserve this trace of the adaptation originally used by reptilian embryos to hatch out of their egg-shells. Botanists had not begun to suspect the fact and significance of the alternation of generations found in mosses, ferns, and flowering plants, without which their methods of reproduction cannot be understood. The mobile sperm of the maidenhair-tree and of cycads, retained from the time when plants depended on films of moisture for the fertilization of their eggs, a good hundred million years ago, was unknown. Comparisons between bloods and other fluids as a measure of divergence in evolution were not dreamt of. Most surprising was the paucity of material then available in palaeontology. Nothing was known of the close series of related species in lineages of Jurassic ammonites, Cretaceous sea-urchins, and Tertiary horses, elephants, and camels, or of fossils like *Archaeopteryx*, and many others which serve as indicators of the structure of precursors of the various classes of vertebrates and of the intermediate evolutionary stages between them. In fact, all the cases now used to demonstrate evolution in the most unequivocal manner were discovered since Darwin wrote his Essay in 1844. It is a matter for wonder that with the meagre materials at his disposal he was able to steer a straight course across a largely uncharted ocean of ignorance, with rocks of falsehood right across his path.

On 5 July 1844 Darwin wrote a letter to his wife in which he requested her in the event of his death to devote £400 to the publication of his Essay, and to secure the help of Lyell, Hooker, or some other suitable person to edit it. 'If, as I believe, my theory in time be accepted even by one competent judge, it will be a considerable step in science.' Knowing as he did what a fundamental contribution to biology he had made, the question arises why Darwin did not publish it himself. Only to Hooker did he give it to read. The most that Darwin allowed himself was that in the second edition of the *Journal of Researches* of the voyage of the *Beagle*, he included two statements which, with the help of hindsight, the present reader can recognize as prophetic though they must have presented riddles to the readers of 1845. The first of these statements concerns the ground-finches of the Galapagos Islands which played so important a part in opening Darwin's eyes to the possibility that species were not immutable: 'Seeing this gradation and diversity of structure in one small, intimately related group of birds, one might really fancy that from an original paucity of birds in this archipelago, one species had been taken and modified for different ends.' This was a discreet suggestion that the different species of Galapagos ground-finches had descended with modification from one ancestral species. The other statement related to the principle of succession of types, the resemblance between extinct fossil forms that once inhabited a region and the species now living in the same area. With well-placed emphasis for the benefit of those, if there were any, who appreciated the significance of the word 'hereafter' in the following passage, it ran: 'This wonderful relationship on the same continent between the dead and the living will, I do not doubt hereafter throw more light on the appearance of organic beings on our earth, and their disappearance from it, than any other class of facts.' Here was a public recognition that the appearance of new species might be no more mysterious than the extinction of old ones.

For Darwin's procrastination in publishing a full account of his theory when he had written it out in 1844 there were several reasons, the first of which was his innate caution. In that same year 1844 an anonymous book was published under the title *Vestiges of the Natural History of Creation* in which the author, by skilful speculation with flowing style but lamentable ignorance of many facts of geology and biology, put forward a theory of evolution. It was very crude and might have been written by a man like Benoît de Maillet in the eighteenth century. It was a mixture of Cuvier's progressionism, Lamarck's tendency to perfection, Paley's teleological final causes and design, and Scriptural orthodoxy. It allowed for spontaneous generation of organisms by means of electric currents, and it derived terrestrial animals from marine animals, reptiles from fishes and mammals from birds in a manner that made Darwin shudder, all the more because the names that were popularly attributed to the anonymous author included Darwin himself, besides the Prince Consort, among others. This fact is in itself of interest because it shows that some persons suspected that Darwin had become converted to the transmutation of species. The author of the book was Robert Chambers and the suspicion that attached to him for having written it, although never admitted, compelled him to withdraw his candidature for the office of Lord Provost of Edinburgh. This also was significant for Darwin because he had already regarded Lamarck as having harmed the cause of transmutation of species, and he was anxious that his own work should not suffer in the minds of his contemporaries by association with *Vestiges*. Actually, *Vestiges* served Darwin well, for twenty-four thousand copies had been sold and it was very widely read and discussed by the time the *Origin of Species* was published. It called attention to the subject, however clumsily, and acted as a lightning conductor for the torrent of opposition that it raised in both scientific and religious circles, which deflected and blunted some of the attacks that were later to fall on Darwin. The opposition to the idea of transmutation of species was not negligible, for in addition to the orthodox and uninformed majority, it still included Lyell, Sedgwick, Herschel, Whewell and Hooker. Darwin's broadside must not misfire.

Chapter 7

Barnacles and the 'Origin of Species'

'At last gleams of light have come,' Darwin wrote to Hooker on 11 January 1844, 'and I am almost convinced (quite contrary to the opinion I started with) that species are not (it is like confessing a murder) immutable.' As W. F. Cannon has aptly remarked, it was murder that Darwin was contemplating, murder of everything that Lyell had stood for with his uniformitarian principle of eternal stability. Darwin went on, 'I think I have found out (here's presumption!) the simple way by which species become exquisitely adapted to various ends. You will groan and think to yourself, "on what a man have I been wasting my time and writing to". I should five years ago have thought so.' Hooker was the only man to whom Darwin confided his great secret, and to him later in that year, 1844, Darwin sent his Essay on species; but it made little impression on Hooker. Although Lyell continued to be the revered, but often challenged, master, Hooker had become Darwin's closest confidant and in the spring of 1845 Darwin wrote again saying, 'I hope this next summer to finish my South American geology, then to get out a little zoology, and hurrah for my species work.' The geology was finished with the publication of the *Geology of South America* in 1846, and the 'little zoology' began. It was his study of barnacles and was to last eight long years.

Barnacles are a small and obscure group of animals that defied all attempts to classify them in their proper place in the animal kingdom until in 1830 Vaughan Thompson found that their young stages of development were similar to those of Crustacea, which fixed their systematic position as a highly specialized sessile group in that class. This in itself must have attracted Darwin's attention because of his interest in the evidence that embryology provided in support of evolution. He had, however, become interested in barnacles before his conversion to transmutation of species, because as he explained in his *Autobiography*, when on the coast of Chile he found a curious, burrowing form of barnacle that differed so much from all others that a new sub-order had to be made to put it in, and this gradually led him to take up the study of the whole group. From October 1846 on he borrowed and begged barnacles from all over the world and eventually had ten thousand specimens to study. The whole house was so firmly held in the grip of this work on Darwin's 'beloved barnacles' that when one of his children went out to tea with his little friends he asked his hosts in all seriousness about their father, 'where does he do his barnacles?'

There was another reason why Darwin devoted so much work to those forbidding animals. This was, as he confided to Hooker, because of his 'long self-acknowledged presumption in accumulating facts and speculating on the subject of variation' without having worked out his due share of species. His intensive study of barnacles, living and fossil, provided Darwin with invaluable evidence for the problem of species that always occupied pride of place at the back of his mind. On the one hand he obtained practical experience of the amount of variation to be found between individuals in the same species living in nature; on the other he was able to see how different groups had varied and given rise to the different families of barnacles in the order. 'I have been struck with the variability of every part in some slight degree of every species,' he wrote to Hooker on 13 June 1849. 'Systematic work would be easy were it not for this confounded variation, which, however, is pleasant to me as a speculatist, though odious to me as a systematist.' Here was the evidence on variation that he had been looking for.

This excursion into systematics and taxonomy brought Darwin face to face with the problems of zoological nomenclature. The rules of procedure required that the earliest name that could be found with a description of a species subsequent to the tenth edition of Linnaeus's *Systema naturae* published in 1758 had priority and was the reigning name for the species, and the name of its describer had to follow the name of the species immediately. Darwin considered that this practice was pernicious because it tended towards unnecessary multiplication of species and genera by naturalists and carelessness in description and definition as a result of the desire to see their name in print. As he wrote to Hugh Strickland, 'I find every genus of Cirripedia has half a dozen names, and not one careful description of any one species in any one genus.' He categorically refused to add his name to the new species that he described and he also refused to apply the law of priority in cases which would have meant calling one well-known barnacle *Balanus* by the name of another equally well-known barnacle *Lepas*: 'cannot do it, my pen won't write it—it is impossible.' Further, he protested, 'I cannot bring myself to reject *very well-known* names . . . for obscure ones' merely because they were inadequately described at an earlier date. Today machinery exists for the recognition of *nomina conservanda* by the International Commission on Zoological Nomenclature.

In 1848 Darwin made a striking discovery. Barnacles are normally hermaphrodite, but in some species he found minute individuals like parasites lodged under the mantle of other individuals, and he correctly identified them as dwarf or 'complemental' males: 'little husbands,' as he once described them. He wrote to Hooker, 'I should never have made this out had not my species theory convinced me, that an hermaphrodite species must pass into a bisexual species by insensibly small stages: and here we have it, for the male organs in the hermaphrodite are beginning to fail, and independent males ready formed.' Here was not only a remarkable example of adaptation but evidence supporting his view that cross-breeding was of particular significance. The complemental males, living like parasites on the bodies of the larger hermaphrodites, may have been the starting-point for a suggestion of genius that he made at about this time in a letter to an unidentified correspondent: 'What interesting investigation would be the comparison of the parasites of the closely allied and representative species of birds of Britain and North America'; a remark that anticipated by a hundred years the recognition of one of the most profitable lines of research in parasitology, as recently developed by Jean Baer and Theresa Clay, who have shown that indications of the affinities of the hosts may in some cases be obtained from the affinities of their parasites which, being more conservative in their uniform environments, have varied less and evolved more slowly.

The work on barnacles was published in two monographs on the living forms and two on the fossils, in 1851 and 1854. They remain the standard works of reference on the subject. The time that Darwin spent on barnacles or Cirripedes may seem excessive in view of the fact that he held in his head the key to the most important advance ever made in biology but had not published it. Huxley considered that the patient toil that Darwin put in on the barnacles was an act of great wisdom because, like all naturalists at that time, he had had no proper training in biological science but saw the necessity for it and did not shirk the labour involved in acquiring it. Darwin himself recognized three stages in his career as a biologist: 'the mere collector at Cambridge; the collector and observer in the *Beagle* and for some years afterwards; and the trained naturalist after, and only after the Cirripede work.'

The barnacle years were not a happy period in Darwin's life. His family had increased; Anne had been born in 1841, Mary born and died in 1842, Henrietta born in 1843, George in 1844, Elizabeth in 1847, and Francis in 1848. In 1849 Darwin was advised to try Dr Gully's Water-cure Establishment at Malvern and spent nearly four months there, and it seemed to do him some good in spite of Dr Gully's forbidding him to take more than six pinches of snuff a week, an allowance that was soon stopped altogether. He returned to Malvern in 1850 for a short time, and in 1851 he took his daughters Anne and Henrietta there in March. In April, Anne's health gave grounds for anxiety, and Darwin hurried to Malvern alone, for his son Leonard had been born the previous year and Horace was expected, so that his wife had to remain at Down. The letters exchanged between them during the agonizing week before Anne's death on 23 April are among the most pathetic that can be read. As soon as he felt strong enough, Darwin composed a little ode on the child that they had loved so dearly, the most beautiful thing that he ever wrote. Horace was born on 13 May. Darwin returned to his barnacles.

On 9 September 1854 Darwin was able to get back to his species work and began to sort out his mass of notes. Of his Essay of 1844 he afterwards wrote in his *Autobiography*:

At that time I overlooked one problem of great importance; and it is astonishing to me, except on the principle of Columbus and his egg, how I could have overlooked it and its solution. The problem is the tendency in organic beings descended from the same stock to diverge in character as they become modified. That they have diverged greatly is obvious from the manner in which species of all kinds can be classed under genera, genera under families, families under suborders, and so forth; and I can remember the very spot on the road, whilst in my carriage, when to my joy the solution occurred to me; and this was long after I came to Down.

From a letter to George Bentham in which Darwin wrote, 'I believe it was fifteen years after I began before I saw the meaning and cause of the divergence of the descendants of any one pair,' this carriage-ride must have taken place in 1852.

Darwin specified that he had not solved this problem when he wrote his Essay of 1844, and this has been the subject of some misunderstanding. Not only that Essay but the Notebooks on Transmutation of Species, begun in 1837, contain splendid descriptions of the principle of branching and sub-branching of the evolutionary tree. What he was referring to in 1852 was not the fact of divergence, but a causal explanation of how it occurs and how it increases. 'How does the lesser difference between varieties become augmented into the greater difference between species?' The problem was no longer only one of branching or splitting one species into two but of widening the split. The solution was that 'the more diversified the descendants from any one species become in structure, constitution and habits, by so much will they be better enabled to seize on many and widely diversified places in the polity of nature.' In other words, divergence is related to the existence of a multiplicity of ecological niches to which organisms may become progressively adapted and, in so doing, diverge from one another more and more.

Early in 1856 Lyell suggested to Darwin that he should commit his views on species to paper, and his brother Erasmus constantly told him, 'you will find that someone will have been before you.' He had his Essay of 1844 as a basis to start on, but he subjected all the links in his evidence and chains of argument to a fresh analysis, as a result of which some of his earlier views underwent extensions and changes. One of his first steps was to breed pigeons, domestic animals that show wide differences between breeds, all of which have diverged from the parental blue rock-pigeon by artifical selection practised by man. 'I want to get the young of our domestic breeds, to see how young, and to what degree the differences appear.' Accordingly he joined the Columbarian and Philoperista pigeon-fanciers' clubs, and obtained and kept specimens of all the most important breeds that he could procure in Britain and in Europe. Chloroform had recently been discovered, and Darwin was able to kill his birds humanely and to prepare skeletons of all his breeds. He also bred them and found that when he crossed different breeds they often produced offspring that reverted to the condition of the original, slaty-blue rock-pigeon. As Darwin realized, reversion means that the characters of the blue rock-pigeon can remain hidden for hundreds of generations, before emerging again, but the real significance of this fact, which is that, thanks to the particulate mechanism of heredity, variance may be conserved indefinitely, was hidden from him because he had no alternative to blending inheritance as a theory of heredity.

Darwin also compared the skeletons of different breeds of rabbits, collected information on stripes in donkeys and different breeds of horses, and compared the wings of wild and domestic ducks to see what differences had arisen between species living in nature and under domestication.

Another field in which his ideas underwent further development was that of the size of populations in which variation took place most extensively. He was led to investigate this problem as a result of the implications of certain facts that he had recorded in his Notebook of 1837 relating to the numbers of species contained in different genera. Humboldt had shown that the ratio of numbers of genera to numbers of species of plants in France is 1 to 5·7, but in Lapland 1 to 2·3, while Deshayes's comparable figures for these ratios in genera and species of shells were 1 to 4·2 in North Africa and 1 to 1·15 at St Helena. There was Leopold von Buch's observation that the number of species of plants on Tristan da Cunha and St Helena was very small, and his query whether it might be possible to discover which are the genera that split most easily into distinct and different species. Darwin also remembered the observation made by Elias Fries that species are more closely related to each other in genera that contain many species than they are in genera that contain few species. From these simple facts Darwin concluded that variability was greater in species belonging to genera that contained many species than in genera that contained few species. He had learnt from John Gould that with birds, species tend to have wide ranges if the genera to which they belong have wide ranges, and he was soon able to satisfy himself that the same principle applied to plants.

By 18 June 1856 Darwin was able to explain to his American botanist friend Asa Gray that the reason why genera and families with few species are correlated with narrow ranges of geographical distribution is because extinction is the cause of both facts. These conclusions had far-reaching consequences, because as it appeared to be a universal rule that species belonging to large genera are most variable, it implied that wide-ranging, much diffused, common species abounding in individuals vary most. This in turn leads to the further conclusion that species inhabiting large areas will be exposed to more severe competition than inhabitants of smaller areas and will reach higher stages of evolution in a given time. This is why the centre of origin of the major groups of land animals is in the tropical and temperate regions of the largest land mass, the Old World, from which emigrations have successively taken place to the ends of the habitable earth, under competitive pressure from more highly organized, later products of evolution in the original centre. 'Hence,'

Darwin continued, 'it is the most flourishing, or, as they may be called, the dominant species, those which range widely, are the most diffused in their own country, and are the most numerous in individuals, which oftenest produce well-marked varieties, or, as I would consider them, incipient species.'

This conclusion modifies the implications of Darwin's earlier argument found in the Notebook of 1837 and the Essay of 1844, that 'if in any country or district all animals of one species be allowed freely to cross, any small tendency in them to vary will be constantly counteracted.' This again was the dead hand of blending inheritance from which Darwin could never free himself, but the facts of the distribution of genera, species, and varieties, the extents of their ranges and their degrees of affinity, had forced him to believe that it was, after all, possible to overcome the resistance to change imposed by blending inheritance, provided that variations were sufficiently numerous. This bore directly on the importance of isolation that Darwin had previously thought was indispensable if variation was to persist. Now, he still regarded isolation as important in preventing interbreeding of varieties with the parent stock and in keeping habitats and ecological niches unoccupied. 'If, however, an isolated area be very small, either from being surrounded by barriers, or from having very peculiar physical conditions, the total number of inhabitants will be small; and this will retard the production of new species through natural selection, by decreasing the chances of favourable variations arising.'

Modern research in genetics has completely confirmed Darwin's conclusion that species rich in numbers of individuals vary most. R. A. Fisher and E. B. Ford have shown that the amount of variation that occurs in a species is an equilibrium between mutation increasing it and natural selection decreasing it, and variance is therefore proportional to size of population. In abundant species, individual survival is less fortuitous and more selective than in rare species. The question of the importance of isolation for the start of a new species is more complicated. Darwin admitted that 'I do not believe that one species will give birth to two or more species, as long as they are all mingled together within the same district,' a conclusion that has been confirmed by Ernst Mayr and extended by recognition of the fact that isolation may be ecological and genetic as well as geographical. 'Nevertheless,' Darwin went on, 'I cannot doubt that many new species have been simultaneously developed within the same large continental area.' Further, 'I must still believe that in many large areas all the individuals of the same species have been slowly modified.' This introduces the concept of transmutation without splitting, bringing about changes in a species to such an extent that in time the later forms differ from the earlier by an amount equivalent to a difference between species.

Next, Darwin had a running fight with his friends Lyell and Hooker over the question of oceanic islands and the former existence of land connections between them and neighbouring continents across wide oceans, which they advocated to explain the geographical distribution and existence of plants and animals on such islands. Darwin complained to Lyell on 16 June 1856 that Edward Forbes makes a continent right across the Atlantic Ocean from Europe to North America and another continent extending to the Sargasso Sea, Hooker makes one from New Zealand to South America and further across the South Atlantic Ocean to Kerguelen Land, T. V. Wollaston makes Madeira a relic of a former continental extension of Europe, and S. P. Woodward wants to make continents extend to every island in the Atlantic and Pacific Oceans, all to explain the distribution of a few living species, which means that these continental extensions and land-bridges have disappeared without trace in deep water within the life-span of existing species. Darwin had had more personal experience of oceanic islands, and of the ranges of species, than anybody else, and it made his geologist's blood boil to hear such irresponsible speculation by a new generation of 'catastrophists' who 'make continents as easily as a cook does pancakes'.

To Hooker he had already protested that 'it shocks my philosophy to create land' (which made Hooker very indignant), and to Lyell, whom he taunted with the threat that he, Lyell, would go down in history as the greatest catastrophist of all time, he wrote a devastating letter demolishing the arguments for continental extensions and land-bridges. The east and west coasts of America are inhabited by shells that have been constantly distinct since the Miocene period, and the same is true of the east and west coasts of Africa; this means that these coasts have remained substantially as they are for a length of time infinitely longer than the life-span of existing species. All oceanic islands except St Paul's Rocks and the Seychelles are volcanic or coralline and require no continental extensions to explain their existence. Being volcanic or coralline, oceanic islands rising out of ocean depths present a picture totally different from that which would result from a deep submergence of existing continents because the majority of their mountain ranges, which would be supposed to become islands, are neither volcanic nor coralline. There is therefore no justification for the view that oceanic islands are the remains of submerged continents, the depth of subsidence of which would have to be out of all reason if continental extensions had existed and since been sunk to the depths of the oceans. Finally, if continental extensions and land-bridges had existed, it would be impossible to explain why so many plants and animals, particularly amphibia and mammals, had not reached and populated oceanic islands and invaded other continents. To invoke a land-bridge to explain a similarity of five per cent of species inhabiting two continents makes the problem nineteen times more difficult, since it would be necessary to explain why the other ninety-five per cent of species did not avail themselves of the land-bridge and cross it. It is impossible to explain the present distribution of plants and animals over the globe if these land-bridges had existed and the continents had not been separated since the Secondary era, with water-gaps between Africa and Madagascar and between Asia and Australasia. The only isthmuses required are those of Suez and Panama, the latter intermittent, and an isthmus across the Bering Strait. It has never been explained why such good scientists as Lyell and Hooker held views so untenable for so long.

Instead of making hypothetical continents to explain the inhabitants of oceanic islands, Darwin contended that it was much more consonant with scientific principles to study methods of fortuitous dispersal open to such inhabitants, the lengths of time that they, their seeds, or their eggs can survive immersion in sea water, and the speeds and directions of ocean currents flowing past the shores of continents towards oceanic islands. This, Darwin had been doing for some time. It has sometimes been said that Darwin's work on evolution was purely observational and implicative, and that he used the method of experiment only when breeding cultivated plants and studying cross-pollination and insectivorous and climbing plants. This is erroneous, for his studies on methods of dispersal were conducted by the most ingenious if simple experiments to determine whether and for how long seeds, snails, or frog-spawn could survive immersion in sea water or desiccation in air. Of 87 species of seeds immersed for 28 days, 64 germinated. Nuts germinated after 90 days' immersion, and some seeds after 137 days. If the average rate of flow of Atlantic Ocean currents is 33 miles a day, even the survivors of only 28 days' immersion might have travelled nearly a thousand miles. West Indian seeds are drifted by the Gulf Stream to Norway, and to Darwin's great amusement Hooker was mortified at their successful germination. The Darwin children entered into the fun with enthusiasm and always hoped that the seeds 'would beat Dr Hooker'. Later, Darwin learnt that nestling petrels on the island of St Kilda had been found with crops full of nuts that Hooker identified as West Indian, which the parent birds had picked out of the ocean to feed their young: 'a funny little fact after my own heart.' Darwin teased Hooker for this by saying, 'I believe you are afraid to send me a ripe *Edwardsia* pod, for fear I should float it from New Zealand to Chile.'

Another possibility is that seeds are eaten by fish and the fish by birds that fly long distances and either vomit the seeds or pass them out with their droppings. Even if the bird dies, its body may float and its crop containing the seeds may be washed up on a distant shore. From a ball of earth sticking to a bird's foot, Darwin raised 82 seedlings. Yet another possibility is that seeds may be transported by icebergs, and Darwin had the cockles of his heart warmed by the news that erratic boulders deposited by icebergs had been found in the Azores, as he had suspected. Another possibility again is that seeds, spores, and insects might be transported by wind to oceanic islands. He had had experience of this method of dispersal when at sea in the *Beagle*, and when he learnt that a high proportion of the beetles on Madeira were wingless, he was able to explain this fact and to show that it was an adaptation preventing these insects from being blown out to sea once they had reached there. He therefore had no difficulty in showing that oceanic islands were populated by fortuitous dispersal.

Meanwhile, Darwin had started writing his great book on species on 14 May 1856; it was to be called Natural Selection and to be as complete as his materials allowed. On 25 July Lyell wrote to Hooker, 'Whether Darwin persuades you and me to renounce our faith in species or not, I foresee that many will go over to the indefinite modifiability doctrine.'

The timing of his progress is important. On 13 October of that year he finished Chapter II, which with Chapter I covered 'Variation under domestication'. Chapter III, 'On the possibility of all organic beings occasionally crossing and on the remarkable susceptibility of the reproductive system to external agencies,' was finished on 16 December; Chapter IV covering 'Variation under nature' on 26 January 1857; Chapter V on the 'Struggle for existence as bearing on natural selection' on 3 March; Chapter VI, 'On natural selection,' on 31 March. Chapter VII, 'Laws of variation: varieties and species compared,' and Chapter VIII, 'Difficulties in the theory of natural selection in relation to passages from form to form,' including 'Transitions of organs,' were both finished on 29 September. Chapter IX, 'Hybridism,' was finished on 29 December, and Chapter X, 'Mental powers and instincts of animals,' on 9 March 1858. There was also an unnumbered chapter on 'Geographical distribution'. On 14 April he started a correction for Chapter VI and the 'Discussion on large genera and small and on Divergence'.

After all this work, he went to Dr Lane's Water-cure Establishment at Moor Park near Farnham, from which he wrote an idyllic letter to his wife: 'The weather is quite delicious. Yesterday, after writing to you, I strolled a little beyond the glade for an hour and a half and enjoyed myself—the fresh yet dark green of the grand Scotch firs, the brown of the catkins of the old birches, with their white stems, and a fringe of distant green from the larches, made an excessively pretty view. At last I fell fast asleep on the grass, and awoke with a chorus of birds singing around me, and squirrels running up the trees, and some woodpeckers laughing, and it was as pleasant and rural a scene as ever I saw, and I did not care one penny how any *late 12* The first page of the third Notebook on Transmutation of Species, 1838, with a pencil note of priority on selection.

late 13 Down House, the corner of the study where the *Origin of Species* was written. photograph of Sir Joseph Hooker and engravings of Sir Charles Lyell and Josiah Wedgwood hang above the mantelpiece.

Plate 14 Alfred Russel Wallace, 1869, photograph.

Plate 15 Thomas Henry Huxley, 1857, photograph.

of the beasts or birds had been formed.' He returned, however, to this knotty problem and finished his 'Discussion on large genera' on 12 June 1858.

On 14 June he started on 'Pigeons' but this, as his Journal said, was 'interrupted', because on 18 June 1858 he received from Alfred Russel Wallace a short paper containing a succinct but perfect statement of Darwin's own theory of evolution by natural selection. Wallace was then at Ternate in the Mollucas, and he accompanied his paper with the request that if Darwin thought it sufficiently novel and interesting, he would do him a kindness by sending it to Lyell. The thunderbolt had fallen from a sky that was already clouded by serious illnesses of his daughter Henrietta, and of his eighteen-months-old baby son Charles who died ten days later.

On the same day that he received Wallace's paper, Darwin forwarded it to Lyell with a letter saying, 'Your words have come true with a vengeance—that I should be forestalled. You said this, when I explained to you here very briefly my views of "Natural Selection" depending on the struggle for existence. I never saw a more striking coincidence; if Wallace had my MS sketch written out in 1842, he could not have made a better short abstract! Even his terms now stand as heads of my chapters. . . . So all my originality, whatever it may amount to, will be smashed, though my book, if it wili ever have any value, will not be deteriorated; as all the labour consists in the application of the theory.'

Darwin was particularly troubled in his conscience whether it would be unfair to Wallace if he also published a summary of his own work: 'as I had not intended to publish any sketch, can I do so honourably, because Wallace has sent me an outline of his doctrine. . . . Do you not think his having sent me this sketch ties my hands? . . . I would far rather burn my whole book, than that he or any other man should think that I had behaved in a paltry spirit. . . . About a year ago I sent a short sketch of which I have a copy, of my views to Asa Gray, so that I could most truly say and prove that I take nothing from Wallace. . . . Would you object to send this and your answer to Hooker to be forwarded to me, for then I shall have the opinion of my two best and kindest friends.' They were indeed good friends, not only to Darwin but to science. Darwin's qualms were allayed and his originality was not smashed, because Lyell and Hooker insisted that an extract from Darwin's Essay of 1844 and the letter written by him to Asa Gray in 1857 should be published together with Wallace's paper. The joint paper was read before the Linnean Society of London on 1 July 1858 and published in the Society's *Journal of Proceedings* on 20 August, under the title 'On the tendency of species to form varieties; and on the perpetuation of varieties and species by natural means of selection.' At long last, Darwin's hand had been forced and he was obliged to publish the theory on which he had been engaged for over twenty years.

On the scientific world the publication of Darwin's and Wallace's joint paper had singularly little effect. 'Our joint productions,' wrote Darwin, 'excited very little attention, and the only published notice of them which I can remember was by Professor Haughton of Dublin, whose verdict was that all that was new in them was false, and what was true was old.' The President of the Society, at the subsequent annual general meeting, concluded dismally that 'The year . . . has not, indeed, been marked by any of those striking discoveries which at once revolutionize, so to speak, the department of science on which they bear.' The only person who noticed what had happened was Alfred Newton, who read the joint paper and found 'a perfectly simple solution of all the difficulties that had been troubling me for months past.'

On Darwin himself, the effect was to force him once

more to follow Lyell's and Hooker's advice and lose no time in writing 'an abstract' of his whole work so as to lay it before the public without waiting to finish the large book on which he had been engaged. At the King's Head Hotel, Sandown, Isle of Wight, he began writing in late July 1858, using the materials that he had collected for his large work which contained long drafts of ten chapters, to which he added four more. As he went on, he found that however hard he tried to condense it, the book became longer and longer and that it was impossible to entertain the original idea that it should form a paper or series of papers to be published by the Linnean Society. It had to be a book, and of fair size, and it may now be called by the name of its title: *On the Origin of Species by means of Natural Selection, or the preservation of favoured races in the struggle for life.* He finished the last chapter on 19 March 1859. To J. W. Judd he afterwards confided that when writing the *Origin* he had seldom been able to write without interruption from pain for more than twenty minutes at a time. It is small wonder that when he had finished it he said, 'I am weary of my work. It is a very odd thing that I have no sensation that I overwork my brain; but facts compell me to conclude that my brain was never formed for much thinking,' a conclusion with which few will agree although they may sympathize.

The book followed the same general lines as the Essay of 1844, modified as regards the order in which some of the subjects are treated, and the new conclusions to which he had since come. The chapter devoted to 'Difficulties on theory' was so carefully thought out that practically no objections to it were afterwards raised that Darwin had not himself foreseen, guarded against, and explained. One of these difficulties is to understand how initial and transitional stages might account for the production of the electric organs of fishes. These organs are clearly adaptive and confer advantage on their possessors because the electric discharges that the organs give off are powerful enough to kill prey and to deter predators. The question is, what adaptive function did these organs perform at earlier stages of evolution so as to be accessible to the improving action of natural selection, before they were powerful enough to kill and deter? Darwin's defence was, 'we must own that we are far too ignorant to argue that no transition of any kind is possible,' which shows how well he remembered his Paley in a passage used in very different context: 'From the confessed and felt imperfection of our knowledge, we ought to presume that there may be consequences of this economy that are hidden from us.' In the case of electric organs, the explanation is as follows. The organs are developed from muscles, and all muscles when they contract produce weak electric discharges. H. W. Lissmann has shown that weak discharges serve to give the fish information of the proximity of solid objects, on the principle of radar. Darwin's prediction of the possibility of transitional stages leading on to the production of electric organs has therefore been fully verified.

The differences in structure and instinct between the different castes of social insects present the remarkable fact that many of the castes such as workers are sterile and leave no offspring. This fact incidentally disproves any possibility that these castes might have resulted from inheritance of acquired characters or of the effects of use and disuse because these animals leave no inheritance at all. Darwin observed that there is variation and gradation in the castes and also between different species of social insects in which the social instincts present different levels of complexity. He therefore pointed out that there was nothing to prevent the possibility that the diversity of castes had evolved slowly as a result of variation and natural selection applied to the community as a whole, the combined efficiency of which is the target of selection, working on the effects of the genetic constitutions of the queens and drones. In one place the *Origin* contains a small trace of Cuvier's work: 'I believe that animals have descended from at most only four or five progenitors, and plants from an equal or lesser number.' Four was the number of *embranchements* into which Cuvier split the animal kingdom because they were so different in structure (p. 8), and Darwin here showed that he believed that they had evolved independently.

The *reductio ad absurdum* of the alternative view of the special creation of species, illustrated in the Essay of 1844 with reference to the rhinoceroses of Java, Sumatra, and Malacca, was replaced in the *Origin* by a passage of shorter and more radical treatment. Referring to adherents to the old view he asked:

> Do they really believe that at innumerable periods in the earth's history certain elemental atoms have been commanded suddenly to flash into living tissues? Do they believe that at each supposed act of creation one individual or many were produced? Were all the infinitely numerous kinds of animals and plants created as eggs or seed, or as full grown? and in the case of mammals, were they created bearing the false marks of nourishment from the mother's womb? Although naturalists very properly demand a full explanation of every difficulty from those who believe in the mutability of species, on their own side they ignore the whole subject of the first appearance of species in what they consider reverent silence.

Although he had decided to avoid the subject of the evolution of man in the *Origin* 'as so surrounded with prejudices,' he felt that it would be disingenuous to omit all mention of it, for he knew all along that it was the *pons asinorum* of his readers. It therefore received discreet recognition in the Conclusion: 'When the views entertained in this volume on the origin of species, or when analogous views are generally admitted,' among the benefits that will accrue will be that 'light will be thrown on the origin of man and his history.'

Of his style of writing, Darwin afterwards said that 'there seems to be a sort of fatality in my mind leading me to put at first my statement and proposition in a wrong or awkward form' which required much work to correct. That he succeeded is shown by the fact that the *Origin* is recognized as a masterpiece of English literature. From Lyell, Darwin learnt many lessons, and it is not impossible that one of them was derived by Lyell himself from Gibbon for whose literary skill Lyell had profound admiration. The lesson was that a frontal attack on a fortress is less likely to succeed than an operation of 'sap and mine'. T. J. B. Spencer has suggested that this was why Lyell recommended to Darwin caution, unprovocative speech and 'sapping and mining'. It was certainly well learnt.

Darwin's participation in the voyage of the *Beagle* was the result of a string of fortunate accidents and conjunctions, and the publication of the *Origin* also had to run the gauntlet of a number of hazards. Early in 1859 Lyell had suggested to John Murray that he might be interested in Darwin's 'important new work,' and Murray readily agreed; he had already published the second edition of Darwin's *Journal of Researches* in 1845 with success. 'I have learned with pleasure from Sir Charles Lyell,' Darwin wrote to Murray on 31 March, 'that you intend to publish my work on the Origin of species, but before deciding and offering any terms you desire to see my MS,' after which he described the book. Murray replied on 1 April, 'I hasten to thank you for your obliging letter of yesterday, and for the interesting details regarding your work on species. On the strength of this information, and my knowledge of your former publications, I can have no hesitation in swerving from my usual routine, and in stating at once, even without seeing the MS, that I shall be most happy to publish it for you on the same terms as those on which I publish for Sir C. Lyell.' Darwin replied immediately accepting the offer, but adding that he felt bound, both for Murray's sake and his own, to say that if after looking over part of the MS he did not think it likely to have a remunerative sale, he completely and explicitly freed him from his offer, and with that he sent Murray the first six chapters.

Murray was so bewildered and sceptical of the scientific soundness of the book that he thought 500 was the largest number of copies that it would be prudent to print. He therefore decided to ask the opinion of George Pollock. Pollock, on the other hand, considered that Darwin had brilliantly surmounted the difficulties, and suggested an edition of 1,000 copies. Murray then consulted Whitwell Elwin, editor of the *Quarterly Review* which Murray published. Elwin called on Lyell as the man who had advised publication, because Elwin was of contrary opinion, and the esteem in which he held Darwin and the value of his researches made him anxious to persuade both author and publisher to reconsider the desirability of publishing the book in its present form of an abstract of a larger work. Lyell told Elwin that it was important that Darwin should without delay publish the results of so many years of his work, but Lyell had apparently not read the MS, and he suggested that Darwin might publish his observations on pigeons accompanied by a brief statement of his general principles. When these suggestions were forwarded by Murray to Darwin, he replied that they were impracticable. Murray thereupon started to print the book.

There was a little difficulty over the title which Darwin wanted to be An Abstract of an Essay on the Origin of Species and varieties through Natural Selection, because the word 'Abstract' was his only excuse for not giving references and facts in full; but Murray not unnaturally objected and the book received the title by which it is so well known. Darwin began correcting proofs on 25 May 1859 and passed the last revises for press on 10 October. He offered to pay Murray for the large number of corrections that he had felt obliged to make. The *Origin* was published on 24 November 1859 and the whole edition of 1,250 copies priced at fifteen shillings was bought up by the booksellers on the same day. A second edition was called for immediately and published on 7 January 1860. Meanwhile, Darwin, 'half-killed' with exhaustion after writing his 'accursed book' in thirteen months' and ten days' 'hard labour', was despondently taking the waters at Ilkley, waiting for the storm to break over his head.

Chapter 8

The Reception of the 'Origin'

'How extremely stupid not to have thought of that,' exclaimed Huxley when he read the *Origin*. Until then he had remained critical of theories of transmutation, partly because he did not think that the evidence in their favour was strong enough, and partly because he could not think of a cause that might bring it about. As late as June 1859, nearly a year after the joint Darwin-Wallace paper was read before the Linnean Society, Huxley had not realized what had happened, for he gave a lecture at the Royal Institution on 'Persistent Types of Animal Life' in which he referred to 'that hypothesis which supposes the species at any time to be the result of the gradual modification of pre-existing species, a hypothesis which, unproven, and sadly damaged by some of its supporters [sc. Lamarck and *Vestiges*], is yet the only one to which physiology lends any countenance. . . .' After reading the *Origin* he had no more doubts about the truth of evolution and he became Darwin's supporter with such energy and staunchness that he earned the name of 'Darwin's bulldog'. By a fortunate chance a review-copy of the *Origin* was sent by *The Times* to him, and the review that appeared in that leading London daily newspaper on Boxing Day 1859 contributed greatly to securing a fair hearing for the book.

Huxley recognized that natural selection was the only known mechanism capable of explaining evolution, and he also saw that it could explain why evolution had been rapid in some groups and slow in those others that produced 'persistent types'. But with his puritanically rigorous criteria of scientific proof he maintained that natural selection would be *proved* to be the method by which new species arose only when it could be shown that natural selection had resulted in the production of a species that was infertile with its parent species. This proof is now available after nearly fifty years of intensive research in genetics and population studies; but it is important to note that Darwin himself did not claim to be able to show this. In a letter to F. W. Hutton on 20 April 1861 he said, 'I am actually weary of telling people that I do not pretend to adduce evidence of one species changing into another, but I believe that this view is in the main correct, because so many phenomena can thus be grouped and explained. . . . I generally throw in their teeth the universally admitted truth of the undulations of light . . . admitted because the view explains so much.'

The attitudes of the other two of Darwin's three musketeers were equally interesting. Hooker published his *Introduction to the Tasmanian Flora* early in November 1859, after the joint paper by Darwin and Wallace in 1858 but before the publication of the *Origin*. In his *Flora of New Zealand* (1853–5) Hooker had adhered to the permanency of species; now in his Tasmanian Flora he used the theories of transmutation and of natural selection as working hypotheses, and found that they explained the problems of affinity and geographical distribution of plants much better than was possible under the view of immutability. Generalizing the results of his observations, Hooker wrote, 'This element of mutability pervades the whole vegetable kingdom; no class nor order nor genus of more than a few species claims absolute exemption, whilst the grand total of unstable forms generally assumed to be species probably exceeds that of the stable.' Noticing that species of plants are subjected to natural operations some of which induce and others oppose variation, he regarded the action of natural selection in checking indefinite variation and in bringing about the extinction of unprofitable varieties as responsible for giving a temporary appearance of fixity to species.

It was all the more important that these conclusions should have been reached from observations on plants, in which no explanations involving Lamarckian views of the action of 'inner feelings' or of the effects of inheritance of use, disuse, or acquired characters, can be invoked at all. It was therefore natural that Darwin should have welcomed Hooker's work, for, as Darwin said, Hooker 'admits the truth of the descent and modification of species and supports this doctrine by many original observations.' Shortly after the *Origin* was published, Hooker wrote to Darwin, 'Oh Lord! how little we do know and have known, to be so advanced in knowledge by one theory. If we thought ourselves to be knowing dogs before you revealed Natural Selection, what damned ignorant ones we must surely be now we do know that law.'

Lyell read the *Origin* in proof, praised it very warmly, and made a few suggestions for its improvement, but he was chary of accepting its conclusions immediately, because he saw very clearly that if he conceded anything he would have to concede the whole, since 'the case of Man and his Races and of other animals, and that of plants, is one and the same.' Lyell therefore presented the curious spectacle of a man who advocated uniformitarianism to prevent Scriptural interference in geological theory, but was nevertheless too orthodox to accept with equanimity the possibility that man, also, might have evolved from lower animals. Darwin replied to Lyell's objections in detail, and with success, because Lyell decided to admit the theory of evolution in the new edition of his *Elements of Geology*. 'I honour you most sincerely,' Darwin wrote to Lyell on the day before the *Origin* was published; 'to have maintained in the position of a master, one side of a question for thirty years, and then deliberately give it up, is a fact to which I much doubt whether the records of science offer a parallel.' Darwin had secured the support of the greatest zoologist, greatest botanist, and greatest geologist in Britain, where, among the others who rallied to his side within the first year after publication of the *Origin*, in addition of course to Wallace, were R. E. Grant, Alfred Newton, Sir John Lubbock, Leonard Jenyns, H. W. Bates, and Searles Wood, zoologists; H. C. Watson, F. Boott, and G. J. K. Thwaites, botanists; Andrew Ramsay, J. B. Jukes, and H. D. Rogers, geologists; W. B. Carpenter and Sir Henry Holland, physiologists; and the Rev. Charles Kingsley, Canon H. B. Tristram and Herbert Spencer. Spencer adhered early to evolution; in 1852 he had published an essay, 'The Development Hypothesis,' in which, by *reductio ad absurdum* rather than by scientific evidence he showed that the alternative assumption of special creation of species was untenable. Writing on 3 March 1860 to Hooker, after rehearsing the list of his supporters, Darwin remarked that 'should the book be forgotten in ten years' (according to the prophecy of an eminent naturalist), with such a list, I feel convinced the subject will not. The outsiders, as you say, are strong.' His opponents in the early days were indeed numerous, but as Darwin wrote again to Hooker on 15 May 1860,

They may all attack me to their hearts' content. I am got case-hardened. As for the old fogies in Cambridge, it really signifies nothing. I look on their attacks as a proof that our work is worth the doing. It makes me resolve to buckle on my armour. I see plainly that it will be a long uphill fight. But think of Lyell's progress with Geology. One thing I see most plainly, that without Lyell's, yours, Huxley's, and Carpenter's aid, my book would have been a mere flash in the pan. But if we all stick to it, we shall surely gain the day. And I now see that the battle is worth fighting.

One of the earliest accounts of the reaction to the *Origin* expressed by ordinary naturalists was given by the entomologist Roland Trimen, who was working in the Insect Room of the British Museum in December 1859. He wrote:

> One day I was at work in the next compartment to that in which Adam White sat, and heard someone come in and a cheery, mellow voice say, 'Good-morning, Mr White;—I'am afraid you won't speak to me any more!' While I was conjecturing who the visitor could be, I was electrified by hearing White reply, in the most solemn and earnest way, 'Ah, Sir! if ye had only stopped with the *Voyage of the Beagle*!' There was a real lament in his voice, pathetic to any one who knew how to this kindly Scot, in his rigid orthodoxy and limited scientific view, the epoch-making *Origin*, then just published, was more than a stumbling-block—it was a grievous and painful lapse into error of the most pernicious kind.

Later on the same day, Trimen saw Darwin in the Bird Room and was warned against him by a clergyman friend who was also present as 'the most dangerous man in England'.

Sedgwick, the veteran catastrophist, who had guided Darwin's first footsteps in geology nearly thirty years before, was appalled at the *Origin*. 'I have read your book with more pain than pleasure. . . . You have *deserted*—after a start in that tram-road of all physical truth—the true method of induction. . . . You do not deny causation. I call causation the will of God; and I can prove that He acts for the good of His creatures.' In other words, unable to attack Darwin on his facts he attacked him on his method and his materialism on the grounds that he had 'deserted' the Baconian principles of inductive science and had indulged in 'hypothesis', a word which it was then fashionable to regard as implying disrepute. Darwin, as he himself had explained, deliberately used the method of hypothesis as the only one that could lead to the discovery of new general principles. His position was that *if* species are the result of evolution by natural selection, then such facts as uniformity of plan of structure, resemblances between embryos, abortive organs, classification of groups within larger groups, and continuity of distribution of species geographically in space and geologically in time would be expected to occur, and they do occur.

Sedgwick was answered by a philosopher greater than himself: Huxley, who counter-attacked, 'There cannot be a doubt that the method of inquiry which Mr Darwin has adopted is not only rigorously in accordance with the canons of scientific logic, but that it is the only adequate method.' To make certain that the nonsense was well and truly exposed, Huxley continued:

> Critics exclusively trained in classics or in mathematics, who have never determined a scientific fact in their lives by induction from experiment or observation, prate learnedly about Mr Darwin's method, which is not inductive enough, not Baconian enough, forsooth for them. But even if partial acquaintance with the process of scientific investigation is denied to them, they may learn, by the perusal of Mr [John Stuart] Mill's admirable chapter 'On the Deductive Method,' that there are multitudes of scientific inquiries in which the method of pure induction helps the investigator but a very little way.

It is a sad commentary on the state of philosophy of science at that time that there were men who thought that the principle of inductive reasoning was to be ascribed to Bacon, and that inductive methods could be separated from deductive methods in research.

Some critics like W. S. MacLeay understood so little of the problem and the principles with which the *Origin* deals that they could see little difference between Darwin's theory and that put forward by Lamarck. They included John Edward Gray of the British Museum who complained bitterly to Darwin that 'You have just reproduced Lamarck's doctrine, and nothing else, and here Lyell and others have been attacking him for twenty years, and because *you* . . . say the very same thing, they are all coming round.' There would be no point in wasting time on such expressions of ignorance except to deal with the implied suggestion that Darwin had plagiarized Lamarck. That such a suggestion was current is shown by what Darwin wrote to Baden Powell on 18 January 1860: 'No person, not even the most ignorant, could suppose that I meant to arrogate to myself the origination of the doctrine that species had not been independently created. The only novelty in my work is the attempt to show *how* species became modified, and to a certain extent how the theory of descent explains certain large classes of facts; and in these respects I received no assistance from my predecessors.' Darwin has been reproached for the harsh things that he said about Lamarck in his private correspondence, but this does not alter the fact that Darwin was only speaking the truth when he said that he got not a fact or idea from Lamarck's book.

On the contrary, instead of owing anything to Lamarck, Darwin was and sometimes still is subjected to attacks that should have been directed at Lamarck and not at him at all. It has, for instance, been argued that Darwin's efforts to prove that species are not constant required that species could not be exactly delimited, and that he failed to prove this because he never succeeded in breaking down the distinction that exists between species. This objection shows how little the objectors understood the problem, for it was Lamarck, not Darwin, who claimed that species merge into each other if a sufficient number of closely allied species are studied together. Darwin, on the other hand, was always careful to recognize that species are well defined even if their limiting characters may be not only difficult to detect but changeable. Even in his first Notebook, written in 1837, he defined a species as 'one that remains at large with constant characters. . . . Between species from moderately distant countries there is no test but generation whether good species.'

From the historical accident that the notion of inheritance of acquired characters has come to be known as 'Lamarckism', and the fact that Darwin accepted the notion, it might be thought that Darwin was indebted to Lamarck for this. But in relying on the supposed inheritance of acquired characters as a source of variation, Darwin was not indebted to Lamarck, for Lamarck did not originate this age-old folk-belief, which is found in ancient Greek mythology and the Old Testament. It was believed by Diderot and Erasmus Darwin among countless others, and nobody would have thought of doubting it till the close of the nineteenth century, when August Weismann called it in question; it was exploded by progress in the study of genetics in the twentieth. The number of men before the nineteenth century who rejected the inheritance of acquired characters can be counted on the fingers of one hand; they include Lucretius, Charles Bonnet, Immanuel Kant, and Charles White.

After the *Origin* was published, Patrick Mathew claimed indignantly that he was the originator of the theory of natural selection in a book entitled *Naval Timber and Arboriculture* that he published in 1831. In 1865 Mr Rowley, of the United States, drew Darwin's attention to the fact that William Charles Wells had recognized the principle of natural selection in a paper on 'An account of a white female, part of whose skin resembles that of a negro,' read before the Royal Society in 1813, but only printed with his *Two Essays on Dew and Single Vision* in 1818. The principle of natural selection was clearly stated in each of these two works which were completely ignored and unknown; but they were only speculations and their authors were in no way qualified to support them with evidence or to generalize their application. On the other hand, James Hutton, the founder of modern geology, towards the end of the eighteenth century put forward a remarkable suggestion that selection of variations resulted

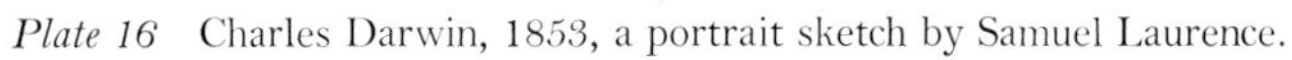

Plate 16 Charles Darwin, 1853, a portrait sketch by Samuel Laurence.

Plate 17 Down House from the entrance.

Plate 18 Down House from the garde

in adaptation, but it remained in his manuscript notebook and was not published until brought to light in 1947 by Sir Edward Bailey.

The heaviest onslaught against the *Origin* was an anonymous, very long, hostile, and speciously disingenuous review that Richard Owen published in the *Edinburgh Review* for April 1860, referring to himself in the third person. Darwin was not deceived. Owen had been a student of Cuvier and shared his teacher's repudiation of transmutation. He dominated the stage in anatomy and palaeontology in Britain with an enormous reputation that has not stood the test of time. Of the review itself Darwin wrote, 'it is extremely malignant, clever, and I fear will be very damaging. . . . It requires much study to appreciate all the bitter spite of many of the remarks against me; indeed I did not discover all myself. He misquotes some passages altering words within inverted commas.' Such conduct was nothing exceptional in Owen's behaviour, which was dictated by an arrogance and jealousy that would stop at nothing to gain priority for himself. He did not shrink from obtaining access to material on which other scientists were working, and by this means he was able to anticipate their announced papers by publishing a note on the subject himself a few days before, a trick that he played on Gideon Mantell and on Huxley. In the *Origin* Owen sensed that he had met a master who had been his personal friend but who would eclipse him and must at all costs be destroyed, while at the same time Owen's priority must be upheld. The result was what can best be described in the words used of Owen by the *London Review* in 1866: 'So far as we can gather from his communication, he denies the Darwinian doctrine, admits the accuracy of its basis, and claims to be the first to point out the truth of the principle on which it is founded.'

Owen had a vicarious second hit at Darwin when he coached Samuel Wilberforce, Bishop of Oxford, for the review that the bishop wrote of the *Origin* in the *Quarterly Review*, which revealed Owen's technique but failed to hide the bishop's ignorance, prejudice, and incompetence to deal with the subjects at issue. The Wilberforce-Owen duet performed again. Well aware that the most unpalatable aspect of Darwin's theory was its applicability to man, Owen opened his attack on that front at the Oxford meeting of the British Association for the Advancement of Science in 1860. On 28 June he claimed that the brain of the gorilla presented more differences, as compared with the brain of man, than it did when compared with the brains of the lowest primates. Huxley promptly gave these assertions a direct and unqualified contradiction, together with a promise to publish the evidence, which he subsequently did in his book *Man's Place in Nature*.

At the meeting on 30 June, Henslow was in the chair. Huxley had not thought of attending but was persuaded in friendly fashion to do so by none other than Robert Chambers, the anonymous and unrecognized author of the *Vestiges of Creation* which, when it appeared, Huxley had criticized very harshly. Bishop Wilberforce read a paper aimed straight at Huxley, for which again he had been crammed by Owen. 'In a light scoffing tone, florid and fluent,' to quote a listener, 'he assured us there was nothing in the idea of evolution; rock-pigeons were what rock-pigeons had always been. Then, turning to his antagonist with a smiling insolence, he begged to know, was it through his grandfather or his grandmother that he claimed his descent from a monkey?' Huxley described his reply in a letter to F. D. Dyster.

It was great fun—I had said that I could not see what difference it would make to my moral responsibility if I *had* had an ape for a grandfather, and saponaceous Samuel thought it was a fine opportunity for chaffing a savan. However, he performed the operation vulgarly and I determined to punish him—partly on that account and partly because he talked pretentious nonsense.

and when I got up I spoke pretty much to the speech—that I had listened with great attention to the Lord Bishop's speech but had been unable to discover either a new fact or a new argument in it—except, indeed, the question raised as to my personal predilections in the matter of ancestry—That it would not have occurred to me to bring forward such a topic as that for discussion myself, but that I was quite ready to meet the Rt. Rev. prelate even on that ground—If, then, said I, the question is put to me 'would I rather have a miserable ape for a grandfather, or a man highly endowed by nature and possessed of great means and influence, and yet who employs these faculties and that influence for the mere purpose of introducing ridicule into a grave scientific discussion'—I unhesitatingly affirm my preference for the ape. Whereupon there was unextinguishable laughter among the people—and they listened to the rest of my argument with the greatest of attention. . . . I happened to be in very good condition and said my say with perfect good temper and politeness—I assure you of this because all sorts of reports were spread about, e.g. that I had said I'd rather be an ape than a bishop.

The excitement was intense. Lady Brewster fainted and had to be carried out. Darwin's old shipmate Robert FitzRoy stalked about holding a Bible over his head, shouting, 'the Book, the Book'. Hooker was called upon to speak, and he described the final scene in a letter to Darwin.

My blood boiled . . . I swore to myself that I would smite that Amalekite, Sam, hip and thigh if my heart jumped out of my mouth. . . . so there I was cocked up with Sam at my right elbow, and there and then I smashed him amid rounds of applause. I hit him in the wind at the first shot in ten words taken from his own ugly mouth; and then proceeded to demonstrate in as few more: (1) that he could never have read your book, and (2) that he was absolutely ignorant of Botanical Science. . . . Sam was shut up—had not one word to say in reply, and the meeting was dissolved forthwith, leaving you master of the field after 4 hours' battle.

Outside Britain, the battle over the *Origin* was begun

in the United States before it was published. Louis Agassiz had published an *Essay on Classification* in which he put nature forward as the result of a divine plan involving the creation of species where they now occur, and if in discontinuous areas, separately in each of them. Asa Gray had meanwhile been studying the flora of North America and comparing it with that of Japan, when he found that the plants of the eastern United States and of Japan had many genera, many representative species, and some even of the same species in common. Gray already knew Darwin's views, and at a meeting of the American Academy of Arts and Sciences on 11 January 1859 he claimed that it was scientifically preferable to suppose that each species had a single, local origin and subsequently underwent changes in its range, and that 'the idea of the descent of all similar or conspecific individuals from a common stock is so natural, and so inevitably suggested by common observation, that it must needs be first tried upon the problem; and if the trial be satisfactory, its adoption would follow as a matter of course.' Agassiz's answer was to reaffirm that species were originally created in the positions that they now occupy, and to say that 'the warfare which so many species wage upon others was in itself an insuperable objection to the assumption that any one species could have originated in a single pair.' But evolution does not proceed from single pairs; it occurs in populations of individuals all evolving together (p. 194). The debate went on at subsequent meetings and Agassiz could do nothing more than try to cast doubt on Asa Gray's facts and put in a plea for spontaneous generation which, like the pupil of Cuvier that he was, he needed to repopulate the world after each catastrophe.

When the *Origin* was published, Agassiz castigated Darwin's book as 'a scientific mistake, untrue in its facts, unscientific in its method, and mischievous in its tendencies.' Gray immediately accepted Darwin's theories but with the curious belief that natural selection was not incompatible with teleological design, which he tried to make responsible for controlling and directing the variations on which natural selection acts. Darwin pointed out that if this were the case and variation was directed, it would be necessary to believe that the tail of the Fantail pigeon was led to vary in number and direction of its feathers in order to gratify the caprices of a few pigeon-fanciers. The argument went on for some time, and eventually Asa Gray was obliged to admit that he was unable to provide logical opposition to Darwin's view that variation was random and uncontrolled. Meanwhile the views expressed in the *Origin* were more and more widely accepted in the United States, one of the first to proclaim his adherence to them being Chauncey Wright.

In France, the homeland of the idea of transmutation from the beginning of the eighteenth century, Darwin's theories first met with strong opposition led by Élie de Beaumont and Pierre Flourens. The latter was perpetual secretary of the Academy of Sciences, which in 1870 turned down a candidature for Darwin to become a corresponding member and only admitted him in 1878 in the Section of Botany. In so doing the Academy behaved like the President of the Royal Society of London who, in 1864, when awarding to Darwin the Copley Medal, the highest honour the Society could bestow, tried to convey the impression that the *Origin* was expressly omitted from the grounds of the award. Darwin's supporters in France in early days after the publication of the *Origin* were therefore few, but they included the Marquis Gaston de Saporta, who first suggested that the evolution of flowering plants was correlated with the appearance of insects that carried out cross-fertilization, and Albert Gaudry, whose palaeontological researches showed that in their descent mammals followed not one but several parallel lines of evolution. Darwin's supporters eventually included P. Broca,

C. Dareste, Edgar Quinet, Ernest Renan, and Alfred Giard who first introduced Darwin's views into university teaching, at Lille in 1872. The city of Paris endowed a professorship of organic evolution at the Sorbonne, the first chair of its kind, for Giard in 1888. While the facts of evolution were gradually accepted, French scientists preferred Lamarck's theories to natural selection for their explanation.

In Germany the *Origin* was at first received with caution. It was accepted by E. H. Du Bois-Reymond and Count Keyserling, and a German translation by H. G. Bronn, published in 1860, was the first of the foreign translations to appear. Presently Fritz Müller, a German living in Brazil, provided valuable support for Darwin in his book *Für Darwin*, and Ernst Haeckel threw himself with such enthusiasm into the cause that Darwin himself shuddered at the excess of his zeal in drawing up evolutionary trees of animals and speculating too far beyond the evidence. It is unquestioned, however, that Haeckel succeeded in placing evolution at the centre of thought, not only in biology but in ever-widening contexts. Anton Dohrn, founder of the Naples Zoological Station, also became a strong supporter of Darwin.

In Switzerland the botanist Alexander Moritzi published in 1842 a theory of transmutation of species based on the absence of distinction between species and varieties, series of forms revealed by comparative anatomy, passages between classes of organisms, the results of artificial selection of domestic animals, the succession of fossils, the obligatory imperfection of the geological record because the earliest organisms had soft bodies, and the impossibility of imagining a process of special creation: 'Where does the substance of organisms come from? Did the Creator get it out of nothing, or from the substances and fluids of which the earth is composed . . . ? Did the Creator make the organs separately one by one to put together a living being subsequently?' It is tragic that this remarkable work fell on deaf ears and its author into complete oblivion. There was a man who by his own efforts came to reject catastrophism and to substitute causal for teleological explanations in biology—he ascribed transmutation to the action of the environment—and, like Mendel, was totally ignored by his contemporaries. On the publication of the *Origin*, Moritzi was already dead; the zoologist Ludwig Rütimeyer was one of the first Swiss to accept its theories, and the botanist Alphonse De Candolle gradually became a supporter. François Jules Pictet, the palaeontologist, showed great respect for Darwin's views, even if he only went a short way with him.

In Belgium evolution was accepted by the botanists Leo Errera and Jean Massart, Edward van Beneden, the embryologist, and the palaeontologist Louis Dollo who propounded the law of irreversibility in evolution. In Holland the first to support the theory of evolution was the zoologist P. Harting.

It is interesting to consider the reception of the *Origin* in the Austrian Empire, not only because of the opinions of biologists in Vienna, but also because the Empire then comprised Bohemia and Moravia, now Czechoslovakia, and particularly Brünn where Gregor Mendel lived and worked. As early as 1852, Franz Unger, professor of plant physiology in Vienna, published his opinion that species were not fixed, and that the vegetable kingdom had 'gradually developed step by step.' These views acquire additional importance from the fact that from 1852 to 1853, Unger's pupils included Mendel, who must have absorbed these ideas.

Such ideas were then politically dangerous to hold, for after the revolutionary outbreaks of 1848, Austria concluded a Concordat with the Vatican in 1855, as a result of which unorthodox views were frowned on. Attempts were even made to oust Unger from his post as a corrupter of youth. Nevertheless, when the *Origin* was published in German, Mendel obtained a copy, and the fact that he studied it carefully is shown by the marks that he made in the margins. Contrary to what has sometimes been said, it is clear that Mendel accepted the theory of evolution, in the classic paper on genetics which he read at Brünn in 1865.

R. A. Fisher has pointed out that although Mendel's paper does not mention Darwin, it reflects the difficulties with which Darwin had had to contend from his reliance on blending inheritance. As if to help Darwin in his search for adequate sources of variation and for a means to avoid the supposed quashing of variation by interbreeding that blending inheritance demanded, Mendel pointed out that some of these difficulties were overcome by the system of particulate inheritance that he had discovered. In particular, Mendel stressed the fact that if parents differing in 7 pairs of genes are crossed, the number of possible combinations to be found in individuals of the second generation of offspring is no less than 16,384 among which there will be 2,187 different genetic constitutions. The breeding of a mere 100 or 200 offspring goes nowhere near allowing all possible combinations to show themselves; and the significance of this demonstration is that, contrary to the notion of blending inheritance, interbreeding does not quash variation but increases it.

It is said that Mendel felt that there was something missing in Darwin's work, and this is perfectly true; as mentioned above, it was an explanation of the source of heritable variation. It is also said that Mendel hoped that his own experiments would provide the information that was lacking; and this is also true, as will be seen in the next chapter, where it will be shown that Mendelian genetics provides exactly the mechanism required to explain evolution by natural selection.

It is interesting to note that at the meeting of the Brünn

Natural History Society immediately preceding that at which Mendel read his classic paper, in 1865, the geologist Alexander Makowsky gave a general account of Darwin's theories. Later in the same decade, the botanist Ladislav Celakovsky also supported Darwin and performed for the evolutionary tree of plants the same service that Haeckel rendered for animals.

In Russia, Ilya Mechnikov has described the adoption of Darwin's theories as having taken place all the more easily because they had no other views to displace, and they spread as on virgin soil. Shortly before the *Origin* was published, the veteran embryologist Karl Ernst von Baer expressed his conviction, based on geographical distribution, that forms now perfectly distinct have descended from a single parent form; and in a letter to Huxley he said that he had expressed the same views as Darwin. Later, however, von Baer repudiated the unwarranted elaboration on his own laws of embryonic resemblance out of which Haeckel had constructed his 'theory of recapitulation,' according to which the embryo of an animal represented the adult form of its ancestor, a view that is now discredited. Haeckel's exaggerations had the effect of making von Baer reject Darwin's views as well as Haeckel's. Meanwhile Darwin's views were strongly supported by the researches of the brothers Alexander and Vladimir Kovalevsky in embryology and palaeontology respectively and by the botanist Kliment Arkadyevich Timiriazev. Mechnikov himself showed that an evolutionary basis was essential for the study of comparative pathology. The Museum Darwinianum was founded in Moscow by Alexander Eric Kohts in 1905.

Such opposition to the *Origin* as was expressed and published, in Britain and abroad during the first few years after its publication, had no scientific significance whatever, and Darwin had little to worry about. 'I could myself write a more damning review than has as yet appeared,' he said. Presently, however, an attempt was made by H. St G. Mivart, a zoologist who accepted the truth of evolution, to show that natural selection was powerless to account for initial stages of adaptations, in a book in which he misquoted Darwin and twisted his meaning grievously. Darwin was obliged to conclude that religious fervour had led Mivart to act not in good faith, but the argument had to be answered, and was, in a section that Darwin added to the sixth edition of the *Origin*. In the cases mentioned, including those of the giraffe, whalebone whale, flat-fishes, mammary glands, flowers of orchids, movements of climbing plants, protective resemblance, and mimicry, Darwin was able to show that on the principle of gradation there was no evidence to support the view that initial stages could not be of advantage. In this Darwin has been fully vindicated by modern research, which has revealed a number of cases in which the function that the structure in question performed in the initial stages is not the same as that which it performs now. One of the best examples of this is provided by electric organs (p. 151) developed out of muscles, the electric discharges from which served to give the fish information of proximity of solid objects. Another example is flight in birds, where it can be shown that feathers first appeared as heat-insulators when the animals became warm-blooded, and conferred progressive advantage from the start of their appearance. Next, enlargement of the feathers increased the surface of the body conferring advantage progressively at each stage to an animal gliding from branch to branch, as in *Archaeopteryx*, which from the structure of its muscle-attachments, breast-bone, and brain can be proved to have glided but not flown. Finally, the increase in power of the breast-muscles converted the glider into an active flyer. Selection makes organisms take a zigzag course in evolution.

A more dangerous attack on natural selection was made

by Lord Kelvin, who proclaimed that the physical data on the rate of cooling of the earth proved that its age was much less than had previously been supposed, and probably not less than 20 or more than 40 million years. This was a subject to which Darwin had paid particular attention as a geologist. If Kelvin was right, it meant that so little time was available for the pageant of evolution to have taken place that it could not have been achieved by natural selection of fortuitous variations. Instead, design and direction would have to be invoked, which was exactly what Darwin had always fought against. He attached little weight to the physicists' estimates of the age of the earth because they differed so widely: 'I feel a conviction that the world will be found rather older than Thomson [Kelvin] makes it.' Darwin's uncanny dumb sagacity was well founded, for the discovery of radio-activity has made nonsense of Kelvin's arguments and has lengthened the estimated age of the earth to over 4,000 million years, sufficient to allow evolution by natural selection of fortuitous variations to have done its work. There is therefore no reason to repudiate natural selection and to invoke design and direction on the score of the age of the earth.

Even more dangerous, though in fact no better founded, was the argument put forward in 1867 by Fleeming Jenkin, who argued that the chances of favourable single variations (mutations) becoming incorporated in a population were infinitesimally small because of the infrequency with which two similar variants were likely to meet and because, under the prevailing notion of blending inheritance, such variations would be swamped and annihilated by interbreeding with the rest of the population. This was damaging to the theory that natural selection worked by accumulation of fortuitous, favourable, single variations, and it increased the difficulty of accounting for a sufficient supply of variation for natural selection to work on. Darwin defended his position by leaning more heavily on the production of variation as the result of the effects, then supposedly inherited, of use and disuse and of the action of the environment in evoking acquired characters, and by admitting that natural selection, although the chief cause, might not be the only cause of evolution. With the knowledge then at his disposal there was nothing else that he could do. These modifications constitute the chief difference between the sixth and earlier editions of the *Origin*.

As is now well known, the facts of Mendelian inheritance make these concessions on the part of Darwin completely unnecessary, and the reason why this is so may best be introduced with reference to the last of the fronts of attack levelled against natural selection, which will form the subject of the next chapter.

Meanwhile, as part of the study of how the *Origin* was received, it may be observed that it was not only from the attacks of his opponents that Darwin needed protection, for some of his supporters persuaded him to make changes in the later editions of the *Origin* which were not improvements on the first edition. In that edition Darwin had referred to an observation made by Samuel Hearne that the black bear swims for hours 'with widely open mouth, thus catching, almost like a whale, insects in the water.' Darwin went on, 'I can see no difficulty in a race of bears being rendered, by natural selection, more and more aquatic in their structure and habits, with larger and larger mouths, till a creature was produced as monstrous as a whale.' This argument was treated with such misrepresentation and abuse by Darwin's opponents who made it mean that he thought a bear could be turned into a whale, and it proved so unpalatable to some of his friends that Darwin struck it out in subsequent editions; but he always regretted that he had jettisoned his bear and continued to protest that his argument was sound, as indeed it, and Hearne's observation, are.

Another instance in which Darwin's own better judgment was subsequently overridden by unsound views of his over-enthusiastic supporters is to be seen in his discussion of the light that embryology throws on evolution. In the Essay of 1844 (p. 129) he had shown that transmutation of species explains why embryonic stages of different but related animals may be very similar, because they are descended from a common ancestor and have inherited from him these embryonic similarities that are evidence of affinity, while the different adult forms have diverged. In the *Origin*, Darwin considered the question whether the embryonic stages of descendants resembled the adult stages of their ancestors, and, in the fourth edition published in 1866, concluded judiciously that the embryo may be 'a picture, more or less obscured, of the progenitor, either in its adult or larval state.' He also saw that in some cases embryonic or larval stages represent no ancestral condition whatever: 'the various larval and pupal stages of insects have thus been acquired through adaptation, and not through inheritance from some ancient form.' He even saw that modified larval forms might be the starting-point for the evolution of new classes of animals, 'and the first larval stage certainly would not represent the former condition of any adult or ancient form.' These views are fully in line with modern conclusions that lineages can evolve, not from the adult but from the youthful stages of their ancestors, a mode of evolution known as paedomorphosis.

In his work *Für Darwin* published in 1864, Fritz Müller claimed that the characteristic larva of Crustacea, called the nauplius, represented the adult ancestor of Crustacea. It is now realized that this view must be mistaken, because the adult ancestors of Crustacea and of their relatives, millipedes and worms, must have had bodies containing large numbers of segments, as shown by trilobites, fossils 600 million years old; whereas the nauplius larva had only three segments in its little body, and its form is an adaptation to secure wide distribution in the sea before the development of the adult forms that live on the sea bottom with limited powers of locomotion. The nauplius larva is evidence of affinity between the different kinds of Crustacea that possess it, but provides no information on what the adult ancestor of Crustacea was like. Unfortunately Darwin accepted Müller's argument and incorporated it in the later editions of the *Origin*.

In 1866 Ernst Haeckel, in his enthusiastic search for ancestral forms with which to populate the evolutionary trees that he drew up, elaborated the relation between embryos and ancestors into the theory of recapitulation (p. 173), which claimed that the succession of embryonic stages in the development of a descendant directly represented the succession of adult ancestors in the evolutionary history of that descendant. This view, now known to be contrary to the evidence and discarded, is reflected in the later editions of the *Origin*.

It should be added that Darwin's appeal to embryology for evidence in support of evolution is not in any way affected by the necessity to drop the additions that he made to the later editions of the *Origin* because of the views of Müller and Haeckel. Nothing detracts from the importance of the fact that resemblances between embryos occur, and that these resemblances are evidence of their affinity and descent from a common ancestor, and therefore of evolution.

Yet another example of misplaced zeal on the part of Darwin's friends was Herbert Spencer's expression 'survival of the fittest' which Wallace urged Darwin to adopt as an improvement on the term 'natural selection', because he had had difficulty in making persons understand that natural selection did not imply a personal selector, which artificial selection did. To Huxley's regret Darwin accepted this 'unlucky substitution' in later editions of the *Origin*.

In fact, survival of the fittest is not a substitute for natural selection, but a gloss on the struggle for existence such as is to be found in the works of many authors including Erasmus Darwin and, even, Lucretius. It conveys nothing of the meaning of how adaptations arise and become more effective or how evolution is brought about. Indeed, the 'fittest' can survive without any evolution taking place at all. At best, it is little more than tautological if fitness is a condition for survival; at worst, the use of the superlative implies more than is intended. It lays too much stress on survival when what is really meant is the favouring of those parents that are most proliferous. Instead of adopting the survival of the fittest as an alternative to natural selection, Darwin would have been better advised to return to the description that he gave of natural selection in his Notebook when he showed (p. 99) that it exerted pressure and was 'a force like a hundred thousand wedges trying to force every kind of structure into the gaps in the oeconomy of nature, or rather forming gaps by thrusting out weaker ones.'

Chapter 9

Modern Views on Natural Selection

In order to appreciate the present position in regard to Darwin's theory of natural selection, and the part that it plays in evolution, it is necessary to consider the general principles of Mendelian genetics, which can be done in simple terms. Mendel's paper had been published in 1866, but it attracted no attention at all, although the journal in which it appeared was not very obscure, and the subjects with which it dealt, hybridization and heredity, were very germane to the arguments that raged round the *Origin of Species*. R. A. Fisher has pointed out that this lack of attention to Mendel's work was probably due to the divorce between the studies of mathematics and of biology, that resulted in naturalists of the mid-nineteenth century being devoid of any appreciation of the importance of mathematical symbolism. As already mentioned (p. 29), Darwin himself afterwards regretted that he had never proceeded far enough to understand 'something of the great leading principles of mathematics,' for, as he sadly admitted, 'men thus endowed seem to have an extra sense.'

In 1900 Mendel's paper was discovered by three men who had independently performed breeding experiments that led to exactly the same results as those of Mendel, and who were very surprised that they had been forestalled. They were all of them botanists: the German Carl Correns, the Austrian Eric von Tschermak, and the Dutchman Hugo de Vries. In Britain William Bateson, and in France

Lucien Cuénot, followed them closely and showed that the principles of Mendelian genetics applied to the Animal Kingdom as well as to the Plant Kingdom.

The material on which de Vries performed most of his experiments, the evening primrose (*Oenothera lamarckiana*), is peculiar in that the offspring of a plant may consist of a number of different types, quite different from the parent plant, that have arisen suddenly and ready-made with all their characters, and breed true. To the process of change that produced these new types, de Vries gave the name of 'mutation', and as it appeared to give rise to new species, in 1901 he published his Mutation Theory, which attributed the origin of species to sudden, discontinuous variation, and claimed that the gradual variation on which, according to Darwin, natural selection worked, was not the starting-point of new species.

Unfortunately the evening primrose, as is now known, has a complicated and untypical genetic constitution; it is a hybrid of a peculiar kind that frequently reverts to its constituent types by an exceptional process quite different from that now understood by the term 'mutation' as applied to a hereditary particle or gene discovered by Mendel. Mutation is defined as the inception of a heritable variation caused by a fortuitous change in the structure of a gene. Genes are chemical molecules, present in pairs in the nucleus of every cell of plants and animals, one gene of each pair having been derived from each parent. Mendel showed that the two members of a pair of genes might be similar, in which case the individual is said to be homozygous, or dissimilar when it is called heterozygous. When the members of a pair of genes are dissimilar, Mendel found that one gene might be dominant over the other, which is called recessive, and that the dominant gene determined the production of a particular character in the individual and concealed the character controlled by the recessive gene.

Mendel's most important discovery was that whether the two members of a pair of genes are similar or dissimilar in an individual, they never contaminate one another, and that they separate from each other cleanly, or segregate, when the individual forms its germ-cells. Each germ-cell never contains more than one member of each pair of genes, and the genes are distributed among the offspring in a simple pattern known as Mendel's Law. The fact that genes do not contaminate each other is the proof that inheritance is not blending but particulate. At each division of a cell the genes are accurately replicated and continue to be self-copying until a mutation occurs and the gene is changed in its structure and in its effects; but it then continues to self-copy itself in its new condition until it mutates again.

Another advance of fundamental importance in biology was made when T. H. Morgan and his colleagues proved that genes are carried in chromosomes, elongated bodies in the nuclei of all cells, and that the genes are arranged in a particular linear order along the length of the chromosomes. C. D. Darlington elucidated the structure and function of the chromosome mechanism and showed that it itself has also evolved.

Mutation normally takes place at a certain rate which in a number of different species of plants and animals has been estimated at roughly one mutation in every half-million pairs of genes in a generation. Physical and chemical agents have been discovered that accelerate the normal rate of mutation, but these agents bear no relation to the quality of the mutations obtained, and the characters determined by these mutations do not adapt the organisms to these agents. This means that mutations are not adaptive responses to environmental conditions, and it is why mutations are said to be random events.

The first examples of mutations of genes that were known to geneticists resembled the 'mutations' of de

Vries's evening primroses in that the characters that they controlled were clear-cut and well marked, and arose ready-made without any previous selection. Early geneticists therefore contended that natural selection of finely graded heritable variations played no part in evolution at all. As mutation was (and is) the only process known by which heritable variation arises, and as the effects of use and disuse, the effects of the action of the environment on the bodies of the parents, and so-called acquired characters were shown not to be inherited, geneticists in early days claimed that evolution took place by mutation producing discontinuous variation.

As the first genes to be studied had these clear-cut effects, and as many of them had lethal results and killed the organisms that carried them, Darwinian selectionists rejected the mutationists' theory, because it did not provide for the gradual changes that were believed to have produced evolution. Furthermore, far from conferring improvement in adaptation, the mutations seemed to be pathological, and provided no explanation of how adaptations arose and became perfected. The result of this conflict of views was that during the first twenty years of the twentieth century, evolutionary studies and theories were in a state of chaos and confusion.

The solution to the problem came in an unexpected manner. It gradually became clear that each of the two schools of thought objected to the other for reasons which further research showed to be erroneous and unfounded. The possibility that mutations and recombinations of genes might be the source of the heritable variation that produces evolution was suggested in 1926 by S. S. Chetverikov, who pointed out that it was necessary to apply genetic analysis to wild populations of animals and plants living in nature, in order to study their variability and their powers of transmitting heritable variability to their offspring. These researches were carried out by him and by his colleagues, who found that in wild populations of the fruit-fly (*Drosophila*) very large numbers of individuals were heterozygous and carried recessive genes that had mutated, but whose effects were hidden by those of their dominant partners. This means that those heterozygous individuals do not breed true, and that their offspring are bound to show heritable variation. It thus became possible to explain the origin of heritable variation as a result of mutation of genes, but further researches were necessary before it was possible to show how natural selection acts on the products of such variation, and this was achieved largely by the work of R. A. Fisher.

Darwinian selectionists, Fisher showed, had to learn two lessons. As more and more genes were identified throughout the Plant and Animal Kingdoms, including Bacteria, and the effects of their mutations were studied, it became clear that the wide and discontinuous effects of the mutations that were first observed were only the more obvious and easily detectable extremes of a range in which the majority produce only slight effects. For the same reason the mutations first observed had deleterious effects because organisms are delicately adjusted systems more likely to be upset and damaged by large and discontinuous changes than by small and gradual steps.

The Mendelian mutationists also had to learn two lessons. On the one hand they found that although individual genes might be associated with particular characters, their control of those characters is subject to and affected by all the other genes, which constitute an organized gene-complex in each organism. As a result of previous mutations the gene-complexes of organisms in nature contain countless pairs of dissimilar genes (that is, are heterozygous), so that when they segregate at the formation of the germ-cells and are recombined in random fashion at fertilization, astronomically large numbers of possible permutations of genes can occur. In some of such reshuffled gene-complexes the effects of a particular gene are accentuated, in others they are reduced. This means that the effects of mutations are not necessarily clear-cut but may produce variations that grade insensibly into each other.

In other words, the effects of any given mutation can be altered by changes in the gene-complex, but these changes in the gene-complex are subject to selection, and this has been proved experimentally by R. A. Fisher and E. B. Ford. A mutant gene that confers advantage on the organism (there are such) automatically undergoes accentuation of its effects by the preferential survival of those reshuffled gene-complexes that produce this result. Such genes then control characters that are called dominant and they have gradually *become* dominant as a result of selection. Conversely, mutant genes that are disadvantageous, the vast majority, undergo automatic reduction of their effects by the preferential survival of those reshuffled gene-complexes that reduce these effects until the gene in question fails to show 'its' character at all if its corresponding dominant gene is present with it. Such repressed characters are then called recessive, and they have gradually *become* recessive as a result of selection. Here, at the heart of Mendelian genetics, is incontrovertible evidence of selection producing gradual change. In this way, in 1930, R. A. Fisher effected the integration of Darwinian selection and Mendelian genetics into a synthetic theory by showing that far from being antagonistic they are mutually indispensable, and between them provide exactly the mechanism required for evolution by natural selection.

Moreover, the effects of any given gene are dependent not only on the other genes of the gene-complex but also on the factors of the environment. It used to be thought, by Darwin among others, that some characters are 'innate' and others 'acquired'; but research in experimental embryology as well as in genetics has shown that this view is mistaken. Nothing would seem to be more 'innate' than the pair of eyes that vertebrate animals have had since the Silurian period, 400 million years ago. Yet today a fish embryo made to develop in water containing certain simple salts such as magnesium chloride develops not a pair of eyes but one single median eye like a cyclops. This shows that the organism's genes are not capable of producing a normal organism unless the environmental factors are also normal. It also shows that 400 million years of normal environment have done nothing to 'fix' the character of paired eyes.

Every character of a plant or an animal is a response, resulting from the interaction between the genes inside and the environmental factors outside. Every character has a genetic basis in the organism's genes without which it would not develop at all and is therefore to that extent 'inherited', but only partly, because every character is also the result of interaction of the genes with the environment and is therefore also 'acquired'. No character owes its existence to heredity or environment alone, and strictly speaking no character is either inherited or acquired. What is inherited is a packet of genes transmitted from the parents with the capacity to respond to environmental conditions in certain ways, some of which are called normal for the species in question in its normal environment, and those are the ways that are adaptive and that natural selection favours. It may, in passing, be noticed that the dependence of the characters of an organism both on the genes that it inherited and on the conditions of the environment in which it developed, invalidates the comment that Mendelian genetics is equivalent to scientific Calvinism, as has been advanced. At a time when it was imagined that there was an unalterable one-to-one correspondence between each gene and 'its' character, such a comment might have been valid to describe the then-supposed predestination of an organism as a result of the genes that it inherited at fertilization of the egg out of which it developed. But since it is known that genes affect each others' effects and that these are subject to environmental conditions, there is no rigid predestination of the characters of an organism. All that the genetic legacy determines is the wide range of limits within which the characters of an organism may develop in accordance with the limitless contingencies to which it may be subjected.

It will be clear from this demonstration that the expression 'inheritance of acquired characters' is meaningless. The question at issue must be put differently, and it must be asked whether a character that is developed as a response by the organism to the reaction between its genes and certain environmental factors can be 'built in' to the organism's descendants produced through sexual reproduction and transmission of genes, so that the character is developed in the absence of the environmental factors that called it forth originally.

Experiments have so far failed to show that adaptive characters evoked by environmental stimuli can be transmitted to offspring through consequent mutation of genes, which are the only known vehicles of heredity. Nor have any experiments succeeded in showing that environmental stimuli can evoke mutations that determine characters adapted to that environment. The great problem is to understand not only how new characters arise, but, even more important, how new *adaptive* characters arise, characters that confer advantage to their possessors in their environments. Darwin's solution of the problem was to point out that as variations are fortuitous, or, in modern terms, mutations and recombinations of genes are random, heritable variations will arise and if some of these confer advantage on their possessors they will give rise to heritable adaptations, capable of further improvement by natural selection. This is the accepted view.

Without straying from established principles of natural

selection and Mendelian genetics, attempts have been made to imagine mechanisms by which the production of heritable adaptations might be facilitated and accelerated. The fact that an animal during its lifetime can respond adaptively to environmental stimuli, as when skin thickens from the effects of friction, or muscles enlarge after subjection to heavy work, must itself be the result of long-continued natural selection, working on variants that showed different responses to the environmental stimuli, and conferring advantage of preferential survival on those that respond by producing the most efficient adaptation. Some variants have lower thresholds of stimulation than others, and can be selected until the response takes place to minimal and eventually to substituted stimuli without the necessity for the particular stimuli that originally called forth the response. This effect, discovered by C. H. Waddington and known as genetic assimilation, might provide a possible formal explanation of the production of heritable adaptations, but the characters on which it has so far been demonstrated are few. An alternative hypothesis due to C. Stern supposes that the genetic constitution that enables an animal to respond adaptively to the environment involves genes in the heterozygous state (or 'in single dose'), and that when these genes if advantageous are present in the homozygous state (or 'in double dose'), having been inherited from both parents, they determine the production of the adaptive character without the original environmental stimuli. In either case the result would be due to the selection of genetic variants without involving any inheritance of acquired characters in the Lamarckian sense. Whether either hypothesis accords with fact can be determined only by further experiments.

These considerations bear closely on Darwin's attempts to discover the causes of variation (p. 87). When he compared a dwarf plant grown from seed in the lowlands with a dwarf plant that owes its size to an alpine environment, he was comparing a variation of genetic origin (a mutation, or 'monster' because it differs from its parents) with a variation of environmental origin (that Darwin called an 'adaptation'). They happen to be similar and the lowland dwarf mutant (an individual that contains a gene which has undergone mutation) can be called a 'genocopy' (to use P. B. Medawar's term) of the alpine form. Conversely, the alpine form can be called a 'phenocopy' (R. Goldschmidt) of the mutant. The same applies to Darwin's example of a puppy born in a temperate climate with a thick coat (a mutation or 'monstrosity'), contrasted with a puppy born in a temperate climate with a normal coat which grows thicker ('adaptation') when moved to a cold climate. From Darwin's point of view the most important conclusion to be drawn from the results of these experiments, as it also is for those who recognize natural selection of variations resulting from mutation and recombination of genes as the mechanism of evolution, is the fact that modifications brought about by changes in the factors of the environment do not produce evolution; this is only achieved by changes in the genes.

The consequences that follow from these major advances in biology are numerous, and here only three can be considered. The first relates to the fact that genes are discrete particles that never contaminate each other but are replicated exactly, until they mutate after which they are replicated exactly in their new condition. This provides the complete disproof of blending inheritance; variance is conserved indefinitely and not halved at each generation; far from obliterating variation, interbreeding spreads and increases it, by random recombination of genes. At one stroke Darwin's chief difficulties are solved; Fleeming Jenkin's objection that single variations (mutations) could not be perpetuated but would be swamped in the population is groundless; reversion to ancestral type is explained by the conservation during many generations of genes whose original effects can reappear when the appropriate gene-complex is reconstituted as a result of interbreeding and recombination; the source of heritable variation is found in mutation and recombination of genes; and mutations not only need not but must not be more frequent than a low value, which is itself subject to alteration and control by natural selection.

From this low natural rate of mutation a consequence follows that appears paradoxical until thoroughly understood. Mathematical analysis has been applied to the effects of selection at different degrees of intensity, and it has been shown that no mutation can become established in a population if there is even a slight degree of adverse selection operating against it. But practically every new mutation at its first appearance and in the environmental conditions in which it occurred *is* opposed by natural selection. At first sight this might appear to be the doomsday of the theory of evolution by natural selection of mutations, but further study shows that this is far from being the case. As just mentioned, a mutant gene that confers no benefit on the organism is reduced by selection o the recessive condition, and organisms in nature have been found to be full of recessive genes whose effects are masked by their corresponding dominant partners. This state of affairs continues until the gene-complex and/or the conditions of the environment change, as is bound to happen sooner or later. Every environment is always deteriorating, even if only because other competitive species are evolving in it. Under the changed conditions, one or other of the hitherto suppressed recessive genes may produce effects that confer advantage under the new conditions. This is why evolution is opportunistic and undesigned. Numerous examples of this phenomenon have been demonstrated experimentally, of which only two can be described here.

In man there is a gene that affects the red blood-corpuscles and produces abnormal molecules of haemoglobin that become attached to one another end to end thereby producing rods that distort the cells and make them look like sickles. In conditions of oxygen-want these cells break down and cause thrombosis that usually kills the man. The gene producing this condition is not unexpectedly recessive. But if there happens to be endemic malaria in the environment, this gene confers advantage because the malaria parasite cannot enter a red blood-corpuscle containing the abnormal haemoglobin. The population then strikes a balance between those individuals that are homozygous for the normal dominant gene and liable to die of malaria, those that are homozygous for the recessive gene and liable to die of thrombosis, and those that are heterozygous and protected from both calamities, and therefore favoured, as A. C. Allison showed.

The second example is provided by the history of the peppered moth in Britain. A hundred years ago a mutation occurred that turned the insect black, which made possessors of this gene conspicuous on the tree-trunks and lichens where the moths rest and so made them an easy prey to birds. The gene in question was kept down by constant adverse selection, but as in the case of most genes the same mutation occurred again and again, with the same result; until by the coming of the industrial revolution and the heavy pollution of soot on vegetation near industrial centres, the resting-places of the moths became black. Now it was the turn of the black moths to be favoured and the original grey moths to fall victims to birds. The expectation of life of the two varieties of moths in natural and in industrial areas has been measured by H. B. D. Kettlewell and found to agree with the theory that the normal gene confers advantage in natural surroundings and the black gene in industrial areas. In these areas the black variety, which was extremely scarce when it first appeared a hundred years ago, has supplanted its parent grey variety. Here, then, is an example of a character that first appeared as the result of a mutation and was acted upon adversely by selection, and that now confers advantage, again as the result of selection, because of the biologically unpredictable change in environmental conditions brought about by the industrial revolution. The peppered moth has evolved from grey to black, the blackness has become intensified, the change was brought about by natural selection of a variation due to a mutation, and this little piece of evolution has taken place in a hundred years under observation by man (Plates 19-23).

Since the majority of genes after they have mutated are deleterious and subjected to adverse selection against the characters that they control, there can be no basis for the view that genes are *directed* to mutate in advantageous directions so as to produce adaptive effects. Agencies such as the fulfilment of design, effects of use and disuse, inheritance of acquired characters, inner feelings, and others have been invoked or invented precisely to direct mutation along adaptive paths. This simply does not happen, there is no 'favourable breeze' of mutations; they mostly get knocked out by selection. As R. A. Fisher has aptly expressed the matter, 'every theory of evolution which assumes, as do all theories alternative to Natural Selection, that evolutionary changes can be explained by some hypothetical agency capable of controlling the nature of the mutations which occur, is involving a cause which demonstrably would not work, even if it were known to exist.' So only natural selection is left, and it is selection, not mutation, that controls evolution.

The same conclusion has to be drawn from studies in palaeontology. That science has now reached a stage where the degree of variability of fossil populations and the speed at which they evolved can be measured. It has been shown, by G. G. Simpson, that the rate and direction of evolution is not correlated with degree of variability nor with generation-time, but with change of environment and ecological conditions, to which organisms failed or succeeded in becoming adapted by selection. Natural selection can explain why evolution has been rapid in some lineages and slow in others as Huxley realized, because the mechanism of genes is capable of producing either diversity or stability, as required under pressure or permitted under absence of pressure by selection. Diversity is the result of mutation and recombination of genes and of their possibility of 'crossing over' from one chromosome to the other when germ-cells are formed. Stability is possible because the genes are particles that do not blend or contaminate each other but persist by replication, and mutate at a slow rate. Selection determines which possibility is adopted.

Evolution is not synonymous with the origin of species. Evolution is change resulting in more efficient adaptation to the environment and can result either in increased organization or in degeneration. Only when evolution has progressed so far that descendants cease normally to breed with the original type (although they may be made to do so) is a new species formed. A species can be regarded as a gene-pool and the formation of a new species involves the splitting of a gene-pool into two. This can be observed taking place in nature in a number of cases that Bernhard Rensch has called 'ring-species', of which gulls in Britain may be taken as an example.

The lesser black-backed gull and the herring gull occupy the extreme ends of a horseshoe-shaped range extending round the Arctic Circle and overlapping in Britain. They vary progressively in colour and habit round the ring, but the British lesser black-backed gull can breed with its neighbours eastwards in Scandinavia and these with their neighbours eastwards in Siberia, North America, and so on round again to Britain. But the easternmost gull of the horseshoe, in Britain, is the herring gull, which differs from the lesser black-backed gull not only in colour, cry, and behaviour, but in nesting habits, preferring cliffs instead of the inland moors of the other gull, and is dispersive in winter instead of migratory. In other words, these two gulls are ecologically isolated in Britain and behave as separate species in spite of their belonging to the same gene-pool followed either way round the ring. When the ring is interrupted by extinction or any other cause the gene-pool will be snapped into two, and the two gulls in Britain will be completely distinct species. They have undergone selection in different directions and the result has been the conversion of geographical varieties into species as Darwin contended, reproductively isolated as Huxley demanded. They also show that evolution does not take place from single pairs but in populations numerous enough for the recombinations of genes that take place at each generation to provide a sufficient heritable variation for natural selection to work on. A reasoned estimate of the population of man's ancestors a million years ago, when australopithecine man-like apes were turning into pithecanthropine ape-like men (p. 216) is 125,000.

It is a measure of Darwin's extraordinary flair for significant detail in the study of species living in nature, that he recognized the importance of a case of ring-species as early as 1839, when he wrote in his Notebook, 'Hooded crow and Carrion crow have in Europe different ranges—latter not going north of the Elbe,—yet they meet in one wood in Anhalt and there every year produce hybrids—now this is independent good case, but very odd since these crows are mixed in England—for I presume Carrion Crow is found in Edinburgh.' The facts of their distribution and interbreeding are confirmed by the most recent authority, K. H. Voous who records that the range of the hooded crow extends from the Elbe to the Yenisei, with the carrion crow to the east and west of it, in western

Europe and eastern Asia. All along the boundary where the two ranges overlap interbreeding occurs. The hooded crow reached Scotland after the retreat of the ice at the end of the last Glacial period, while the carrion crow reached the British Isles later from southwestern Europe. Although they now interbreed where they meet, there can be little doubt that eventually the large populations where they do not meet will come to have different gene-pools and become separate species.

Natural selection emerges as the paramount factor in evolution, to a greater extent than Darwin himself would have been prepared to admit. Mutation is the cause of heritable variation, but it is selection, not mutation that determines the direction and speed of evolution. As natural selection is the contribution that Darwin made to science, his theory, refined by more recent knowledge, is the one that holds the field. The progress of ideas during the past hundred and fifty years may be summarized conveniently in the form of questions and answers, as follows.

LAMARCK

question: What causes adaptive variations to occur?
answer: Fulfilment of needs by action of inner feelings, inheritance of acquired characters, effects of environment.

DARWIN

1st question: What causes variation?
answer: I do not know.
2nd question: What causes any variation that happens to be adaptive to be preserved so that it can modify the descendants of its possessors?
answer: Natural selection.

TODAY

1st question: What causes heritable variation?
answer: Random mutation and recombination of genes.

2nd question: What causes any heritable variation that may become adaptive under changed conditions to be preserved until those changed conditions arise?

answer: Preservation of genes as recessives until, under changed conditions and after reshuffling of the gene-complex, their effects may become adaptive and they become dominant as a result of natural selection.

The formulation and general acceptance of the present synthetic theory of evolution has coincided with the reversal of a curious trend that set in among biologists after the publication of the *Origin of Species*. This new and powerful interpretation of the world of life was largely due to Darwin's observations on living plants and animals in nature, and his realization of the importance of ecological niches to which organisms become adapted; but no sooner was this great work in the hands of biologists than they rushed indoors, into their laboratories, and for fifty years devoted their energies and thoughts to research in comparative anatomy and embryology, and neglected the study of variation, selection, and adaptation in natural populations of animals and plants. The reason for this paradoxical situation was that the dominant influences in teaching were those of Huxley and of Haeckel. The classic researches of the former inspired students with interest in what could be learnt from the structure and functions of the organs of a type, while the latter kindled enthusiasm in the search for ancestral types to place on the appropriate levels of ancestral trees. To this static treatment of evolution, devoted to the study of its products, has succeeded a dynamic approach aimed at the analysis of the processes by which evolution works.

It is only within the last fifty years that biologists such as Julian Huxley, Richard Hesse, and Charles Elton have re-established the importance of field studies and ecology, a branch of science practically founded by Darwin, while

Plate 19 Normal and melanic varieties of the peppered moth on a natural, unpolluted, lichen-covered tree trunk in an unpolluted area. In this environment the normal variety was the overwhelmingly preponderant type a hundred years ago.

'late 20 Normal and melanic arieties of the peppered moth on soot-polluted lichenless tree 'unk in an industrial area. In this nvironment the melanic variety is ne overwhelmingly preponderant ype, and the change has occurred rough natural selection of genes. 'hotos by courtesy of Dr H. B. D. ettlewell.

Plate 21 (*left*) Robin preying on the melanic (i.e. non-adaptive) variety of the peppered moth on a lichen-covered tree trunk in a rural area.

Plate 22 (*below*) Redstart preying on the normal (i.e. non-adaptive) variety of the peppered moth on a soot-polluted tree trunk in an industrial area. Photos by courtesy of Dr N. Tinbergen.

animal behaviour was shown to be accessible to experimental study by Karl von Frisch, Konrad Lorenz, and Nikolaas Tinbergen; genetical analysis was applied to ecological situations by Edmund Brisco Ford, Theodosius Dobzhansky, and G. Ledyard Stebbins, and combined studies in taxonomy, geographical distribution, and isolation were instituted at the hands of Ernst Mayr and Bernhard Rensch. The mathematics of selection have been studied by R. A. Fisher, J. B. S. Haldane, and S. Wright. Only the names of some pioneers are here mentioned. The result has been that evolution can now be studied experimentally in the field and made to yield direct evidence on variation and selection. Towards the end of his life, when Darwin was asked by his son Leonard whether it would be possible to observe evolution happening under natural conditions, the reply was given that if facts were properly collected they might reveal evidence of evolution 'perhaps in no more than fifty years'. It was a good estimate.

If a reader should be so impressed by the successful solution of so many problems relating to evolution by natural selection that he is in danger of imagining that this subject is exhausted, and that there is little more to discover in it, he must immediately be disabused. Darwin himself would have been the first to do so and to protest that enough is never known about anything. Expressing this view he wrote in 1869, 'If I lived twenty more years and was able to work, how I should have to modify the *Origin*, and how much the views on all points will have to be modified!' His views have had to be modified probably less than he thought, for science progresses not by the reversal of principles well established by observation and experiment, but by extension and refinement of results already obtained out of which new principles emerge. This is what relativity theory did to Newton's physics and future research will do to Darwin's evolution. It is part of the achievement of both these men that they not only made fundamental discoveries but opened up whole new fields of research that had never been thought of before and in which further advances in knowledge can be made. This was what T. Dobzhansky meant when he paradoxically said that 'the true greatness of a scientist may lie in the fact that his work carries the seeds of its own obsolescence.' An indication of the directions in which some of these 'seeds' are likely to grow may be found in Ernst Mayr's appreciation of certain fields in which knowledge of natural selection and genetics and the way in which they interact is still very deficient. The following are examples, limited in number to half a dozen.

Fitness has been defined as a measure of the contribution made to the gene-pool of the next generation. Fitness cannot be ascribed to any given gene because its effects depend on the other genes in the gene-complex, and on the living and physical environments of the organism, none of which is constant. How, then, should fitness be measured? Some characters, such as mutation-rate, degree of inbreeding or outbreeding practised, and sex ratio of males to females, are not significant for the survival or succumbing of any given individual, but are of great importance for the survival of the species. How are such characters controlled by natural selection? Genes are known to determine systems of enzymes which control the synthesis of particular chemical compounds out of which living matter of organisms is built up. What is the mechanism of the interaction of genes on each other in the gene-complex and of their co-operation in regulating the structure and function of the organism?

Populations in nature are constantly invaded by migrants from other neighbouring populations of the same species with which, of course, they are fertile. The difference between the contents of a seed-bed or breeding-pen and a population in nature is that in the latter the effects of outbreeding and recombination of genes are far more important in giving rise to variability than is mutation. How far, then, can the results of experiments conducted on closed populations like those of a breeding-pen be applied to open populations in nature? At the periphery of the geographical range of a species natural selection is more stringent because the environmental conditions are likely to be marginal and to that extent different from those to which the bulk of the species is adapted, and the interchange of genes or 'gene-flow' is more restricted than in the centre of the range. What are the genetic differences between populations at the periphery and at the centre? Many examples are known of species that are indistinguishable from one another by eye, but are nevertheless different species because they will not interbreed. This is because they have different gene-pools. Darwin knew of the possibility of such species now known as sibling species: 'Species may be good ones and differ scarcely in any external character.' Their gene-complexes have changed but their structure has remained constant. How does a gene-complex change without changing the visible structure of an organism?

These examples, each of which could form a research programme for a generation, must suffice to show that evolution theory will itself evolve.

Chapter 10

Variation, Man, and Emotions

When Darwin finished writing the *Origin,* he still had notes and material to form the basis of three more books. The first of these was *Variation of Animals and Plants under Domestication,* for which he started to look over his manuscripts on 9 January 1860, only two days after the publication of the second edition of the *Origin.* He began to write on *Variation* on 24 March 1860, but it was not published until 1868. The reasons for this delay were that Darwin continually found new subjects for research and experiment that fascinated him in many fields, including the structure and methods of pollination in orchids, the different lengths of stamens and styles in flowers of primroses, flax, and loosestrife, and the insectivorous habits of sundew, his work on which forms the subject of Chapter 11. Research and publications on these subjects came out like a cascade between 1862 and 1865. Darwin also had to prepare the third and fourth editions of the *Origin* which were published in April 1861 and December 1866 respectively. The health of his children was often a cause of anxiety. In the summer of 1862 his son Leonard was very ill with scarlet fever, and his wife also caught the disease; 'We are a wretched family and ought to be exterminated,' he wrote to Asa Gray, 'there is no end of trouble in this weary world.' As for himself, he was wretchedly ill all through the year 1864.

In the Introduction to *Variation,* Darwin reminded his readers that he had promised in the *Origin* to publish the evidence and the references for the conclusions to which he had come in that book, and this new work was the first instalment in the fulfilment of that promise. At the same time it contained a restatement of the principles of natural selection, and of the impossibility of admitting design in variation. *Variation* covered the subjects treated in the first two chapters of the large work which had been interrupted when he began to write the 'abstract' that became the *Origin*, and was therefore a continuation and amplification of that work.

The object of *Variation* was to study and show the amount and kind of change that had been brought about under artificial conditions of selection by man since the domestication of animals and cultivation of plants had been practised. It described the variability of these plants and animals and the differences between them and their wild ancestors, in the cases where these could be identified. Darwin's method was to study specimens of the chief breeds, to inquire into their fertility when crossed, to breed some of them himself and follow the inheritance of their characters and the appearance of reversion to what he assumed was their ancestral type; he also took into account the changes that took place when previously domesticated animals were turned back to the wild and became feral. He collected what information was then available on domesticated animals and cultivated plants in the antiquities of Egypt and Mesopotamia, the writings of India and China, and the results of archaeological researches into the contents of Swiss lakeside dwellings and Danish middens.

Dogs were domesticated very early; during the Neolithic period they belonged to only one race but during the Bronze Age they belonged to several races, and Darwin inclined to the view that they originated from different species of wild ancestor in different parts of the world, for instance wolves and jackals, under intensive artificial selection by man for the different uses to which they could be put and also for pets. The peculiarities of some breeds such as the pug, he thought, might have arisen suddenly as a sport or what would now be called a mutation but had become accentuated and fixed by human selection. He noted that all domesticated dogs bark, which no wild species of the Canidae does. In contrast to dogs, cats do not show a number of originally different breeds in any one country, although the breed found in any one country may differ from that found in another. That cats are variable is seen from the fact that breeds are different, but the uniformity of cats within a given country Darwin ascribed to the comparative absence of artificial selection practised by man owing to their intractable and independent nature and rambling nocturnal habits, which make control of their mating difficult.

Horses are extremely variable, and Darwin stressed the difference between the South American ponies that he had seen and the imported Spanish horses, which were their known sole ancestors three hundred years before. Horses have been selected solely for their utility in different directions. The ass is represented by four breeds in Syria but only one in Europe, the reason for which Darwin ascribed to the fact that in Europe owners of donkeys have always been poor persons in no position to breed large numbers or to exercise selection. In this manner Darwin was able to find a correlation between the practice and the effects of artificial selection. His explanation of the fact that domestic geese are so uniform was that 'no one makes a pet of the goose' or selects different breeds of it as has been so intensively done with rabbits, pigeons, poultry, canaries, and goldfish. Other domesticated animals considered in the book are pigs, cattle, sheep, goats, peacocks, turkeys, guinea-fowl, honey-bees in which artificial selection cannot be ordinarily practised because of the mating habits involving the nuptial flight of the queen, and silk-moths which present the interesting phenomenon of a species that shows variation in the cocoon stage without much effect on the condition of the adult insect.

Cultivated plants are not treated in such detail as domesticated animals in *Variation*, but Darwin draws an important conclusion from the fact that no useful plants have come from the Cape of Good Hope, Australia, New Zealand, or America north of Mexico or south of the River Plate, nor from any oceanic island. If cultivated plants owed their present condition to long-practised selection by man, their absence from those regions is readily explained by the fact that the regions were inhabited by men who either did not cultivate the land at all, as in South Africa and Australia, or who cultivated it very imperfectly, or again because they were uninhabited by man.

With his intense desire for tangible and visible explanations of the apparent facts that came to his notice, Darwin had ever since 1840 wanted to frame an hypothesis that would cover heredity and include acquired characters and the effects of use and disuse, variation, graft-hybrids, hybridization, reversion to ancestral type and atavism, regeneration, reproduction, and embryonic development. The result was his provisional hypothesis of pangenesis that he printed at the end of his book on *Variation*. Carrying the war straight into the camp of those critics of the *Origin* who had objected to his use of the method of hypothesis, Darwin quoted a remark by William Whewell in the *History of the Inductive Sciences*: ' "Hypotheses may often be of service to science, when they involve a certain portion of incompleteness, and even of error." Under this point of view I venture to advance the hypothesis of Pangenesis, which implies that the whole organization, in the sense of every separate atom or unit, reproduces itself. Hence ovules and pollen-grains—the fertilized seed or egg, as well as buds—include and consist of a multitude of germs thrown off from each separate atom of the organism.'

These germs he called gemmules, and as the cell-theory as applied to animals was not yet sufficiently well established, Darwin preferred to say that the gemmules were given off from all parts of the animal and carried in the blood-stream to the germ-cells. The gemmules were made responsible not only for the hereditary resemblance between offspring and parent but also for the development of the structures in the offspring. A reserve of gemmules in the tissues served for regeneration in case parts were lost; malformations and monstrosities were due to gemmules reaching the wrong destination in the offspring; variations were caused by irregularities in the numbers of gemmules derived from different parts of the parents' bodies; the existence of abortive or vestigial organs and the fact of reversion to ancestral type were explained as a result of the preservation of ancestral gemmules from several generations back; and the fact that mutilations were not transmitted by inheritance was accounted for by the presence of sufficient gemmules from previous generations. On the other hand, as gemmules were imagined as being in constant production in the organism, a gemmule from an organ that had been modified by the environment or by the effects of use and disuse would perpetuate that modification in the offspring, and in this manner Darwin accounted for the inheritance of acquired characters, of which he had no reason to doubt.

It was a brave attempt to explain a number of phenomena which at that time were either completely outside the bounds of scientific knowledge such as heredity and experimental embryology, or imperfectly studied and misunderstood like variation and regeneration, or which simply do not occur like the effect of a previous sire on a subsequent sire's offspring, so that Darwin's hypothesis of pangenesis could not possibly avoid falling into fundamental errors. For instance, it was not even known that fertilization involves the fusion of one sperm nucleus with one egg nucleus before Oskar Hertwig observed this in 1875. Darwin still believed in 1868 that several pollen-grains or several sperms were required to fertilize one egg. In spite of the observations made by William Harvey in the seventeenth century and of the experiments conducted by Étienne Geoffroy-Saint-Hilaire and Camille Dareste in the nineteenth, it had not yet been realized that embryonic development is not the unfolding and enlargement of anything preformed but a fresh creation of differentiation in each successive generation, an epigenesis, in which a point-to-point correspondence of gemmules from part of parent to corresponding part of offspring simply does not occur. Acquired characters and the effects of use and disuse are not inherited, Mendelian genetics provides the explanation of heredity and of variation, and the fact that all cells of the body contain the full complement of genes allows replacement of lost parts to take place by regeneration where this faculty is not impaired by other limiting factors. Francis Galton's experiment of transfusing blood from rabbits of one breed into those of another and finding that this had no effect on the characters of the offspring which, on the hypothesis of pangenesis, should have been affected by the gemmules in the transfused blood provided a practical disproof of the hypothesis.

The hypothesis of pangenesis is in some ways a reminder of how little biological science in the middle of the nineteenth century had progressed since the time of the classical Greeks. Although Darwin, with his complete lack of historical sense, was unaware of it until informed by William Ogle, an hypothesis practically identical with pangenesis had been advanced by the author of *Peri gones* in the Hippocratic corpus about 400 B.C. It is, however, with the hypotheses put forward by the French philosophers in the eighteenth century that pangenesis may best be compared. Under the influence of Descartes, visible and tangible 'mechanistic' explanations were looked for in science, and this fashion led to the adoption of the view that embryonic development was the unfolding, 'development', and enlargement of an already preformed miniature organism in the egg. When sperms were discovered by Ludwig Hamm in 1677, a furious controversy arose between the 'ovists' who maintained that the next generation was preformed in the egg and the 'spermatists' who denied this and maintained on the contrary that the next generation was preformed in the sperm. Some enthusiasts even claimed to have detected a miniature man in sperms.

On either view, it may be noted, only one parent contributed to the inheritance of the characters shown in the offspring. When it was realized that half-breeds like mulattos in man or equine mules showed characters that they had obviously inherited from both parents, these crude views had to be abandoned, and Maupertuis suggested in 1745 that seminal particles from both parents contributed to produce and determine the characters of the offspring. These particles were supposed, like Darwin's gemmules, to come from all parts of the body of the parents and to reproduce them, part for part, in the offspring. Buffon's theory of 'organic molecules', put forward in 1749, supposed that these molecules were indestructible elements absorbed with the food and built into the body of the parents until these were full-grown, when the organic molecules were supposed to accumulate in the reproductive organs where they formed the seminal fluids of both sexes. Buffon accounted for the characters of the offspring and its sex by supposing these to be the result of the relative preponderance of organic molecules contributed to the offspring by one or other of the parents. Diderot's theory of 'filaments' put forward in 1769 was similar, and it attempted to account for the production of monstrosities, either deficient of parts or possessing parts in excess of normal, by supposing that different 'filaments' had different predetermined prospective fates. This and other similar hypotheses marked a period of sterile premature speculation.

As the facts of Mendelian inheritance and of experimental embryology make Darwin's hypothesis of pangenesis untenable, it is of interest to consider more closely the conclusions to which Darwin came on heredity as a result of the breeding experiments described in *Variation* and others of his writings. He knew of course that sports, now called mutations, arise suddenly and are inherited. He also knew that self-fertilization and inbreeding for several generations produce strains that become quite constant in their characters although they may have come from very variable species. Such strains are now known as 'pure lines' following the experiments of W. Johannsen, and they breed true because they are homozygous for all their genes. Darwin knew of the phenomenon which since Mendel's work is called segregation, and he described it clearly in terms of characters though not of hereditary factors: 'some characters refuse to blend, and are transmitted in an unmodified state either from both parents or from one. . . . I know of a good many varieties, which must be so called, that will not blend or intermix, but produce offspring quite like either parent . . . I crossed the Painted Lady and Purple sweet peas, which are very differently coloured varieties, and got, even out of the same pod, both varieties perfect, but none intermediate.'

Darwin even obtained a fair approximation to a simple 3 to 1 Mendelian ratio after crossing the common snapdragon with the peloric variety; the first generation of hybrids (F_1) were all common, and when these were allowed to sow themselves the second generation (F_2) consisted of 88 common to 37 peloric. Here, in addition, was the phenomenon of dominance and of the extraction of the recessive form from the heterozygote. He knew of what are now called F_1 uniformity and F_2 variability, which are used as tests for simple Mendelian inheritance: 'When two well-marked races are crossed the offspring in the first generation take more or less after either parent or are quite intermediate between them, or rarely assume characters in some degree new. In the second and several succeeding generations, the offspring are generally found to vary exceedingly, one compared with another.' Here, if only he could have realized it, was the complete experimental disproof of blending inheritance and the evidence for particulate inheritance.

Once, indeed, he came within a hair's-breadth of making Mendel's discovery when he wrote to Huxley in 1858, 'Approaching the subject from the side which attracts me most, viz., inheritance, I have lately been inclined to speculate, very crudely and indistinctly, that propagation by true fertilization will turn out to be a sort of mixture, and not true fusion, of two distinct individuals, as each parent has its parents and ancestors. I can understand on no other view the way in which crossed forms go back to so large an extent to ancestral forms.' For that brief moment Darwin caught a glimpse of the particulate nature of inheritance and of the non-fusion, non-contamination of its factors, as well as of a preview of Weismann's theory of the germ-plasm. This glimpse of the significance of reversion enabled him to see the difference between the hereditary transmission of factors and the embryonic development of characters, for when characters are hidden and only appear in later generations, they are determined by factors that are hereditarily transmitted during the intervening generations in which they do not undergo embryonic development.

Although Darwin therefore had knowledge of the essential facts on which Mendel established his Laws, he failed to grasp their significance. The main reason for this was probably that the results of most crosses between different varieties with which he was familiar involved a number of pairs of genes and gave mongrels which, by their generally intermediate characters, appeared to support the idea of blending inheritance. This serves to underline the good fortune and genius of Mendel in selecting as material for his crossing experiments varieties that differed in only a few pairs of genes and therefore revealed the facts of segregation and non-contamination. Another reason that probably prevented Darwin from making Mendel's discovery was that he was so deeply imbued with the principle of correlation of parts in an organism that it would have been difficult for him to conceive of characters as being controlled by units. As Jean Rostand has aptly put the matter, 'Il ne serait jamais venu à l'esprit de Darwin d'envisager la fragmentation du patrimoine héréditaire.' Nevertheless, although it has not stood the test of time or increased knowledge, the hypothesis of pangenesis stands as a remarkable attempt to make a generalization.

Variation of Animals and Plants under Domestication was published on 30 January 1868 and the whole edition of 1,500 copies was sold in a week. Darwin had originally intended and hoped that he would follow it with similarly documented and detailed books on variation in nature and on natural selection which would cover the remaining subjects in the *Origin* in greater detail and use all the material that he had collected for his large book. Before *Variation* was printed, however, and while waiting for proofs, Darwin had become so heartily sick of the subject that for relaxation he turned to another, the *Descent of Man*. This topic had never ceased to engage his close attention since the time in 1837 and 1838 when he wrote his Notebooks on Transmutation of Species which already contained many of his basic ideas. 'Man in his arrogance thinks himself a great work worthy the interposition of a deity. More humble and I believe truer to consider him created from animals.' Memories of Tierra del Fuego and a visit to the Zoo are reflected in the following: 'Let man visit Ourang-Outang in domestication, hear expressive whine, see its intelligence when spoken to, as if it understood every word said—see its affection to those it knows, —see its passion and rage, sulkiness and very extreme of despair; let him look at savage [Fuegian], roasting his parent, naked, artless, not improving, yet improvable and then let him dare to boast his proud pre-eminence.' The evolutionary significance of behaviour did not escape Darwin: 'The passion of the doe for the victorious stag, who runs the skin off horns to fight, is analogous to the love of women to brave men.' One wonders whether Darwin witnessed a bullfight and the triumphs of a matador in South America.

In the *Origin* he mentioned very briefly that with the help of his theory 'Light will be thrown on the origin of man and his history.' His new book was to give chapter and verse for this claim. Restricting his subject to the evolution of one species, man, in the state of knowledge prevailing at that time, he was deprived of the help that might have been forthcoming in the case of other groups of animals from their affinities, geographical distribution in past and present times, and their representation in the fossil record. This left for consideration the evidence to be gleaned from comparative anatomy, embryology, and vestigial organs. After acknowledging the priority of Lamarck in claiming an animal origin for man in a scheme of evolution, Darwin had little difficulty in showing that in every single bodily character man differs less from the higher apes than these do from the lower members of the Primates. It must have given Darwin no little satisfaction to throw back into Owen's teeth, word for word, the flat contradiction that Huxley had given to Owen's claim at the memorable Oxford meeting of the British Association in 1860. Contrary to popular error, prevalent now as well

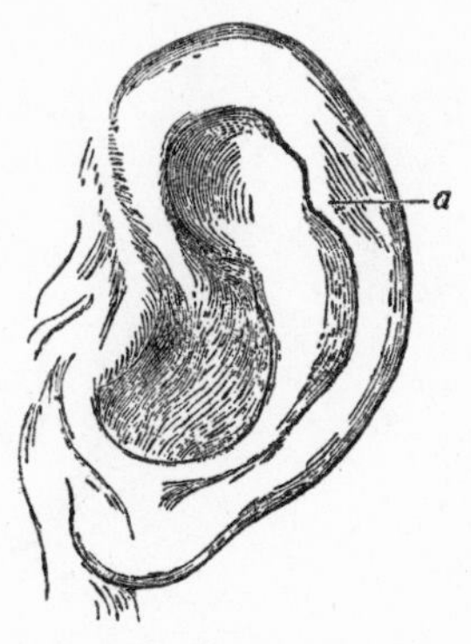

Fig. 15 A human ear showing at *a* the little blunt point projecting from the inwardly folded margin or helix, representing the original point of the pointed ear of the ancestor of Primates. From *The Descent of Man*, 1871.

as then, Darwin never said that man was descended from apes, let alone monkeys; what he claimed was that man's ancestors if alive today would have to be classified among the Primates.

Without going into details of anatomy, Darwin went on to show that man and apes share some parasites, some diseases, and the same susceptibilities to drugs and chemical substances. Baboons are caught by making them helplessly drunk on strong beer: 'an *Ateles* [spider-monkey], after getting drunk on brandy, would never touch it again, and thus was wiser than many men.' Men and apes are subject to similar processes in courtship, reproduction, periods of menstruation and gestation, birth, and lactation. At early stages of development the human embryo resembles the embryo of lower mammals to the extent of possessing a tail that extends backwards behind the hind limbs, a feature in which embryonic man resembles the embryos of lower mammals as well as of apes, for adult apes have no tails. Darwin had realized the importance of this fact as early as 6 January 1839 when he wrote in his Notebook, 'the rudiment of a *tail* shows man was originally *quadruped*.' Among vestigial organs in adult man Darwin

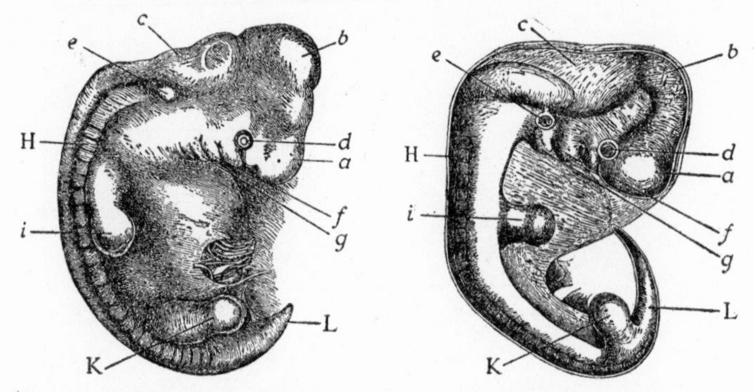

Fig. 16 Illustrations used by Darwin to show the embryo of a man on the left and that of a dog on the right, to emphasise their similarity and affinity. *a*, forebrain; *b*, mid-brain; *c*, hind-brain; *d*, eye; *e*, ear; *f*, first visceral arch; *g*, second visceral arch; H, muscles flanking the vertebral column; *i*, fore-limb; K, hindlimb; L, tail. From *The Descent of Man*, 1871.

enumerated skin and scalp muscles, the original tip of pointed ears now known as 'Darwin's point', hair on the body, wisdom teeth, vermiform appendix, and the immovable vertebrae of the coccyx to which muscles are attached. From all these considerations he drew the simple and unavoidable conclusion that

> man and all other vertebrate animals have been constructed on the same general model. . . . It is only our natural prejudice, and that arrogance which made our forefathers declare that they were descended from demi-gods, which leads us to demur to this conclusion. . . . But the time will before long come when it will be thought wonderful, that naturalists, who were well acquainted with the comparative structure and development of man and other mammals, should have believed that each was the work of a separate act of creation.

That time has come.

Having dealt with man's body Darwin next turned to the origin of man's mind, for the difference between the mental powers of the lowest man and the highest ape are enormous. To show that this gap, for all its width, was not unbridgeable, Darwin used the principle of gradation

Plate 23 Charles Darwin, 1854, photograph by Maull & Fox.

Plate 24 Charles Darwin, 1881, portrait by John Collier.

and comparison. If man shares any instincts and senses with animals there must be the possibility of some transition between them. Man does share with animals the principles of self-preservation, sexual love, maternal affection, and the senses of pleasure and pain, jealousy and rage, pride and shame, excitement and boredom, wonder and curiosity, imitation, attention, memory, and imagination. Some animals are capable of a limited degree of reasoning, and some can use tools; all higher animals have some means of communication with one another, and apes can do this orally by a very rudimentary sort of language. It has been said that man differs absolutely from all other animals in his belief in a deity of some sort, but Darwin had had personal experience of Fuegians who recognized neither god nor devil and practised no religious rite. From all these considerations Darwin drew the conclusion that the differences in mental powers between man and animals was a difference of degree but not of kind.

'I fully subscribe to the judgment of those writers who maintain that of all the differences between man and the lower animals, the moral sense or conscience is by far the most important.' Darwin's approach to this problem was to claim that any animal whatever, endowed with well-marked social instincts, would inevitably acquire a moral sense or conscience, as soon as its intellectual powers had become as well developed as in man. He defended this view by pointing out that many animals are social and that social instincts lead them to take pleasure in one another's company and to perform services for each other. Animal mothers love and comfort their offspring, and adults sacrifice themselves for them. The basis of altruism is there. If to this level of behaviour were added the development of the higher mental faculties and the power of articulate language, the guide to action would be the common good under the influence of approbation or blame from fellow-members of the social group. 'The virtues which must be practised, at least generally, by rude men, so that they may associate in a body, are those which are still regarded as the most important. But they are practised almost exclusively in relation to the men of the same tribe; and their opposites are not regarded as crimes in relation to the men of other tribes.' From what is known of Darwin's opinion of Jehovah, it is most probable that what he here had in mind was the ancient Hebrews whose commandments to abstain from crime within the nation did not extend outside it. The relations between modern nations are still not very different from those. Darwin went on, 'As man advances in civilization, and small tribes are united into larger communities, the simplest reason would tell each individual that he ought to extend his social instincts and sympathies to all members of the same nation, though personally unknown to him. This point being once reached, there is only an artificial barrier to prevent his sympathies extending to men of all nations and races.' This demonstration has been made before, but still awaits fulfilment. Borrowing from Marcus Aurelius the statement that social instincts are the prime principle of man's moral constitution, Darwin concludes by saying that these, with the aid of active intellectual powers and the effects of habit, naturally lead to the golden rule, 'As ye would that men should do to you, do ye to them likewise.' Civilized nations have all once been barbarous, and this historical evidence for ethical progress confirmed Darwin in his belief that '*all* morality has grown up by evolution'. Ethical behaviour can be seen to develop in individuals and to have evolved in societies.

If it be true that man has evolved from lower mammals, there remains the problem of how it was brought about. Physical and mental characters must be considered together, for mental capacities are correlated with the structure and condition of the brain. Since man is variable and has been exposed to competition in the struggle for existence and to changes in climate and environment, and since, further, every improvement in his mental capacities and social instincts must have been adaptive and conferred increased survival value on the favourable variants, Darwin had no doubt that it was by natural selection that man's evolution was mainly brought about. Here Darwin met opposition from an unexpected quarter, his fellow-discoverer of natural selection, Wallace himself. In 1864 Wallace published a paper in which he fully supported the view that, by natural selection, man's body had been improved through the acquisition of the upright posture and bipedal gait, freeing the fore limbs from taking part in locomotion, and above all by the greater development of his brain, which introduced a completely new factor in evolution. In 1869, however, Wallace came to the conclusion that the brain of man in its present state could not have been the result of natural selection because he thought the brain and potential mental capacities of the owest savage little inferior to those of advanced civilized races. He therefore claimed that 'an instrument has been developed in advance of the needs of its possessor,' and since this put natural selection out of court as the cause of this phase of human evolution, Wallace concluded that 'some higher intelligence may have directed the process by which the human race was developed.' The effect of these views on Darwin was to make him regret sadly that his friend had deserted science and taken refuge in mysticism, a trend in Wallace's mind which became accentuated when he indulged in spiritualism. Darwin countered Wallace's argument by showing that there was no evidence to support the view that man's mental capacities had ever preceded his needs, and by claiming that no limit can be set to the advantage accruing from continued improvement of the brain and mental faculties, through natural selection. It must be remembered that at the time when these discussions took place, no fossil forerunners of man were known except for the Neanderthal skull-cap, the significance of which was not understood. A hundred years of research and the discovery of such fossils as *Proconsul*, a Primate close to the ancestors of both apes and men; *Kenyapithecus*, a Primate leading towards the hominids; *Australopithecus*, an ape-faced hominid that walked nearly upright and used simple tools; *Pithecanthropus*, a brutish man who used fire, have done more than Darwin would ever have expected to fill the gaps between man's ancestors and man. While these fossils confirm Wallace's views of the importance of early acquisition of upright gait, they support Darwin's general thesis of progressive improvement through natural selection. They also confirm Darwin's uncannily sound conjecture that the early progenitors of man would be found to have lived in Africa.

As in the case of the *Origin*, Darwin did not pretend to provide evidence that man had evolved from lower mammals; he showed by conclusions drawn from independent lines of evidence in different branches of science how man could have evolved, and indeed in all reason must have evolved. He predicted that the evidence would one day be forthcoming, and that day has arrived, for the series of fossils just mentioned provides the crucial evidence that man did evolve.

Furthermore, the members of this series of fossils satisfy the two requirements that must be met before they can serve as evidence for evolution; they show serial gradations in structure that connect primitive to advanced types, and they follow a temporal sequence that agrees with the geological evidence. They also demonstrate the impossibility of saying, in a close evolutionary series of forms in which the individuals vary widely, where any particular type begins. This gives all the more point to Darwin's prophetic statement that 'in a series of forms graduating insensibly from some ape-like creature to man as he now exists, it would be impossible to fix on any definite point where the term "man" ought to be used.' The very fact that anthropologists have difficulty in giving names to the different stages in this fossil series of men is the result of their transition from one to another, or, in other words, of their evolution.

Anthropology existed before Darwin, but he provided it with its central theme. Meanwhile some anthropologists, jurists, historians, and philosophers did not wait for the *Descent of Man* to act on the cue that Darwin had given them in the *Origin*, and the following pioneer studies in evolutionary cultural anthropology reflect the effect of his work: Sir Henry Maine's *Ancient Law* (1861), N. D. Fustel de Coulange's *La cité antique* (1865), J. F. MacLennan's *Primitive Marriage* (1865), Sir Edward Tylor's *Researches into the Primitive History of Mankind* (1865), Sir John Lubbock's *Origins of Civilisation and the Primitive Condition of Man* (1870), all of which were published after the first edition of the *Origin* in 1859 and before the *Descent of Man* in 1871. It was not long before the lesson of evolution filtered through to all fields of human endeavour, including literature, art, music, and the history of ideas in general. Politics did not escape, and while the evolution of political systems has been a fruitful field for historical study, the method by which biological evolution has been brought about, natural selection, has been pressed into service to provide a 'basis' for political systems of very diverse kinds, by attempting to apply to man in the stage of cultural evolution a mechanism based on selection, genetics, and variation, which operated in the pre-human stage of biological evolution.

Judged from a modern standpoint, there is an aspect of Darwin's magnificent demonstration of the evolution of man that he failed to develop to the full. Wallace had pointed out in 1864 that the appearance of man's brain introduced a completely new factor into evolution, because the efficient function of that brain made further specialization of the body unnecessary, and mind became more important than bodily structure. Darwin accepted this contribution with acclamation, for it explains why man's body has no weapons of offence or defence, while his mind enabled him to defeat enemies, outwit prey and capture it, and overcome environmental hardships. But Darwin did not go on to the conclusion that with the development of the brain and the improvement of the higher mental faculties to the point where experience could be exchanged through speech, stored in cumulative tradition, and passed on from one generation to the next by instruction, example, and guidance, a process completely distinct from the transmission of genes through the germ-cells, a totally new process was started that had never been seen on earth before. It has been called psycho-social evolution by Sir Julian Huxley, and is what has produced civilization. Another fundamental difference between it and biological evolution through natural selection is that while in any given environment natural selection will work solely in accordance with the ecological factors present, there are as many criteria of psycho-social selection as there are kinds of society, because of differences in ethical standards of value, whether accepted by a social group or enforced by a leader, to which individuals are expected to conform. This may be illustrated by the differences between Lycurgus's Sparta or the Germanic tribes described by Tacitus on the one hand, and the modern welfare state on the other. The difference between the results of natural selection and of psycho-social selection are therefore so great that many scientists prefer to restrict the term 'evolution' to the effects of the former during the biological stage, and to leave cultural advance to the sociologist.

Another aspect of the evolution of man with which Darwin very understandably did not deal because of the lack of information then available, is the fact that it has been characterized by delay in bodily development, retention of juvenile ancestral features, postponement of maturity, and prolongation of childhood, which had important repercussions on the prolonged maintenance of the family as a basic social unit. Man when adult resembles his nearest living relatives, the apes, when young. In his smooth forehead, absence of brow-ridges, adult man resembles juvenile individuals of the ancestral forms *Australopithecus*, *Pithecanthropus*, and of apes, while the delayed development of man's teeth, closure of the sutures of the skull, and age of onset of puberty as compared with apes can easily be seen. This mode of evolution where adult descendant resembles juvenile ancestor because the descendant has undergone retardation of development, is known as paedomorphosis, which is the direct opposite to the theory of recapitulation, according to which juvenile descendant was supposed to resemble ancestral adult. This now-discredited theory was put forward by Haeckel with great enthusiasm and forcefulness, and this was probably the reason why Darwin was not led to consider its opposite.

The *Descent of Man* is really two books, for its title also includes the words *and selection in relation to sex*, a subject that occupies nearly three-quarters of the whole work. Natural selection was not the only agency by which Darwin explained the evolution of man. He had mentioned sexual selection in the *Origin*, and the subject had been discussed by Erasmus Darwin. By sexual selection Darwin meant the preferential chances of mating that some individuals of one sex, usually males, would have over other animals of the same species, because of their possession of special structures, colours, and types of behaviour used in courtship display, that would result in their leaving more offspring than their unsuccessful rivals, or because of their possession of weapons used for fighting other males in competition for mates, which would have the same effect. By means of this hypothesis, based on deduction, Darwin sought to explain the appearance, through selection of variants, of those characters additional to the reproductive organs by which one sex differs from the other. Here belong the train of the peacock, the tail of the lyre-bird, the feathers of the amherst pheasant, the mane of the lion, the antlers of the deer, and the nuptial colour of the stickleback, to mention only a few. Darwin then went through the whole Animal Kingdom, from molluscs to man, looking for examples of characters present in one sex that might have resulted from sexual selection. He also looked for patterns of behaviour and other factors bearing on the problem, for sexual selection would operate particularly strongly in species where males were more numerous than females or where polygamy was practised.

Because the theory of sexual selection involves acceptance or rejection of a male by a female, it has been objected that it implies the existence in lower mammals, birds, or fish, of a power of aesthetic discrimination equivalent to that of women. This objection is not valid, for there is no question of the female stickleback or peahen exerting conscious choice; the favoured male is he who by the brilliance of his colouring and the striking nature of his display during courtship causes a sufficient degree of stimulation in the female, up to the point where she automatically accepts him as a mate.

Further research on the behaviour of animals in nature has shown that many of the cases attributed by Darwin to sexual selection are in fact of a different nature. Some of them are warning colours, threatening characters, and recognition marks, that play no part in sexual behaviour but have been evolved for the survival of their possessors and for the species, and have been produced by natural selection. Moreover, there are many cases where courtship activities continue after mating and serve to keep the members of the pairs together. Finally, there are other cases, including divers, grebes, herons, where the display and courtship activities are mutual and also serve as general reproductive stimulation, benefiting the species, and maintained by natural selection. There are, nevertheless, some species in which sexual selection in Darwin's sense occurs: the ruff, peacock, pheasants, and birds of paradise are polygamous species in which male display and the development of special structures may go to such lengths as to be deleterious to the species. In sea-lions the bulls fight for possession of the cows, and have developed to disparately large size. Darwin's theory of sexual selection is therefore a special case in a larger category of processes concerned with reproduction, involving the evolution of characters that are for that reason called epigamic.

Returning to the main subject of Darwin's book, we find that he ascribed to sexual selection many of the differences between the sexes in man, and differences between the races of man, such as the distribution of hair on face and body and the local distribution of fat under the skin. Darwin was careful to say that these views were in need of scientific precision; but when it is considered that some tribes 'are said to choose their wives by ranging them in a line, and picking her out who projects farthest *a tergo*,' and when the presumed result of such selection can be seen in the steatopygy of the Hottentots and of some statuettes of the Old Stone Age, it is not extravagant to claim that sexual selection has been responsible for some aspects of man's evolution.

In his great work on the anatomy of expression, Sir Charles Bell had maintained that man is endowed with certain muscles solely for the sake of expressing his emotions. As this view contradicts the belief that man evolved from lower animals it was a challenge to Darwin, who hoped to deal with the problem in the *Descent of Man*. Lack of space obliged him to devote a separate book to it

Fig. 17 Illustrations used by Darwin to show his principle of antithesis in expression of emotions. In a hostile state of mind at the sight of a man, the dog walks stiffly, head raised, tail erect, hairs bristled, ears pricked, staring eyes. From *The Expression of the Emotions*, 1872.

under the title *The Expression of the Emotions in Man and Animals*, which was published in November 1872 and sold 5,267 copies on the day of publication.

From the days of his early Notebooks on Transmutation of Species and the birth of his first child, Darwin had collected observations on this subject that played no small part in convincing him that man could not be separated from animals. 'Seeing a dog, horse, and man yawn make one feel how all animals are built on one structure,' he wrote; and 'A capital passage might be made from comparison of man with expression of monkey when offended, who loves, who fears, who is curious &c &c &c who imitates.' After describing the facial muscles in man and the means of expression in animals by the emission of sounds and contraction of the skin muscles and erection of feathers or hair, Darwin went through the catalogue of emotions and illustrated how they are expressed by man,

Fig. 18 The same dog as in Fig. 17 on realising that the man is his master. His whole bearing is reversed: crouching position, tail lowered, hair smoothed, ears depressed, eyes relaxed. From *The Expression of the Emotions*, 1872.

and by animals insofar as it possible to identify them in the latter. Suffering, sobbing, anxiety, grief, despair, joy, love, devotion, reflection, meditation, bad temper, sulking, determination, hatred, anger, disdain, pride, shame, surprise, fear, horror, affirmation, negation, all these are considered in turn. In his human material he studied infants, obtained photographs of actors playing parts involving expressions, asked his friends to study lunatics and to describe the expression on the face of a murderer when he was arrested, and he circulated a questionnaire to know whether particular emotions were expressed in the same way by different races of man.

The results of the investigation showed that in many cases expression is not learnt but is innate. Next Darwin was able to formulate three principles underlying the expression of emotions. The first is that certain movements and actions are of service in particular states of mind, in which they relieve sensations and desires; but whenever the same state of mind is induced, however feebly, there is a tendency for the same movements to be made although they may not then be of any use at all. An example of this is found in some persons who express dislike and hostility by raising the upper lip and uncovering the canine teeth as in snarling. It serves no purpose in man, but no doubt did as a threat in ancestral forms where the canine teeth were powerful offensive weapons. As early as 1838 there was an entry in the Notebooks: 'no doubt a habit gained by formerly being a baboon with great canine teeth.'

The second principle is that of antithesis. Certain states of mind result in movements and actions that are useful, but if the state of mind is suddenly and directly reversed into the opposite state, the movements are also reversed. The dog who sees a man approaching advances to meet the intruder with its legs tense, tail stiff and erect, hair bristling on neck and back, eyes staring and round, ears pricked. Suddenly the dog realizes that the man is his master, and immediately all the actions taken are reversed; the legs bend and the dog wriggles and crouches, the tail is lowered and wagged, eyelids relax, ears drop, and the lips hang loosely. None of these actions can be said to be useful, but they are explicable as being the antithesis of those taken up immediately before the change in the situation was perceived. The third principle involves reflex actions such as trembling with fear, anger, or joy that depend on the structure of the nervous system.

The chief expressions of man are the same in different races throughout the world, and the mechanism of expression serves as the first means of communication between mother and infant. At the present day the movements and actions of expression described by Darwin are interpreted not in terms of emotions that presuppose feelings, but of activities that can be observed and compared. It is nevertheless true that this work of Darwin's is the foundation of that aspect of the study of animal behaviour that goes by the name of ethology, and that he made a direct contribution to psychology.

With the publication of the *Expression of the Emotions* the tetrad of Darwin's books specifically devoted to evolution was completed, appropriately, with special reference to that of man. The reaction to this in orthodox circles was naturally hostile, and where resistance to Darwin's theories was shown by the general public it was based on emotional rather than rational lines. Altogether, however, the clamour after the publication of the *Descent of Man* and the *Expression of the Emotions* was less than that which had greeted the *Origin*, partly because that book had drawn the worst of the thunder and partly because the unanswerable case for evolution that Darwin had built up and the impossibility of treating man differently from animals had already resulted in widespread adherence to his views by sensible people. Today no competent person has any doubt about the truth of the evolution of man.

Chapter 11

Plants, Vegetable Mould, and Earthworms

Until the middle of the nineteenth century it was generally believed that the hermaphrodite condition of most flowers, or the presence of both male and female organs in the same flower, was a provision designed to ensure that each flower would set seed as a result of the pollination of its stigma by its own pollen. This view did not satisfy Darwin at all. In his early Notebooks written in 1837 he had already asked himself the question why individuals in a species remain more or less constant, and he had answered it by appealing to the results of interbreeding between different individuals. Of course he knew nothing about genes, but he had grasped the principle of the species as a population of interbreeding individuals, now known as a gene-pool. But if flowers are permanently self-pollinated, which means that the plants that bear them are self-fertilized and no interchange of hereditary factors takes place between individuals, Darwin asked himself how and why species of plants bearing hermaphrodite flowers remain constant at all, for in the absence of interbreeding he would have expected each plant to vary on its own and its progeny to go on varying. He answered this question by going straight to the root of the problem and challenging the view that hermaphrodite flowers are permanently self-pollinated.

Christian Conrad Sprengel in his book *Das entdeckte Geheimniss der Natur* published in 1793 had recognized the part played by insects in transporting pollen from one flower to another, but Sprengel had not appreciated the difference between pollination from another flower of the same plant and pollination from a flower of a different plant. Only in the latter case would there be interbreeding between different individuals. Sprengel did not suspect that there was any special significance in the transportal of pollen from one flower to another. Thomas Andrew Knight in 1799 remarked that 'Nature intended that a sexual intercourse should take place between neighbouring plants of the same species,' and similar opinions were expressed by Joseph Gottlieb Koelreuter and by William Herbert, but again without their appreciating the true significance of the phenomena, or their generality.

In his correspondence with Hooker and Asa Gray in 1856, Darwin drew attention to the probability that trees which, from the fact of their large size, bear vast numbers of flowers would tend to become pollinated by their own pollen unless the flowers of each tree possessed organs of one sex only. This is a good example of Darwin's method of working; from various facts he had formed a hypothesis, that 'flowers are adapted to be crossed, at least occasionally, by pollen from a distinct plant,' and then he proceeded to inquire whether it was true that individual trees tended to have flowers of only one sex. After separating trees from small herbaceous plants, he found that in the British flora 'trees belonging to all Orders have their sexes more often separated than other plants.' The same was found to be true of the floras of New Zealand and the United States by Hooker and Asa Gray at Darwin's invitation, with the additional observation that bushy plants were found to be intermediate between trees and herbaceous plants in their tendency to have flowers of separate sexes. Here was a fact of wide application, but so simple that nobody had noticed it before Darwin ferreted it out. Such a fact must rest on some general principle and have an important meaning, and Darwin devoted much thought and many experiments to this problem in the hope of discovering the full significance of adaptations serving to ensure cross-pollination and interbreeding between individuals.

Orchids provided Darwin with splendid material for analysing the problem further. They have specialized flowers with the lower petal enlarged, forming the labellum on which insects land when they plunge their proboscis into the flower. Many orchids have a long spur containing nectar, into which the proboscis is thrust by the insect. The anthers in these flowers are modified in such a way that the pollen sacs are carried on special organs called pollinia, which become detached from the flower and attached to the proboscis of the insects when they thrust it into the flower. When the insects fly away they carry the pollinia with them, and Darwin found that not until some half a minute after a pollinium has become attached to a proboscis, by which time the insect has had time to fly to a different plant, does the pollinium become bent down to a position where, in the next flower visited, the pollen is rubbed onto the stigma. Furthermore, instead of being dry and powdery like the pollen of flowers that are pollinated by wind, the pollen in the pollinia of orchids is sticky, with the result that it is not lost in the air and wasted but kept in a condition in which it can be applied to the stigma of one flower after another as the insect flies on, until the supply is exhausted. Even this contingency is guarded against by the possibility that as it goes on visiting orchid flowers, the insect collects other pollinia on its proboscis. The whole phenomenon can be observed if a sharpened pencil is thrust into an orchid and withdrawn.

As evidence of adaptation to ensure cross-pollination the case of the orchids is most striking, but the variations which different species of orchids show are equally interesting, for they provide graded series in the perfection of

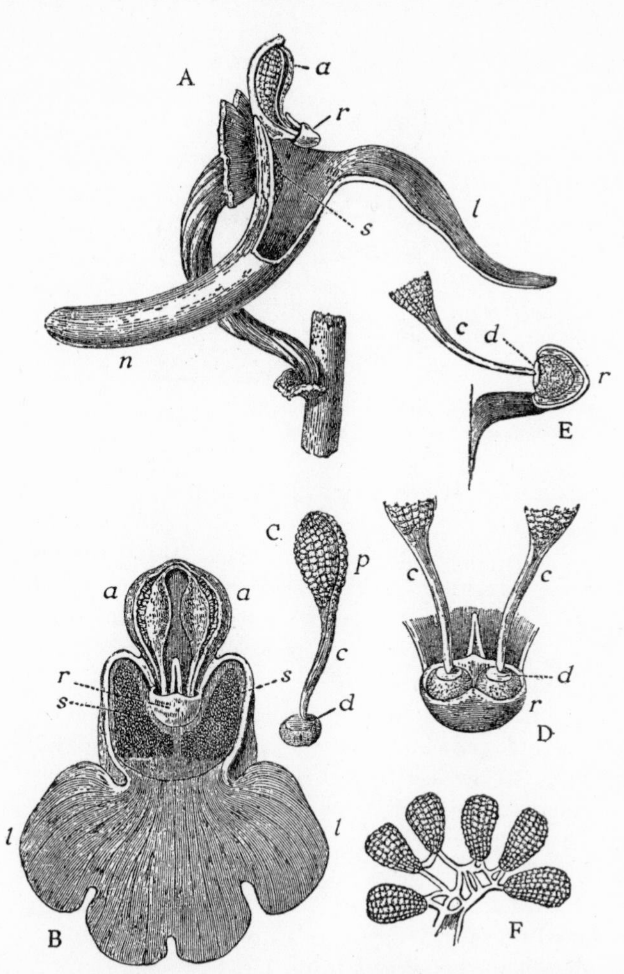

Fig. 19 *Orchis mascula.* A, side view of a flower with all the petals and sepals cut off except the labellum, of which the near half is cut away, as well as the upper portion of the near side of the nectary. B, front view of a flower with all petals and sepals removed except the labellum. C, one pollinium or pollen-mass, showing the packets of pollen-grains, the caudicle, and viscid disc. D, front view of the discs and caudicles of both pollinia. E, section through one side of the rostellum with the included disc and caudicle of one pollinium. F, packets of pollen-grains, tied together by elastic threads. *a*, anther; *r*, rostellum; *s*, stigma; *l*, labellum; *n*, nectary; *p*, pollinium or pollen-mass; *c*, caudicle of pollinium; *d*, viscid disc of pollinium. From Darwin: *On the Various Contrivances by which British and Foreign Orchids are Fertilised by Insects*, 1862.

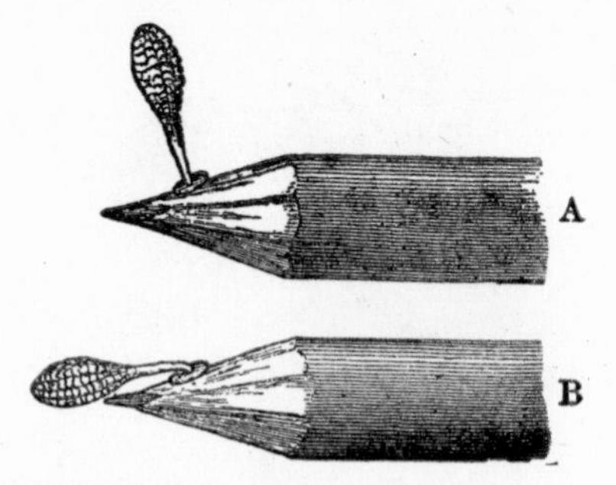

Fig. 20 A, pollinium of *Orchis mascula* attached to a pencil when plunged into the mouth of a flower. B, the same pollinium, after it has become depressed. From Darwin: *Orchids.*

the adaptation which Darwin showed could have been produced and improved by natural selection. He also showed how these adaptations must have been improved, for as the detachment of the pollinia from their own flower and their attachment to the insect depend on the latter inserting its proboscis up to the hilt into the flower, the full advantages of cross-pollination are likely to accrue to those plants whose flowers have nectaries in the longest and deepest spurs. Conversely, as the supply of nectar is important to the insect, if it is a moth as is often the case in foreign orchids, advantages will accrue to those moths that have a proboscis long enough to reach down to the bottom of the nectaries. An orchid was found in Madagascar with a nectary-spur eleven inches long, and Darwin predicted that in Madagascar a moth would be found with a proboscis of the same length. It was found.

These adaptations in so many species of orchids clearly showed that cross-pollination must confer important advantages whatever they were. At the same time, however, there were a few other species of orchids in which the adaptation was modified in the direction of ensuring self-pollination. In the bee-orchid, for instance, the pollinia have stems so slender that the pollen-sacs droop over the stigma of their own flower, the pollen is detached by the

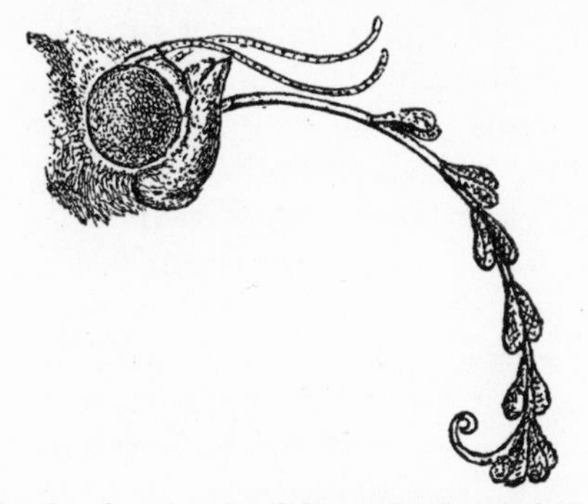

Fig. 21 The head and proboscis of the moth *Acontia luctuosa* with seven pairs of the pollinia of *Orchis pyramidalis* attached to the proboscis. From Darwin: *Orchids.*

slightest vibration, and self-pollination ensues. Darwin noticed, further, that the bee-orchid set more seed than those species adapted for cross-pollination. Whatever the advantages of cross-pollination might be, therefore, they must tolerate the possibility of exceptions, which in the case of the bee-orchid allow greater fertility. But Darwin also found that in a few cases the pollinia had been removed from the flowers of bee-orchids, and this makes it probable that occasionally insects detach them and carry them to other flowers, cross-pollinating them. This was why Darwin was careful to put his hypothesis in the form that flowers are adapted to be crossed, 'at least occasionally,' by pollen from a distinct plant.

The widespread habit of cross-pollination by insects led Darwin to make two generalizations of great importance. The first was that in all species of plants where the flower departs from the regular, radially symmetrical type seen for example in the buttercup, and becomes bilaterally symmetrical as in orchids, foxglove, or snapdragon, or asymmetrical as in cannas, 'the structure of all irregular flowers is governed in relation to insects. Insects are the Lords of the floral world.' The second generalization was the 'invariable rule that when a flower is fertilized by the wind it never has a gaily coloured corolla.' Examples of this fact are familiar in the cones of coniferous trees, catkins of deciduous trees, and the flowers of grasses. Darwin's observation means that in all gaily coloured flowers the colour is an adaptation serving to attract insects to the flowers, and the same is true of scent. There is reason to believe that the origin of flowering plants in the Jurassic period was correlated with the evolution of insects of modern type that appeared at the same time. Darwin continued, 'A similar line of argument holds good with fruits; that a ripe strawberry or cherry is as pleasing to the eye as to the palate,—that the gaily-coloured fruit of the spindle-wood tree and the scarlet berries of the holly are beautiful objects,—will be admitted by everyone. But this beauty serves merely as a guide to birds and beasts, in order that the fruit may be devoured and the manured seeds disseminated.' In this manner Darwin was able to show that objects like flowers and fruits which to man appear to be endowed with beauty were nevertheless produced as adaptations by natural selection, and this answers the objection sometimes raised, that natural selection could not account for the evolution of forms possessed of beauty.

The immediate object that Darwin had in mind when he published his book *On the Various Contrivances by which British and Foreign Orchids are Fertilized by Insects* on 15 May 1862 was 'to show that the contrivances by which orchids are fertilized, are as varied and almost as perfect as any of the most beautiful adaptations in the animal kingdom.' It always gave him pleasure to exalt the Vegetable Kingdom. He also had another object in view which emerges from his letter of 23 July 1862 addressed to Asa Gray in reply to the latter's appreciation of the book: 'no one else has perceived that my chief interest in my orchid book has been that it was a "flank movement" on the enemy.' It was a continuation of the campaign that

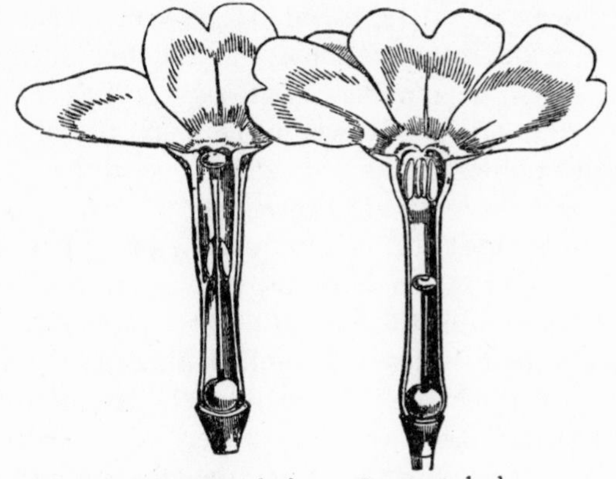

Fig. 22 Flowers of *Primula vulgaris*, the primrose, showing the dimorphism between the long-styled or 'pin-eyed' form and the short-styled or 'thrum-eyed' form. From Darwin: 'On the two forms or dimorphic condition in the species of *Primula*', 1862.

he never ceased to wage in support of his theory of the origin of adaptations by natural selection of infinitesimal variations, and, as such, a sequel to the *Origin*.

In primroses and cowslips Darwin found more material bearing on this problem. It had long been known that these flowers exist in two forms: one, called 'pin-eyed', has a long style reaching up from the ovaries in the base of the flower to the stigma in the tubular part of the flower, while the five stamens are set deep down in the tube; the other, called 'thrum-eyed', has a short style reaching to a stigma only half-way up the tube while the five stamens are set high up at the mouth, at the level of the stigma in the pin-eye. The same dimorphism is found in many species of *Primula*, and it had been regarded as a case of variability without significance. By tying labels onto plants and observing them in successive years Darwin found that each form maintained the same character, which was therefore hereditary, and he also found that all flowers borne on any one plant were of the same form. No intermediate forms could be found. He collected hundreds of plants from different stations, and the two forms were roughly equal in numbers, but as a result of careful measurements of size and weight he found that the thrums have larger pollen-grains and set more seed than the pins.

Thus far, observation. Proceeding to experiment, he covered a number of plants just before their flowers opened: they set no seed. To prove that the covering was not itself responsible for this result he covered other plants and dusted their styles with pollen himself: they all set seed. He was thus able to prove that the significant factor in covering the plants was the prevention of visits to the flowers by insects. Next he tested the effects of pollinating pin flowers with pin pollen (taken from a different plant so as to avoid any complications that might result from self-pollination) and with thrum pollen, and thrum flowers with thrum pollen and pin pollen. The results were that pin flowers pollinated by pin pollen, and thrum flowers pollinated by thrum pollen, were much less fertile than pin flowers pollinated by thrum pollen and thrum flowers pollinated by pin pollen. From the structure of the two forms Darwin was then able to show by plunging a proboscis of a dead bumble-bee or a bristle into the mouths of the flowers, that in a pin flower the proboscis is covered with pollen near the tip, at the place where it comes into contact with the stigma when plunged into a thrum flower, and conversely that in a thrum flower the proboscis is covered with pollen at its base, at the place where it comes into contact with the stigma when plunged into a pin flower. Here, then, was a simple mechanism favouring cross-pollination and penalizing pollination between flowers of the same form and, therefore, self-pollination. Here, again, was evidence that cross-fertilization confers some important advantage and that the adaptation ensuring it is preserved by natural selection.

Darwin's experiments had also shown something else,

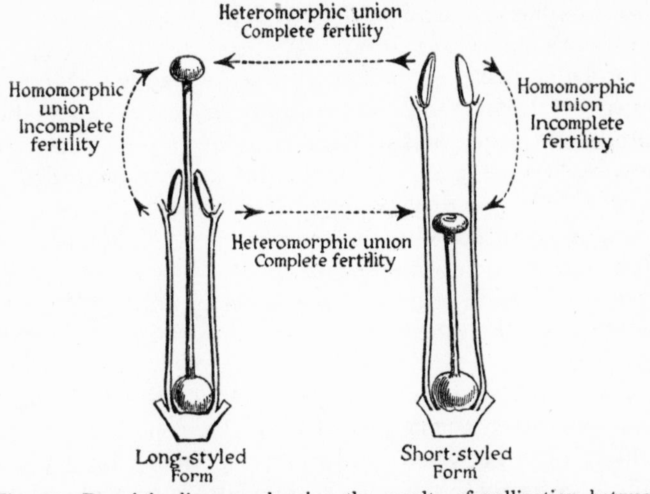

Fig. 23 Darwin's diagram showing the results of pollination between long-styled and short-styled forms of *Primula*.

To a certain extent different species of primroses can be cross-pollinated and produce hybrids, but pollination between flowers of the same form in the same species shows a degree of sterility that is greater than that found between parents of different species. This, incidentally, was positive evidence that no hard and fast line can be drawn between species and varieties on the supposition of universal fertility between varieties of the same species and universal sterility between different species. The bearing of these facts on one of the chief problems in the origin of species was obvious: 'Those who believe in the slow modification of specific forms will naturally ask themselves whether sterility may not have been slowly acquired for a distinct object, namely, to prevent two forms, whilst being fitted for different lines of life, becoming blended by marriage, and thus less well adapted for their new habits of life.'

When Darwin published his observations and experiments on dimorphism and its significance in *Primula* in

1862, eminent botanists in Paris said that his paper was the work of imagination and that the case was so improbable that they did not believe his results. Presently, however, Darwin discovered an even more remarkable case in the purple loosestrife, *Lythrum salicaria*, where the flowers can be of three forms, with long styles, middle-length styles, and short styles, each with two sets of stamens corresponding in position to the length of the style and position of the stigma in the flowers of the other two forms. Each of these three forms is fully fertile with pollen from the other two forms but largely sterile with its own.

Recent research has confirmed Darwin's observations and experiments and provided the explanation for the self-sterility between similar forms. In primroses the difference between pin and thrum plants is controlled by a single pair of super-genes (genes closely linked together), thrum being dominant and pin recessive. The self-sterility results from the antigenic properties of the tissues of the stigmas and styles of the flowers, which affect pollen-grains from plants of the same genetic constitution as themselves, and retard the formation of pollen-tubes. Pollen-grains from plants of different genetic constitution are not thus retarded, and produce pollen-tubes that therefore win the race down the styles and fertilize the ovules. Since pin flowers are always recessive, all their pollen-grains and all their ovules carry the recessive gene. Thrum plants are always heterozygous and carry either one dominant or one recessive gene in their pollen-grains and in their ovules, because their stigmas can only be pollinated by pin pollen which carries only the recessive gene. As half the ovules of thrum flowers carry the dominant and half the recessive gene, pollination of thrum flowers results in the production of seeds that will develop into thrum plants and pin plants, in roughly equal numbers. Pin flowers can only be pollinated by thrum pollen, and

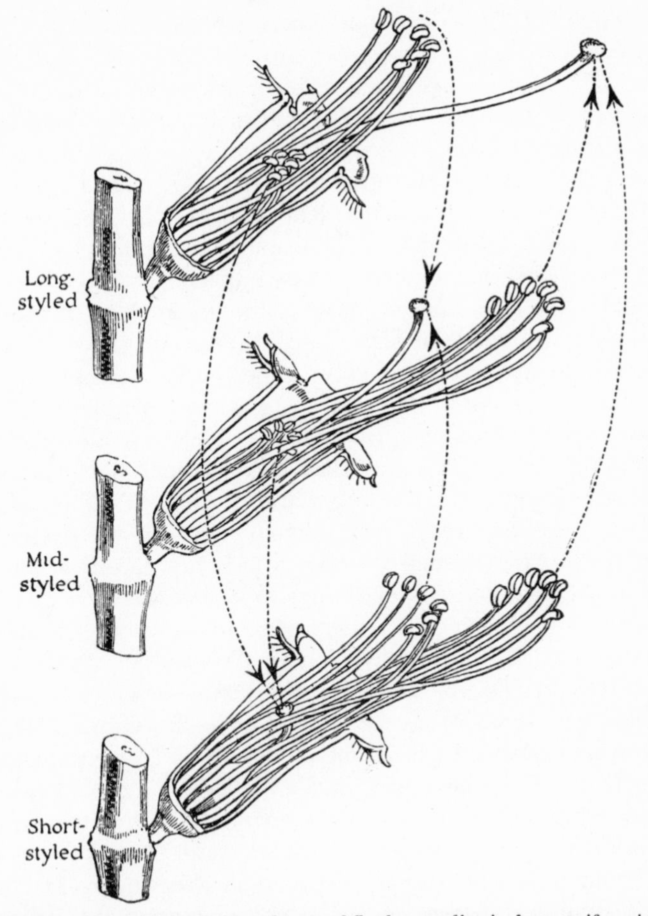

Fig. 24 Flowers of the three forms of ***Lythrum salicaria***, loosestrife, with the petals removed and the near side of the calyx cut away. The dotted lines with the arrows show which pollen must be applied to each stigma to cause full fertility. From Darwin: 'On the sexual relations of the three forms of *Lythrum salicaria*', 1864.

as this can be of two kinds, carrying the dominant or the recessive gene, the result of pollination of pin flowers is the production of seeds that will develop into thrum plants and pin plants, again roughly in equal numbers.

These observations and experiments on flowers with different style-lengths were continued and extended until in 1877 Darwin published a general account of the phenomenon under the title *The Different Forms of Flowers on Plants of the Same Species.* Most of the book is concerned with heterostylic flowers like *Primula* and *Lythrum.* Another section deals with plants that bear hermaphrodite flowers with male and female organs but with the flowers of two kinds: one kind open, fully expanded, with coloured petals like any normal flower, the other kind minute, closed, with vestigial petals devoid of colour. These small flowers, called cleistogamous, being closed cannot admit pollen from any other flower and are therefore self-pollinated and set seed, as in violets. There are also plants like the feather-hyacinth that bear normal flowers and closed flowers, but the latter are sterile and their outer tissues are coloured and conspicuous and serve to attract insects to the normal flowers, which are inconspicuous. A third class consists of species in which the flowers are of two types each containing organs of one sex only, such as catkins. A fourth class contains species in which the flowers may be of two or three kinds, namely, normal hermaphrodite flowers and either male flowers or female flowers or both. In the common ash some trees bear only male flowers, others only female flowers, and others again hermaphrodite flowers. In the maple, one and the same tree may bear hermaphrodite, male, and female flowers. Common thyme plants bear either hermaphrodite or female flowers; sneezewort plants bear hermaphrodite and male flowers. As will be seen, almost every conceivable combination is found in some form or other.

Meanwhile Darwin never lost sight of his main target in all this work, which was to discover the significance of cross-fertilization. He published his results in 1876 under the title *The Effects of Cross and Self Fertilization in the Vegetable Kingdom.* The book begins by reviewing the various adaptations resulting in cross-fertilization that he had found in orchids and in heterostyled plants. There is also the beautifully simple method by which self-pollination is prevented in hermaphrodite flowers by a delay in time between the periods when the organs of the two sexes are ripe in any one flower. For example the protandrous condition in which the pollen ripens before the pistil is found in geraniums, the protogynous condition where the pistil ripens before the pollen in magnolia.

The chief end of fertilization is the production of seed, and this end can be achieved with greater certainty by self-pollination, especially when the flowers are closed and little pollen is required, or lost from injury by weather or insects. But the great fact remains that the vast majority of flowers are open and produce immense quantities of pollen. Why? 'For the sake of determining certain points with respect to inheritance,' Darwin explained, 'and without any thought of the effects of close interbreeding, I raised close together two large beds of self-fertilized and crossed seedlings from the same plant of *Linaria vulgaris*. To my surprise, the crossed plants when fully grown were plainly taller and more vigorous than the self-fertilized ones.' Next he performed the same experiment on *Dianthus caryophillus* with the same result. Both these two species are only sparingly fertile if insects are excluded from them, so Darwin tested a couple of species that are highly fertile when insects are excluded, *Mimulus luteus* and *Ipomoea purpurea*, and here again, 'the crossed seedlings were conspicuously superior in height and in other ways to the self-fertilized.'

In experiments conducted over twelve years on fifty-seven species of plants he found that in the majority of cases the products of cross-pollination were more numerous, larger, heavier, more vigorous, and more fertile than the products of self-pollination, even in species that are normally self-pollinating. Darwin had at last found what the advantage is that accrues from cross-fertilization, for which so high a price is paid by the ingenious adaptations found in so many species and so much pollen wasted; it is hybrid-vigour, now known as heterosis, and Darwin showed that natural selection favours those species that are able to produce it. At the same time he realized that 'the advantages of cross-fertilization do not follow from some mysterious virtue in the mere union of two distinct individuals, but from such individuals having been subjected during previous generations to different conditions, or to their having varied in a manner commonly called spontaneous, so that in either case their sexual elements have been in some degree differentiated.'

This conclusion of Darwin's can be translated straight into the language of modern genetics. Populations in nature are found to contain large numbers of heterozygous individuals in which the normal dominant genes mask the effects of their corresponding recessive genes. From the fact that the latter are recessive it necessarily follows that in their particular environment they are disadvantageous, and the harmful effects of recessive genes will be manifested in offspring produced by self-fertilization because a proportion of these will be homozygous for the recessive gene, without a corresponding dominant gene to mask these harmful effects. In cross-bred individuals, on the contrary, the harmful effects of recessive genes from one parent will be masked by the corresponding dominant genes from the other, and this is why cross-bred offspring are more vigorous.

There is an additional reason why cross-fertilization confers advantage on a species, although it was not known to Darwin. Cross-fertilization brings about the recombination of genes in innumerable possible permutations, and this increases the variability on which natural selection can then act and modify the species by evolution. Unless this is possible, when environmental conditions change, which they inevitably do sooner or later, the species is in danger of becoming extinct. In offspring produced by self-fertilization, or by parthenogenesis where there is, of course, no cross-fertilization, no heritable variations resulting from recombination of genes can take place, and species that reproduce permanently by self-fertilization or parthenogenesis cannot evolve any further. In both the Plant and Animal Kingdoms it is found that under optimal conditions it is common for self-fertilization or parthenogenesis to take place for periods of time such as a season, and to produce enormous numbers of genetically identical offspring, as, for example, with green-fly in summer; but cross-fertilization then takes place and confers its resulting advantages.

From the results of these simple experiments on plants, Darwin had in fact discovered one of the reasons why there are advantages in the existence of two sexes, which supplies an objective answer to the puzzle why there are men and women. Cross-fertilization in plants and animals that consist of more than one cell necessarily involves embryonic development, during which the single fertilized egg-cell becomes transformed into the many-celled adult. It is as an adaptation to that hazardous performance that some germ-cells are large and contain an emergency supply of food for the early stages in the form of yolk. Such germ-cells are called eggs and the organisms that produce them females. But being large, eggs are immobile and play no part in actively finding other germ-cells, without which meeting there would be no fertilization, cross or otherwise. Fertilization is achieved as a result of the fact that organisms of a different kind produce small germ-cells that contain no food, but are able to swim about by means of their whip-like tails. These are called sperms, and the organisms that produce them males. None of the advantages of cross-fertilization would amount to anything in many-celled organisms unless sperms reached and fertilized eggs, and unless the fertilized eggs developed successfully into adult organisms of the next generation.

Darwin always denied that he was a botanist, and it is perfectly true that his approach to problems in botany was quite different from that of professional botanists. While the latter systematically studied the structure and functions of plants as subjects in themselves, Darwin's starting-point continued to reflect his unflinching interest in evolution and natural selection. For example, his observations and experiments on climbing plants were aimed to show the affinities and common descent of plants with the properties of climbing, and to demonstrate the importance of climbing as an adaptation conferring advantage and produced by natural selection.

It had previously been supposed that twining plants had what was called a 'natural tendency' to grow in a spiral, which was no explanation at all. Darwin soon found that it was untrue, for while a twining plant growing up a pole as a support assumes a spiral shape it straightens itself if the pole is removed. The plant twines because the apex of its stem as it grows bends to the side, and the plane of the bend revolves, clockwise or counter-clockwise, with the result that the apex describes a circular sweeping movement. If no obstacle is met by the growing stem the circular movement of the apex continues, but if an object like a pole is hit, the apex revolves round it and the stem becomes wrapped round it. The speeds at which this movement takes place vary in different plants, but in the hop the average speed for a new shoot in hot weather during daytime is about two hours and eight minutes for each revolution. After twenty-seven revolutions Darwin found that the apex of the shoot was describing a circle nineteen inches in diameter.

The advantage of twining as an adaptation is that it enables the plant to reach a height where its leaves are well exposed to sun and air rapidly, in many cases in one

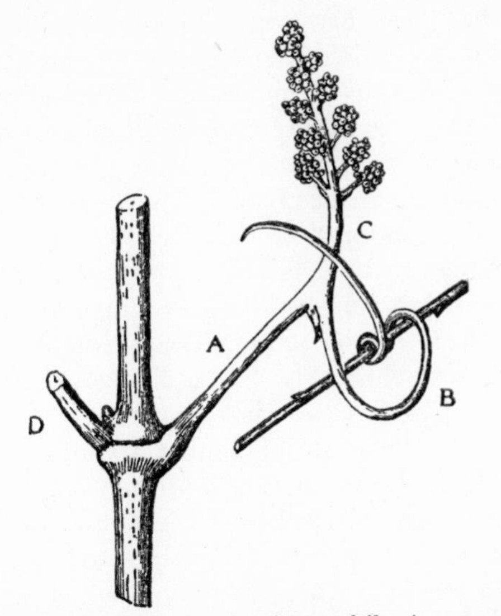

Fig. 25 Flower-stalk of the vine showing tendrils. A, common peduncle. B, flower-tendril. C, sub-peduncle bearing the flower-buds. D, petiole of the opposite leaf. From Darwin: *The Movements and Habits of Climbing Plants*, 1875.

season, without the expenditure of time and synthesis of material involved in the growth of a stout woody trunk, as is the case with trees. Even here a curious little adaptation is found. The maximum diameter of a rod or support that a twining plant will wrap itself round and climb is about six inches, and this prevents it from climbing up a tree with a trunk of wider diameter, up which the climbing plant could only reach a height where it would be shaded by the tree's foliage.

Another group of plants climb by means of the stalks and tips of their leaves, which bend round and clasp twigs and other thin objects with which they come into contact. This is because the under surfaces of the stalks and tips of the leaves are sensitive to contact with solid objects and bring about greater growth of the upper surfaces and thickening of the clasping portions. Some species of

Clematis that have this property of leaf-climbing combine it with ordinary twining, and the two types of behaviour show a gradation that indicates that leaf-climbers evolved from twiners. A further refinement of adaptation is found in the plants that bear tendrils, which are flexible, long, and thin filaments formed from specialized shoots or leaves or parts of leaves or flower-stalks. They revolve in the air like miniature twiners and, when they hit an object, contract into tight spirals that grow thick and strong and effectively keep up the stems of the plants. Tendrils that hit nothing shrivel up. The vine is an example of a tendril-bearer, and other species show a perfectly graded series from leaves like those of leaf-climbers to fully differentiated tendrils. This shows that tendril-bearers evolved from leaf-climbers. The highest refinement of all these adaptations is found in *Ampelopsis*, Virginia creeper, where the tips of the tendrils, when they come into contact with a solid surface, swell into little discs, red in colour and full of fluid that is extruded as a resinous cement and anchors the plant firmly to the surface up which it is climbing. *Climbing Plants* was published in 1875.

The investigation of climbing plants thus presented Darwin with numerous further examples of adaptations showing a graded series by which they evolved with advantages improved by natural selection. 'In accordance with the principles of evolution it was impossible to account for climbing plants having been developed in so many widely different groups, unless all kinds of plants possess some slight power of movement of an analogous kind.' The search for the nature of this power led Darwin, helped by his son Francis, to undertake experiments lasting five years that resulted in the publication of the book *Power of Movement in Plants* in 1880.

Starting from the fact that in climbing plants the growing shoot bends, the problem was to discover the mechanical cause of such bending. The fact of bending of

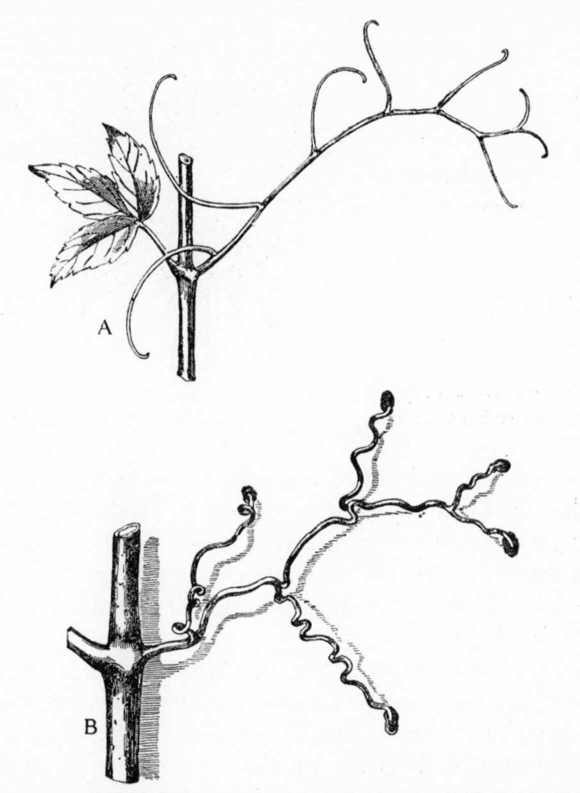

Fig. 26 Ampelopsis hederacea. A, tendril fully developed, with a young leaf on the opposite side of the stem. B, older tendril, several weeks after its attachment to a wall, with the branches thickened and spirally contracted, and with the extremities developed into adhesive discs. The unattached branches of this tendril have withered and dropped off. From Darwin: *Climbing Plants.*

a stem towards the light as a result of unequal elongation on the convex and concave sides had been known for many years, but no agreement had been reached in the analysis of its causes which were attributed to differential warmth and moisture as well as to light acting on the sides of the stem. By means of simple but very ingenious experiments on growing tips of shoots and roots, Darwin

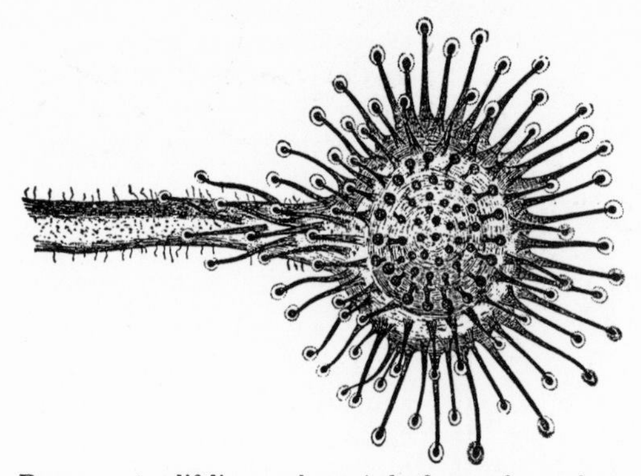

Fig. 27 *Drosera rotundifolia*, sundew. A leaf seen from above, showing the tentacles each ending in a gland. Enlarged three times. From Darwin: *Insectivorous Plants*, 1875.

discovered that the tip of a shoot was sensitive to light but that the bending was due to growth on the side of the shoot away from the light, at a lower level, some way down from the tip. He also found that this growth took place even if the growing tissues were protected from light provided that the tip was exposed to it. This fundamental discovery was ascribed by Darwin to 'some matter in the upper part which is acted upon by light, and which transmits its effects to the lower part.' Similarly in the case of root-tips, it is the tip that is sensitive to gravity and to contact with solid objects and brings about curvature by influencing the growth of tissues further up the root. 'Some influence must therefore be transmitted from the tip along the radicle.' The famous plant physiologist Julius Sachs greeted the Darwins' results with scorn and derision, but from these results have proceeded the whole science of plant-hormones and growth-promoting substances, which still engages physiologists with the most perplexing problems.

In the summer of 1860 Darwin was staying at Hartfield where, he said, 'I was surprised by finding how large a number of insects were caught by the common sun-dew

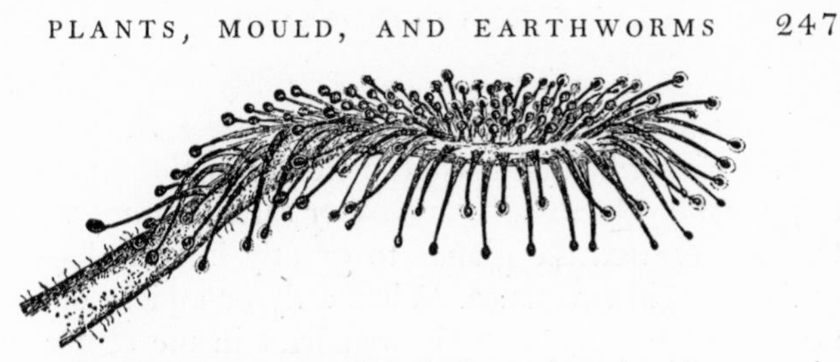

Fig. 28 *Drosera rotundifolia*, leaf, seen from the side.

(*Drosera rotundifolia*) on a heath in Sussex.' He gathered a dozen of these plants and found that they bore fifty-six fully expanded leaves to which were stuck thirty-one dead insects or remains of insects. The leaves of *Drosera* are like round discs, about a quarter of an inch in diameter,

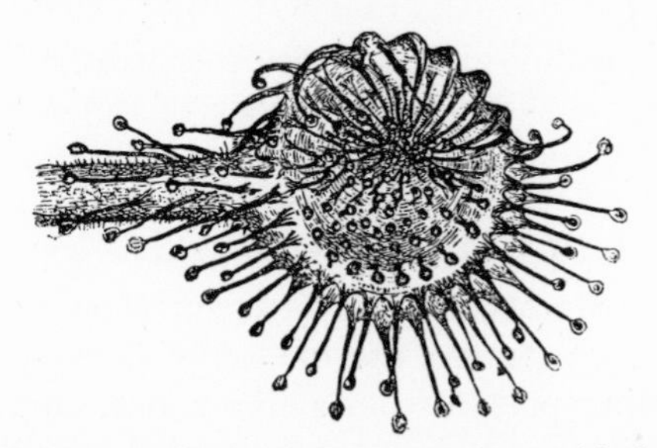

Fig. 29 *Drosera rotundifolia*, leaf, seen from above with the tentacles on the left side inflected and bent over a piece of meat placed on the leaf. From Darwin: *Insectivorous Plants*.

on stalks. The upper surface of the disc bears some hundred tentacles each ending in a gland containing a viscid substance that glitters in the sun, giving the plant its name of sun-dew. When a small object like a fly touches the glands on the tentacles in the middle of the leaf it becomes stuck to the glands, and an impulse is transmitted to the neighbouring tentacles which in the course of a few hours all bend towards the centre where their glands concentrate on the fly.

The same effect is produced if the leaf is immersed in an infusion of raw meat or a solution of ammonia, and this led Darwin to undertake an incredibly large number of experiments to test the nature of this effect. As an example of how widely he cast his net, he found that dilute solutions of gold chloride and of some other salts, but not antimony tartrate, excited the glands to greatly increased secretion of their viscid substance. When a fly or a piece of meat is placed on the glands of the tentacles in the centre of the leaf and the surrounding tentacles bend towards it, the glands of the latter increase their secretion which becomes acid and possesses digestive properties analogous to those of gastric juice in vertebrate animals.

Darwin found that this secretion from *Drosera* would dissolve albumin, muscle, connective tissue, cartilage, bone-fibres, gelatine, and casein, but not epidermis, elastic tissue, chitin, cellulose, and some other substances. Darwin next tested the effects of hundreds of different chemical substances to see which did and which did not cause inflection of the tentacles. Since the bending of the peripheral tentacles follows from stimulation of the glands of the central tentacles, as if by transmission of a nervous impulse, Darwin tested the effects of nerve-poisons and drugs including poison from a live adder, curare, strychnine, digitalin, morphia, and others, but without conclusive results. Benzoic acid was so poisonous to *Drosera* that Darwin suggested to Lord Lister that he might try it on bacteria. After further experiments he found that the impulse causing the tentacles to bend is transmitted through the cellular tissue of the leaf and not through the vessels. The sensitivity of the glands on the tentacles was such that a minute portion of a human hair, calculated to weigh 0·0008 milligrams, was sufficient to excite movement. As Darwin said, regarding instruments available in his day, *Drosera* 'is seventy-eight times more sensitive than a chemical balance.'

The most extraordinary fact about *Drosera*, however, is still to come, for when a fly has been caught and the glands have secreted digestive juice onto it, the products of the digested insect are then absorbed by the glands and passed into the tissues of the plant. To Hooker Darwin confided, 'By Jove, I sometimes think *Drosera* is a disguised animal.' Darwin saw that this fantastic adaptation that enabled *Drosera* to obtain its supplies of nitrogen from animal food was correlated with the fact that it can grow on extremely poor soil and has few roots. After the book *Insectivorous Plants* was published in 1875, a number of botanists in Europe published statements that the digestion of meat by plants is of no use to them. Francis Darwin thereupon fed a large number of *Drosera* plants on meat and compared them with unfed plants under identical conditions. 'On the fed side the leaves are much larger, differently coloured, and more numerous; flower-stalks taller and more numerous, and I believe, far more seed capsules.' The evidence that the insectivorous habit of *Drosera* was an adaptation conferring advantage was complete.

Darwin may not have been a professional botanist; he never had the experience with plants that his barnacles gave him with animals; but as a biologist studying general problems and using plant material for his experiments he was unsurpassed. While he recognized the greater importance of his work on evolution and natural selection, he derived most pleasure from his researches on living plants. This was partly because he loved making observations, particularly on flowers, and partly because he found close argument a great strain. It was with some regret that he realized how his mind had become a machine for grinding general laws out of large collections of facts, and it was a relief for him to turn to experiments on plants. Francis Darwin has described how his father used to stand before a plant for a considerable time and touch it affectionately. This attitude was not understood by his gardener who, when asked about his master's health, replied, 'Oh! my poor master has been very sadly. I often wish he had something to do. He moons about in the garden, and I have seen him standing doing nothing before a flower for ten minutes at a time. If he only had something to do I really believe he would be better.' Francis Darwin, who was closely associated with his father during the last years of his life, has described how for forty years Darwin never knew one day of the health of ordinary men.

In 1881 Darwin called on John Murray with the manuscript of his last book. Murray's son has described the conversation that took place. 'Here is a work,' said Darwin, 'which has occupied me for many years and interested me much. I fear the subject will not interest the public but will you publish it for me?' Murray replied, 'It always gives me pleasure and hope to hear an author speak of his work thus. What is the subject?' 'Earthworms,' said Darwin. *The Formation of Vegetable Mould through the Action of Worms* was published on 10 October 1881, and six editions were called for in less than one year. It took up a problem in which he had been interested from the time when he returned from the voyage of the *Beagle.* It has an indirect bearing on plants for it deals with the production of the soil that is necessary for their life and growth. Near his uncle Josiah Wedgwood's home at Maer Hall in Staffordshire, lime had been spread over the surface of a field in 1827, and ten years later some holes were dug to see a section of the soil. Beneath half an inch of turf two and a half inches of fine mould were found overlying the remains of the lime which had therefore been covered at a rate of about a quarter of an inch a year. Near Down, in 1842, broken chalk had been spread over a field across which a trench was dug in 1871. The chalk nodules were then found to have been buried beneath seven inches of mould, again at a rate of about a quarter of an inch a year.

Earthworms eat decayed leaves and drag them down into their burrows, and they also swallow earth for the

Fig. 30 Section through an excavation of a Roman villa at Silchester showing the subsidence of a floor paved with tesserae, owing to the action of earthworms removing earth from underneath. The subsidence of the floor amounted to nearly 8 inches. From Darwin: *The Formation of Vegetable Mould through the Action of Worms*, 1881.

particles of food that it contains, grind it down to a fine powder in their gizzards, line their burrows with it, and bring it up to the surface where it is ejected as worm-castings. By calculating the weight of worm-castings thrown up on the surface in a square yard of pasture-land overlying chalk, the quantity of soil brought up to the surface by worms in an acre in a year was worked out at eighteen tons. To the depth that earthworms normally burrow, between twelve and twenty inches, the soil is thus constantly passed through them, decomposed and disintegrated, brought to the surface from lower levels, and aerated. These are the processes that result in the formation of mould suitable for the growth of plants. As worms burrow underneath stones and pavements, they slowly but gradually undermine them so that they sink into the soil and eventually become covered. Darwin was able to confirm this fact on ancient buildings such as a fallen sarsen at Stonehenge, Roman pavements at Silchester and Wroxeter, and the pavement at Beaulieu Abbey exposed since its destruction by Henry VIII. Earthworms thus play an important part not only in the ecology of plants but also as geological agents, and Darwin's work on these lowly animals stands as a pioneer study in quantitative ecology.

Chapter 12

The Way to Westminster Abbey

On the man himself, the keynote of Darwin's character was simplicity amounting to naïvety, and a remark by his wife who was no mean judge, made before she married him, may here be quoted, 'He is the most open transparent man I ever saw, and every word expresses his real thoughts.' Darwin's own description of himself as a great overgrown child is singularly appropriate, for the juvenile quality of his nature never deserted him. It emerges from his definition of a good novel which must have in it some character that one can thoroughly love, and if a pretty woman, all the better. It must also end happily like a fairy-tale. His boyish gaiety appears in the mock anger with which he exploded at his bad luck when losing a game, and it permeates his letters and remarks referring to his own work with a dry humour that lent great vividness to his descriptions. In spite of all his objectivity and hard-headedness, he could still live in a fairy-like land of make-believe; for instance, when he learnt that the government of Tasmania had made an unsolicited grant towards the expenses of Hooker's *Flora of Tasmania*, Darwin wrote to Hooker in 1854, 'What capital news from Tasmania: it is really a very remarkable and creditable fact to the Colony. I am always building veritable castles in the air about emigrating, and Tasmania has been my head-quarters of late; so that I feel very proud of my adopted country.'

At one time he thought that the spider-orchid and the

bee-orchid might be different forms of one and the same species, so he asked a friend to mark some spider-orchids and to observe whether they retained the same character in successive seasons, 'but he evidently thought the request as foolish as if I had asked him to mark one of his cows with a ribbon, to see if it would turn next spring into a horse.' As this remark shows, he had a flair for the absurd which he made into fun. After he had put in seven years' hard labour at his barnacles he expressed himself in the same vein, 'I hate a barnacle as no man ever did before, not even a sailor in a slow-sailing ship.'

One day when working at his insectivorous plants, he shouted out of the window at his family on the lawn, 'this confounded *Drosera* has gone all wrong this morning, upsetting my theories and spoiling a year's work.' Peace and serenity of mind returned by lunch-time when the cause of the error had been discovered. On another occasion when he was growing some seedlings, he personified them and complained, 'The little beggars are doing just what I don't want them to.' There was a pleasant paradox, whimsically expressed, in Darwin's letter to John Maurice Herbert in which he said, 'I have long discovered that geologists never read each other's works, and that the only object in writing a book is a proof of earnestness, and that you do not form your opinions without undergoing labour of some kind. Geology is at present very oral, and what I here say is to a great extent quite true.' It still is. On the difficulty of deciding whether the platysma muscle performs voluntary or involuntary movements in expressing emotion, he asked Dr Ogle to shudder with horror and to see whether 'this abominable muscle' contracts. As for coal, the method of formation of which was so difficult to account for, he wrote to Hooker, 'I sometimes think that it could not have been formed at all.'

With the whimsical touch that he used when criticizing

himself Darwin once wrote to Hooker, 'It is an accursed evil to a man to become as absorbed in his subject as I am in mine.' He was writing the *Origin of Species* at the time and under great pressure of work, but this remark has general significance because it reveals his characteristic habit of focusing a beam of attention of such power and concentration on whatever he was doing at the time that anything outside it ran the risk of being completely forgotten. This explains the astonishing instances in which matters simply slipped past his attention. For example, in the summary at the end of the page-proofs of the first edition of the *Origin* he forgot to include the name of Wallace until reminded by Lyell; when writing to Lyell in 1859 about the succession of types, a principle which Owen was claiming to have discovered, Darwin gave references to his own generalizations on the subject, published in the Journal of the voyage of the *Beagle* in 1839, but as L. Eiseley pointed out, Darwin quite forgot that he had himself published a paper on this very subject in 1837.

One of the most remarkable instances of Darwin's obliviousness was on 18 January 1860 when he wrote to Baden Powell and excused himself for not having mentioned Powell's book in the *Origin* because, he explained, it was an abstract of a larger work and he had included no history of the subject. Later, on the same day, after thinking about the letter that he had just written and sent, he suddenly remembered something. 'I have just bethought me of a Preface which I wrote to my larger work, before I broke down and was persuaded to write the now published abstract. In this Preface I find following passage, which on my honour I had completely forgotten as if I had never written it.' Follows a eulogistic mention of Powell's book in the same words as were printed in the Historical Sketch that he thereafter prefaced to all subsequent editions of the *Origin*. Speaking of the fourth edition of the *Origin* Darwin wrote to Hooker, 'The new edition of the *Origin* has caused me two great vexations. I forgot Bates's paper on variation, but I remembered in time his mimetic work, and now, strange to say, I find I have forgotten your Arctic paper!'

Finally there was the case of the book on *Erasmus Darwin*, which consisted of an English translation of an essay on him by Hermann Krause first published in the German journal *Kosmos*, and an introduction by Darwin himself. In his Preface Darwin stated that the linguistic and scientific reputation of the translator, W. S. Dallas, was a guarantee of the accuracy of the translation. Krause's text had been revised and enlarged since its publication in *Kosmos*, and it made somewhat disparaging mention of the book *Evolution Old and New* that Samuel Butler had in the meantime published with the object of showing that the idea of evolution did not originate with Darwin (a fact that Darwin constantly acknowledged), and of restoring the importance of mind in place of accident in the universe, which was an attack on the *Origin*.

When Butler read Krause's *Erasmus Darwin* in English with the adverse comment on his own book and Darwin's assurance of the accuracy of the translation, and then found that Krause's original German paper in *Kosmos* made no mention of Butler's book (which would in any case have been impossible because it had not then been published), Butler concluded that a dishonest attack had been made upon himself. He wrote to Darwin to complain that his book had been condemned 'by anticipation', and Darwin replied courteously, regretted the incident, and explained that Krause had enlarged his essay before it was translated, adding that this was so common a practice that it did not occur to him that it was necessary to state this fact.

With a virulence that bordered on insanity Butler thereupon vilified Darwin repeatedly in print, not only for the alleged attack on himself which in any case he should have laid at Krause's door, but also for ignoring his predecessors who had advocated evolution before him and, most preposterous of all, for claiming the discovery of the principle of natural selection as his own. In doing this Butler merely showed that he was incompetent to appreciate even the general principles of the contribution that Darwin had made to science. As the *Origin* was written in good plain English without technical terms, other debaters and essayists besides Butler have been misled into thinking that without any knowledge of science or experience of nature they were competent to dispute with Darwin on facts and, like Butler, only exposed their own ignorance.

The interesting part of Butler's futile behaviour, however, is the effect that it had on Darwin. In the first place, he gradually recollected that the first proof of the book contained a passage that did include a statement that Krause had enlarged his essay, a passage that Krause asked Darwin to delete, which he did without noticing that in deleting this passage he also deleted the information about Krause's additions to his text. Darwin then drafted a careful letter explaining all this, but before sending it to be published in answer to Butler's accusations of bad faith he submitted it to his family and his friends. The majority advised against taking any notice of Butler's fulminations. A second draft letter met the same fate. In thanking Huxley for his advice, Darwin wrote, 'the affair has annoyed and pained me to a silly extent; but it would be disagreeable to anyone to be publicly called in fact a liar.' Butler was left to go on fulminating and never knew how much care and attention Darwin had devoted to his ridiculous storm in a teacup. Within a fortnight of Darwin's death Butler wrote to his father, 'I feel very sure that he will not keep the reputation he has at present.'

A man of science is obliged from time to time to tear himself away from his researches and to work on committees, commissions, and reports with the object of improving the organization of scientific research, and even in his day Darwin was no exception to this rule. He served as Secretary of the Geological Society of London from 1838 to 1841 and was a member of its Council from 1837 to 1851. He served on the Council of the Royal Society in 1849–50 when he attended on one occasion, and again from 1854 to 1856 when he attended on no less than sixteen occasions.

In 1858 the Trustees of the British Museum instituted an inquiry on the question of the desirability of separating the natural history collections from the antiquities, and Darwin was invited to attend. Against the suggestion that the former should be moved to Kew he stated, on 19 June 1858, 'I think it would be the greatest evil which could possibly happen to natural science in this country if the other collections were ever to be removed from the British Museum and Library,' for he knew that without a complete library the natural history collections would be useless. Instead he made a different suggestion on 23 October 1858 when he wrote, 'If I had my own way, I would make the British Museum collection only a typical one for display, which would be quite as amusing and far more instructive to the populace (and I think to naturalists) than the present enormous display of birds and mammals. I would save expense of stuffing, and would keep all skins, except a few "typicals", in drawers. Thus much room would be saved, and a little more space could be given to real workers, who could work all day.'

When it became known that Her Majesty's Government had decided to move the natural history collections away from Bloomsbury, he was greatly troubled by the destination proposed for them. 'I must express a very strong opinion that it would be an immense evil to remove to Kensington, not on account of the men of science so much as for the masses in the whole eastern and central part of London. . . . I am low at the conviction that Government will never give money enough for a really good library.' A little later he added, 'I can see many advantages in not being under the unmotherly wing of art and archaeology, and my only fear was that we were not strong enough to live without some protection, so profound, I think, is the contempt for and ignorance of Natural Science amongst the gentry of England.' The passage of a century of time has not made much difference to the gentry of England in this respect, but in 1880, in view of the opening of the British Museum (Natural History) at South Kensington in the following year, Parliament voted a special grant to enable the Museum to build up a library to compensate for the loss resulting from separation from the library at Bloomsbury.

In 1881 Mr Gladstone invited Darwin to become a Trustee of the British Museum, and he replied, 'I should have gladly accepted, had my strength been sufficient for anything like regular attendance at the meetings of the Trustees. But as this is not the case, I think that it is right on my part to decline the honour.' Had he accepted, one can only conjecture what would have been the attitude of the Superintendent of the Natural History Departments, Richard Owen.

In 1870 Anton Dohrn consulted the naturalists of the world on his plan to found a station for the study of marine animals and plants. In reply Darwin wrote:

You ask me for my opinion with respect to founding an acquarium with the necessary apparatus, at some favourable station such as Messina for scientific researches. As far as my judgement goes, I can feel no doubt that at present embryological investigations on the lower marine animals are of the utmost importance; and for this purpose your scheme offers obvious facilities . . . Therefore if sufficient funds can be obtained to construct and keep up an acquarium, and if it is found practicable to regulate its use amongst old and new subscribers or strangers, you will no doubt have the good wishes of every naturalist in Europe.

The appeal for funds for the Zoological Station which it was decided to build at Naples was signed in 1873 by Darwin and Huxley, F. M. Balfour, and Michael Foster. To buy a piece of apparatus Darwin offered one hundred pounds, a sum that must be greatly multiplied to appreciate its worth in present currency.

For a man with such a horror of cruelty to man or beast as Darwin had, based on his experience of slavery in Brazil, the savagery of the Fuegians, and the remorseless struggle for existence in nature, and shown by his detestation of the Crimean War and his revulsion at Governor Eyre's brutalities in Jamaica, the question of control of vivisection could not fail to have importance. At the same time, as a man of science he knew that physiology cannot possibly progress except by means of experiments on living animals, and he felt 'the deepest conviction that he who retards the progress of physiology commits a crime against mankind.' In defence of science against the ignorant and obscurantist agitation that arose about 1875 Darwin consulted with his friends. A proposal to limit research in physiology to points on which the bearings in regard to health could already be seen he regarded as puerile, because, 'judging from all other sciences, the benefits will accrue only indirectly in the search for abstract truth.' In other words, pure science must be pursued for its own sake. If Parliament passed stringent laws, which he feared was only too probable, 'seeing how unscientific the House of Commons is, and that the gentlemen of England are humane, as long as their sports are not considered, which entail a hundred or thousand-fold more suffering than the experiments of physiologists,' the result would inevitably be that progress in physiology, which during the previous few years had been practically at a standstill in Britain, would cease altogether. His strictures on the sports of the gentlemen of England contained a strong element of self-reproach, for as a young man he was passionately fond of shooting, until one day he found a bird that had been maimed but not killed during a shoot the day before, and forthwith he resolved to forego a pleasure that involved so much cruelty.

A reasonable Bill for which Darwin worked was introduced in the House of Commons by Lyon Playfair and his colleagues, but it was withdrawn on the appointment of a Royal Commission, before which Darwin gave evidence. The Commission reported early in 1876 and a Bill was passed yielding so much to uninformed sentimental clamour that the progress of science was gravely compromised. To the lasting shame of Britain, Lord Lister was obliged to go to Toulouse to perform the experiments on the power of blood to resist bacterial infection that lie at the base of antiseptic surgery. Darwin had done his best, both for the progress of science and for protecting animals from cruelty, and it must also be remembered that animals no less than men have benefited from the knowledge gained as a direct result of such experiments. He himself said, 'I thought it fair to bear my share of the abuse poured in so atrocious a manner on all physiologists.' Darwin's action was recognized by the Physiological Society which elected him its first Honorary Member.

One more of Darwin's activities designed to facilitate the pursuit of science deserves mention, for it is in many ways the counterpart in favour of botany of what he had done for zoology in supporting the Station at Naples. Not long before he died, Darwin wrote to Hooker saying that he would like to help the work of research at Kew by providing a sum of money to complete and publish an index to the names and authors of all genera and species of plants known to botanists, together with their native countries. As a matter of course Hooker informed the First Commissioner of Works, his administrative superior officer, of Darwin's generous offer and received in reply 'a characteristically illiberal and ill-bred minute' warning him against putting the Board of Works to any expense, 'and this though I expressly stated that your offer involved the Board in no expense or other responsibility whatever,' as Hooker afterwards informed Darwin. The work went ahead and resulted in the *Index Kewensis*, the indispensable instrument of research in botany, but Darwin did not live to see it.

If it is important to help with the organization of scientific research, it is no less important to help scientists when they are in trouble or difficulties, and Darwin's generous feelings in this field were shown no less by the time and trouble that he devoted to such cases than by the pecuniary assistance that he gave. In December 1871 Huxley's health broke down and he was obliged to take a complete rest. In secret Darwin organized a subscription for him and on 23 April 1872 he wrote, 'I have been asked by some of your friends (eighteen in number) to inform you that they have placed the sum of £2100 to your account at your bankers. We have done this to enable you to get such complete rest as you may require for the re-establishment of your health; and in doing this we are convinced that we act for the public interest, as well as in accordance with our most earnest desires. Let me assure you that we are all your warm personal friends and that there is not a stranger or mere personal acquaintance among us.' Darwin's contribution to this fund was £300, and, to the delight of all the subscribers, the fund fulfilled its object.

Later in the same year Hooker was in trouble with his superior the First Commissioner of Works, Acton Smee Ayrton, an ambitious politician without any knowledge of science, who subordinated Hooker as Director of the Royal Botanical Gardens, Kew, to the Secretary of the Board and the London Director of Works. As a result Hooker was subjected to the gravest indignities and obstruction in his work. A full statement of the case, setting out the overbearing behaviour of Ayrton, was drawn up over the signatures of Lyell and of Darwin and nine other distinguished men of science and sent to Mr Gladstone, who was then Prime Minister. A report on Kew had been circulated by Ayrton without previously submitting it to Hooker for comment; the report had been written by his and Darwin's bitter enemy Owen for the purpose of discrediting Hooker, and of securing the transfer of the collections at Kew to the British Museum where, of course, they would have been under Owen's hand. The matter was raised in both Houses of Parliament, and Ayrton was rebuked by a Treasury Minute which laid down that, in all scientific matters, Hooker was master in his own house.

Finally, Darwin had an opportunity of doing a good turn to Wallace. The idea of a civil-list pension for him had occurred to Darwin in 1879, and eventually, on 6 January 1881, Mr Gladstone wrote to Darwin to say that he had decided to recommend a pension of £200 per annum to Wallace. Darwin replied, 'your note just received has given me an extraordinary amount of pleasure, for I was much grieved that Mr Wallace should be so hard worked in his declining years and with failing health.' In spite of his declining years and failing health, Wallace was to live for thirty-two years more, Darwin for only one.

A glimpse of the place that Darwin during his own lifetime occupied in the estimation of students has been given by Henry Fairfield Osborn, who was working in Huxley's laboratory in the Royal College of Science in December 1879. As Osborn was dissecting a lobster Huxley and Darwin came in, and Osborn was introduced as

'an American who has already done some good palaeontological work on the other side of the water.' I gave Darwin's hand a tremendous squeeze and said, without intending, in an almost reverential tone, 'I am very glad to see you.' He stands much taller than Huxley, has a very ruddy face, with benevolent blue eyes and overhanging eyebrows. His beard is quite long and perfectly white and his hair falls partly over a low forehead. His features are not good. My general impression of his face is very pleasant. He smiled broadly, said something about a hope that Marsh with his students would not be hindered in his work, and Huxley, saying 'I must not let you talk too much,' hurried him on into the next room. . . . The instant Huxley closed the door I was mobbed as the 'lucky American' by the ninety less fortunate students of Great Britain and other countries.

The reference to the American palaeontologist Othniel C. Marsh related to the great interest that Darwin took in Marsh's discoveries of extinct toothed birds of the Cretaceous period.

This is perhaps the appropriate place in which to refer to another visit by Darwin to Huxley's laboratory, related by David Garnett. The top of the building of the Royal College of Arts and Sciences in Exhibition Road in London had previously been devoted to the teaching of art, but in Huxley's time the plaster casts and statues had been banished behind sheets in the lecture-room. One day, when the laboratory assistant was setting out the exhibits in preparation for Huxley's lecture on evolution, Darwin came in before any of the students had arrived. 'Don't tell Professor Huxley or any-one else that I am here,' he said, and edged in behind the statuary where he remained in hiding, listening to Huxley's exposition of the Darwinian theory. Not until the Professor and the last student had disappeared did Darwin come out of his hiding-place and steal downstairs into the street.' Garnett's authority for this anecdote of Darwin's hiding behind the Discobolos and the Hermes of Praxiteles was the laboratory assistant himself.

So many owe a debt to Darwin that it is not out of place to consider what Darwin owed to others. From his family, apart from the genetic inheritance from his parents and ancestors, and his upbringing in a comfortable home permeated by an atmosphere of affectionate kindness and high moral standards, Darwin did not consider that he gained much intellectual help. His mother died when he was eight years old and he remembered little of her. Of his father, he said that his mind, though unorthodox from the religious point of view, was not scientific in the sense of generalizing his knowledge under general principles. What Darwin gained from him was probably in the field of practical common sense; for it would otherwise be difficult to account for the success that Darwin made, as a raw young man, of all the unpredictable and exacting problems that presented themselves to him during the voyage of the *Beagle*. Similarly, what he owed to his sisters, the elder of whom brought him up after the death of their mother, was on the human rather than on the intellectual plane.

A special place should, perhaps, be reserved for his brother Erasmus, whose clarity of mind and diversity of tastes cannot have failed to leave their mark on Darwin after their common experiences at Shrewsbury School and Edinburgh University. Erasmus was interested in chemistry and botany, but his health was not robust and his energy was limited. He encouraged Darwin in his favourite practice of reading, which was no small service for an elder brother to perform. The mention of Erasmus in Carlyle's *Reminiscences* called from Darwin the comment that it had little truth or merit, for Darwin was devoted to his brother.

Of his friends, mention has already been made of the help and guidance that he received from Henslow, Lyell, and Hooker during the formative period of the work on the *Origin of Species*, and from Huxley in defending him from attacks after its publication. Mention has already also been made of the stimulation that Darwin received from the writings of Humboldt, Sir John Herschel, and from the works of Paley and a passage in Malthus that produced effects very different from any that these two authors could possibly have intended. There remains only the debt that Darwin may be said to have owed to himself:

I think that I have become a little more skilful in guessing right explanations and in devising experimental tests; . . . I have no great quickness of apprehension or wit which is so remarkable in some clever men, for example Huxley. I am therefore a poor critic; a paper or book therefore excites my admiration, and it is only after considerable reflection that I perceive the weak points . . . My memory is extensive, yet hazy: it suffices to make me cautious by vaguely telling me that I have observed or read something opposed to the conclusion which I am drawing, or on the other hand in favour of it. . . . I think that I am superior to the common run of men in noticing things which easily escape attention, and in observing them carefully. My industry has been nearly as great as it could have been in the observation and collection of facts . . . With the exception of Coral Reefs, I cannot remember a single first-formed hypothesis which had not after a time to be given up or greatly modified . . . My habits are methodical, and this has been of not a little use for my particular line of work. Lastly, I have had ample leisure from not having to earn my bread. Even ill-health, though it has annihilated several years of my life, has saved me from the distractions of society and amusement. Therefore my success as a man of science, whatever this may have amounted to, has been determined, as far as I can judge, by complex and diversified mental qualities and conditions. Of these the most important have been—the love of science—unbounded patience in long reflecting over any subject—industry in observing and collecting facts—and a fair share of invention as well as of common sense.

He recognized that at the cost of losing his appreciation of poetry and other things that delighted him in his youth, his mind had become a 'machine for grinding general laws out of large collections of facts'.

There was one characteristic that Darwin omitted from this very modest and objective appraisal of himself, and that was that he always remained a great overgrown child and, in some respects, childlike in his naïvety. He had no historical sense at all, and he once wrote to Huxley, referring to the parallelism between the works of Erasmus Darwin and Lamarck, 'the history of error is quite unimportant'. It was no doubt partly Darwin's lack of any sense of history that led him to write his astonishingly naïve letter to Baron von Scherzer: 'what a foolish idea seems to prevail in Germany on the connexion between Socialism and Evolution through Natural Selection.' That was on 26 December 1879, and a year later he must have had a shock when he received a letter from Karl Marx asking his permission to dedicate the English edition of *Das Kapital* to him. With great courtesy he refused, and his refusal was based not on political grounds but on his wish not to be associated with direct attacks against Christianity and theism, which introduces the question of Darwin's attitude to religion.

From the position of an orthodox candidate for holy orders when he embarked in the *Beagle*, he had gradually come to see that the Old Testament, from its manifestly false history of the earth and from its attribution to its God of the feelings of a jealous, revengeful tyrant, was no more to be trusted than the sacred books of the Hindus or Mahometans. The morality of the New Testament appealed to him as especially beautiful, but on the one hand he made allowance for the fact that it was interpreted in the light of modern liberal feelings, and on the other he could not recognize the doctrine of eternal punishment as compatible with the concepts of Christian charity. He had therefore gradually freed himself from the thought-forms of institutional religion, and the fact that natural selection does away with the argument from design led him to take an even wider view of the riddle of the universe.

He was also influenced by the problem of suffering and estranged by the pious platitudes and special pleading advanced by theologians, including Paley, to justify it. As he pointed out to himself, suffering may be a preparation for moral improvement in man, 'but the number of men in the world is as nothing compared with that of all other sentient beings, and these often suffer greatly without any moral improvement.' He was, however, able to show that there was some human comfort to be drawn from the argument that if the processes of evolution were regarded as the result of natural laws, 'we cease to be astonished that a group of animals should have been formed to lay their eggs in the bowels and flesh of other sensitive beings; that some animals should live by and even delight in cruelty.' What sort of guidance can it be that has led countless species to evolve to their doom and extinction, as the geological record proves to have been the case? There is no argument possible here. What sort of design is it that requires species to become extinct as a part-condition for the origin of new species that take their places in the economy of nature? When the war of nature and the struggle for existence are fairly faced the problem becomes even more difficult. What sort of providence is it that protects organisms but only if they happen to be of the size, weight, and general constitution nearest to the mean of the species, achieved by natural selection as most efficiently equipped to survive environmental conditions, when those that show variation from this mean and are lighter or heavier than the optimum perish miserably? It was facts like these that Darwin refused to conjure away by special pleading.

'What a book a devil's chaplain might write on the clumsy, wasteful, blundering, low, and horribly cruel works of nature,' he continued, and concluded that the horrors of nature and the atrocious behaviour of its denizens cannot be reconciled with a Creator of allegedly unlimited power and inexhaustible compassion, any more than the extinction of species, the shipwreck of mariners, the death of a gnat snapped up by a swallow, or of a man struck by lightning, the movements of the heavenly bodies, or the fall of earthly things, are to be ascribed to his direct volition. But these calamities need not be laid at the Creator's door if they are the result of natural laws.

The result of his experiences was that 'My theology is a simple muddle; I cannot look at the universe as the result of blind chance, yet I can see no evidence of beneficent design, or indeed of design of any kind, in the details.' The same views are echoed in the answers that he wrote to inquirers, many of them students, who asked him whether belief in evolution was compatible with religion. To two Dutch students from Utrecht, J. C. Costerus and N. D. Doedes, he said:

the impossibility of conceiving that this grand and wondrous universe, with our conscious selves, arose through chance, seems to me the chief argument for the existence of God; but whether this is an argument of real value, I have never been able to decide. I am aware that if we admit a first cause, the mind still craves to know whence it came, and how it arose. Nor can I overlook the difficulty from the immense amount of suffering through the world. . . . The safest conclusion seems to me that the whole subject is beyond the scope of man's intellect.

To another student, Niklaus, Baron Mengden, Darwin wrote in answer to a question on the compatibility of evolution with Christianity, 'I cannot spare the time to answer your question fully—provided it can be answered. Science has nothing to do with Christ; except in so far as the habit of scientific research makes a man cautious in admitting evidence. For myself I do not believe that there ever has been any Revelation.' This famous passage has been seized upon by some as evidence that Darwin was a complete atheist, which is a grave misreading of his character as a scientist, for he would never have allowed himself to make a categorical profession of atheism without evidence, and it was evidence that he constantly craved for. The proof of this is contained in his letter to John Fordyce written towards the end of his life: 'In my most extreme fluctuations I have never been an atheist in the sense of denying the existence of a God. I think that generally (and more and more as I grow older), but not always, that an agnostic would be the more correct description of my state of mind.'

Darwin never failed to make clear that his difficulties in reconciling orthodox beliefs with the evidence of nature were intended for himself alone. To this, the deepest of all problems, he applied the same technique of tolerance that pervades the pages of the *Origin of Species*, where he gave the reasons for his doubts and his conclusions, but never brought any verbal pressure on the reader to follow him. Each must decide for himself, and Darwin never felt any but the most friendly and charitable feelings for those who differed from him in matters of religion, provided that they were honest. His neighbour Lord Avebury has described how Darwin took an active part in parish work. 'Our then clergyman was a wise and sensible man. He and Mr Darwin, though they thought so differently, always worked together, and were firm friends.' This is amply confirmed from both sides. The clergyman, the Rev. J. Brodie Innes, wrote to Darwin, 'We often differed, but you are one of those rare mortals from whom one can differ and yet feel no shade of animosity, and that is a thing of which I should feel very proud if anyone could say it of me.' Darwin's description of their relations was equally generous: 'Innes and I have been fast friends for thirty years, and we never thoroughly agreed on any subject but once, and then we stared hard at each other, and thought one of us must be very ill.'

Darwin's disbelief crept over him at a slow rate and caused him no distress, except for one thing. His wife, throughout her life, maintained a deep conviction of orthodoxy, and Darwin's agnosticism made her sad and uneasy for his sake. They were far too much attached to each other, and the question was much too deep for the matter to be a subject for reproach between them. Instead, shortly after her marriage, and again after the publication of the *Origin of Species*, his wife wrote letters to him in which her love and tact were combined with her depth of feeling to express her solicitude for his earthly happiness and spiritual welfare. She asked for no reply, but the letters were found, each bearing a deeply touching annotation by Darwin.

For all his agnosticism, Darwin was not devoid of faith, but it was the faith of a scientist, that the laws of nature are consistent and that fundamentally order prevails in the universe. As Loren Eiseley has pointed out, it is a remarkable paradox that science which by profession fights so shy of faith in revelation is based on faith of a different kind, but nevertheless faith, that the universe can be rationally interpreted. This was what Darwin felt when he wrote to his old friend Henslow, 'I believe there exists, and I feel within me, an instinct for truth, or knowledge or discovery, of something of the same nature as the instinct of virtue.'

Darwin's views on the relation between science and theology also emerge from his conclusions about the origin of life. In his published works he made no mention of this problem but was content to work out the evolution of animals 'from at most four or five progenitors, and plants from an equal or lesser number,' leaving the reader to decide for himself how they arose. His reasons for doing this were that in the state of knowledge then prevailing, speculation on the origin of life, or even of matter, was unprofitable. He did not hide from himself, or his friends, the fact that if miraculous interposition was not only unnecessary but inadmissible in the evolution of plants and animals, it must be the same with their origin. For the problem of the origin of life Darwin performed the same service that Herschel performed for the origin of species. In a letter which he wrote to G. C. Wallich, Darwin said,

'If it is ever found that life can originate on this world, the vital phenomena will come under some general law of nature.' A little later Darwin amplified this view:

> It is often said that all the conditions for the first production of a living organism are now present, which could ever have been present. But if (and oh! what a big if!) we could conceive in some warm little pond, with all sorts of ammonia and phosphoric salts, light, heat, electricity, etc., present, that a proteine compound was chemically formed ready to undergo still more complex changes, at the present day such matter would be instantly devoured or absorbed, which would not have been the case before living creatures were formed.

In this passage, written in 1871, Darwin anticipated by eighty years the possibility of chemical evolution and the heterotrophe hypothesis of the origin of life that is now held as a result of experiments on 'warm little ponds' that have yielded results very similar to those that he imagined.

It has, for instance, been shown by S. L. Miller that if ultra-violet light or an electric discharge is passed through a mixture of chemical substances as simple as hydrogen, water, ammonia, and marsh-gas, the result is the production of large molecules containing numerous atoms of carbon, oxygen, hydrogen, and also nitrogen and other elements. Some molecules thus formed, known as amino-acids, are the bricks out of which proteins are constructed. It used to be thought that such compounds could be synthesized only by living organisms, for which reason they were called 'organic' compounds. It is now clear that if energy is supplied to mixtures of simple chemical substances under certain conditions, organic compounds are built up without the action of any living organisms at all. Such compounds are found in meteorites.

Originally the energy required must have come from the sun, and it is believed that when compounds produced in this manner reached a sufficient degree of complexity and of concentration in the sea, or a restricted arm of the sea, some molecules such as nucleic acids became surrounded by others forming a membrane, and that this was how cells originated. Nucleic acids have the property of replicating themselves by forcing other appropriate molecules to adhere to templates in the correct order, and this is the chemical basis of reproduction.

The other criterion of life, growth, was met by the fact that the cells were bathed in a 'soup' of molecules similar to those that they contained. They did not need to synthesize their food-materials into their own substance but took them ready-made by absorbing them from their surrounding medium, a method of nutrition called heterotrophic. But as Darwin foresaw, the supply of this food would be absorbed by living organisms faster than it could be replenished. Before this happened it was necessary that some organisms should develop a system of synthesizing their own substance from simpler substances, and so of becoming self-supporting and of acquiring a method of nutrition called autotrophic. This is what genes enable organisms to do, for they determine the production of proteins that act as enzymes in the building up of compounds, using energy. Originally this energy must have been supplied by sunlight working on coloured substances such as the green pigment chlorophyll; and this is still the characteristic mode of life of the Plant Kingdom.

Subsequently, a group of one-celled plants varied in the direction of turning cannibal and devouring their plant brethren, thereby obtaining all their food requirements ready-made, without having to synthesize them. These organisms then lost the equipment of enzymes that had previously enabled them to be self-supporting, and became animals. This is why animals have to eat plants or other animals, and why the continued existence of the Animal Kingdom is dependent on that of the Plant Kingdom. Darwin's 'if' certainly was 'a big if', but it is now taken quite seriously; it is accepted that life evolved from nonliving matter, and the lines along which Darwin formulated the problem are those which promise a solution in principle.

It was inevitable that a man who substituted an automatic natural process for what had previously been regarded as a divine prerogative in the origination and welfare of living species should arouse antagonism among custodians of institutional religion. It was an episode in the struggle between those who believe what they are told or read in revealed or so-called authoritative texts, and those who believe in the body of knowledge slowly built up by observation and experiment, repeatable and demonstrable. By Darwin's time this struggle had already dispossessed the theologians of the physical universe, but they clung tenaciously to the living world. Darwin recognized this as early as 1838 when he wrote in his Notebook, 'We can allow satellites, planets, suns, universe, nay whole system of universe to be governed by laws, but the smallest insect we wish to be created at once by special act, provided with its instincts, its place in nature, its range, etc.'

When Darwin proceeded to dispossess the theologians of the Plant and Animal Kingdoms, including man's body and mind, the theologians regarded him as an atheist, in which view they found themselves in curious agreement with the professional and political atheists who claimed Darwin as one of themselves, and in both cases for the same invalid reason, the *non-sequitur* of equating the rejection of the God of the Bible with disbelief in any God at all. The First Commandment is indeed a powerful deterrent for it affects the opinions even of those who do not accept the Commandments. Actually no man set a higher store by moral virtues than Darwin, and few men set a better example than his loving care for his family and his friends, which he also extended to all plants and animals, and his respect for truth. It seems, however, that loving kindness is not prized so highly if it is regarded as

PUNCH'S FANCY PORTRAITS.—No. 54.
DIET OF WORMS
SAMBOURNE · INV · DEL ·
CHARLES ROBERT DARWIN, LL.D., F.R.S.
IN HIS *DESCENT OF MAN* HE BROUGHT HIS OWN SPECIES DOWN AS LOW AS POSSIBLE—*I.E.*, TO "A HAIRY QUADRUPED FURNISHED WITH A TAIL AND POINTED EARS, AND PROBABLY *ARBOREAL* IN ITS HABITS"—WHICH IS A REASON FOR THE VERY GENERAL INTEREST IN A "FAMILY TREE." HE HAS LATELY BEEN TURNING HIS ATTENTION TO THE "POLITIC WORM."

Fig. 31

of natural instead of supernatural origin, and as, for this reason, Darwin was widely held to be the most dangerous man in England, it was obvious that the Establishment could not recognize the outstanding importance of his contributions to science and to human thought. It is only necessary to remember the honours officially offered to Newton, Davy, and Faraday to be aware of the difference in treatment as regards Darwin.

Indeed, among men of science it would be difficult to find a more striking example than Darwin of the saying that a prophet is not without honour save in his own country, and by honour is here meant official recognition by the nation. Oxford offered him the honorary degree of Doctor of Civil Law in 1870, but the state of his health prevented him from attending the ceremony to receive it. Cambridge awarded him the honorary degree of Doctor of Laws in 1877, and its conferment must have presented an impressive sight because the undergraduates lowered a stuffed monkey containing a musical box on a string over Darwin's head from the balcony of the Senate House. The British scientific societies awarded him all the honours in their power, including the Copley Medal of the Royal Society, but no mark of recognition whatever was bestowed by the Sovereign on the greatest British biologist in history. The Prussian Government awarded him the much coveted *Ordre pour le Mérite*, three foreign universities gave him honorary doctorates, and fifty-seven leading foreign learned societies elected him to honorary or corresponding membership.

The neglect of Darwin by British authorities is all the more poignant when it is considered how extraordinarily English he was. Brought up as a country gentleman to be thoroughly familiar with cultivated plants in spacious gardens and with domestic animals in kennels and stables, passionately fond of riding and shooting, he lived in a country where academic failure did not ruin his career, speed of work counted for nothing, private means could support him without his having to earn his living, and liberal institutions protected him from persecution for his unorthodox ideas. Nowhere but in England would such an environment have been possible in the first half of the nineteenth century, and Darwin played the part perfectly, including an incompetence in foreign languages that went so far as to pronounce the name of the capital city of Austria 'Wye-enn'. He was almost a caricature of an Englishman with his whiskers and, later on, his beard. Furthermore, such intellectual heritage as he enjoyed was purely British, consisting of the principle of uniformitarianism that he had learnt from Lyell, and the purposiveness of adaptation in nature that he had derived from Paley. W. F. Cannon has aptly remarked, 'this heritage is one of the reasons why, if you wish to discover the origin of species by means of natural selection, it is desirable to be English.'

The only British national honour that Darwin received was burial in Westminster Abbey, and even this was resented in some quarters as a desecration. With his genial sense of humour Darwin would have been highly amused: 'Considering how fiercely I have been attacked by the orthodox,' he wrote, 'it seems ludicrous that I once intended to be a clergyman.' But he would have been deeply appreciative, for like Cromwell's russet-coated captain that knows what he fights for and loves what he knows, Darwin never swerved from his conviction that he had acted rightly in devoting his life to science.

When he died, as a result of a heart attack, on 19 April 1882, his family wished that he should be buried at the village of Downe where Down House was, but twenty members of Parliament, a body which then included four professional Fellows of the Royal Society, wrote to the Dean of Westminster and suggested that 'it would be acceptable to a very large number of our fellow-countrymen of all classes and opinions that our illustrious countryman, Mr Darwin, should be buried in Westminster Abbey.' The Dean, George Granville Bradley, cordially acquiesced. If the pursuit of truth be worthy of reverence and honour, there could be no other fitting earthly resting-place for an Englishman who, by his proof of the fact of evolution was the Copernicus, and by his discovery and establishment of the principle of natural selection, was the Newton of the realm of living things.

The funeral took place on 26 April 1882, and the pall-bearers included Darwin's intimate friends, Hooker, Huxley, Wallace, and Lubbock, Canon Farrar, William Spottiswoode, President of the Royal Society, Lord Derby, the Dukes of Argyll and of Devonshire, and James Russell Lowell, the American Minister. Other foreign diplomats represented France, Germany, Italy, Spain, and Russia. An anthem was specially composed for the occasion by Dr Bridge, the sermon was preached by Canon Prothero and Beethoven's Funeral March was played. Darwin's grave is near those of Newton, Faraday, and his friend Lyell.

12,629 19

Chronology

Some important dates in the life of Darwin

1809	12 Feb.	Born at Shrewsbury
1818		Entered Shrewsbury School
1825	22 Oct.	Matriculated in the University of Edinburgh
1827	15 Oct.	Admitted to Christ's College, Cambridge
1831	26 Apr.	B.A. degree
	30 Aug.	Received invitation to sail in the *Beagle*
	27 Dec.	*Beagle* sailed from Plymouth
1835	26 Mar.	Heavily bitten by *Triatoma infestans*
	Sept.	Visited Galapagos Islands
1836	2 Oct.	Landed at Falmouth
1837	13 Mar.	Lived at 36 Great Marlborough Street, London
	July	Opened first Notebook on Transmutation of Species
1838	28 Sept.	Started to read Malthus on Population
	11 Nov.	Successfully proposed marriage to Emma Wedgwood
1839	1 Jan.	Moved to 12 Upper Gower Street, London
	24 Jan.	Elected F.R.S.
	29 Jan.	Married to Emma Wedgwood
	Aug.	*Journal of Researches* (during the voyage of the *Beagle*) published
	27 Dec.	William Erasmus Darwin born
1841	2 Mar.	Anne Elizabeth Darwin born
1842	May	Wrote Sketch of Species Theory
	May	*Structure and Distribution of Coral Reefs* published
	17 Sept.	Moved to Down House, Downe, Kent
	23 Sept.	Mary Eleanor Darwin born (died three weeks later)
1843	25 Sept.	Henrietta Emma Darwin born
1844	July	Wrote Essay on Species
	Nov.	*Geological Observations on Volcanic Islands* published
1845	9 July	George Howard Darwin born
	Aug.	*Journal of Researches*, 2nd edition published
1846	1 Oct.	Began work on barnacles
	end	*Geological Observations on South America* published

1847	8 July	Elizabeth Darwin born
1848	16 Aug.	Francis Darwin born
1850	15 Jan.	Leonard Darwin born
1851	23 Apr.	Anne Elizabeth Darwin died
	13 May	Horace Darwin born
	June	*Monograph of Fossil Lepadidae* published
	end	*Monograph of [recent] Lepadidae* published
1854	Aug.	*Monograph of [recent] Balanidae* published
	9 Sept.	Began to sort out notes on species
	end	*Monograph of Fossil Balanidae* published
1856	14 May	Began to write large work on species
	6 Dec.	Charles Waring Darwin born
1858	18 June	Received complete statement on evolution by natural selection from Alfred Russel Wallace
	28 June	Charles Waring Darwin died
	1 July	Joint paper with Wallace read before Linnean Society
	20 July	Began to write *Origin of Species*
	20 Aug.	Joint paper with Wallace published
1859	24 Nov.	*Origin of Species* published (1,250 copies, all sold on first day)
1860	7 Jan.	*Origin of Species*, 2nd edition published (3,000 copies)
1861	Apr.	*Origin of Species*, 3rd edition published (2,000 copies)
1862	1 Mar.	Paper on Dimorphism in *Primula* published
	15 May	*On the Various Contrivances by which British and Foreign Orchids are Fertilised by Insects* published
1864	30 Nov.	Awarded Copley Medal of the Royal Society
1866	15 Dec.	*Origin of Species*, 4th edition published (1,250 copies)
1868	30 Jan.	*Variation of Animals and Plants under Domestication* published (1,500 copies)
	20 Feb.	*Variation of Animals and Plants under Domestication*, reprint published (1,500 copies)
1869	7 Aug.	*Origin of Species*, 5th edition published (2,000 copies)
1871	24 Feb.	*Descent of Man* published (2,500 copies, and reprint of 5,000)
1872	19 Feb.	*Origin of Species*, 6th edition published (3,000 copies)
	26 Nov.	*The Expression of the Emotions in Man and*

		Animals published (7,000 copies, and reprint of 2,000)
1874	June	*Structure and Distribution of Coral Reefs*, 2nd edition published
	autumn	*Descent of Man*, 2nd edition published
1875	2 July	*Insectivorous Plants* published
	Sept.	*Climbing Plants* published
	end	*Variation of Animals and Plants under Domestication*, 2nd edition published
1876	5 Dec.	*Effects of Cross and Self Fertilisation in the Vegetable Kingdom* published
1877	Jan.	*Fertilisation of Orchids*, 2nd edition published
	9 July	*Different forms of flowers on plants of the same species* published
1879	19 Nov.	*Life of Erasmus Darwin* published
1880	22 Nov.	*Power of Movement in Plants* published
1881	10 Oct.	*Formation of Vegetable Mould through the action of Worms* published
1882	19 Apr.	Died at Down House
	26 Apr.	Buried in Westminster Abbey

Bibliography

The literature on Darwin, evolution, and natural selection is immense. No attempt is made here to give more than a very restricted number of titles of general works.

First come Darwin's own books, of which the titles are given under the dates of their publication in the Chronology of his life, on p. 278. *The Origin of Species* (6th edition) is available in the World's Classics (Oxford University Press), and *The Voyage of the Beagle* (2nd edition) in Everyman's Library (Dent). In addition the following (which were not published during Darwin's life) are available:

Sketch on Species written in 1842, and Essay written in 1844, published in *Evolution by Natural Selection* (Cambridge 1958).

'Darwin's Ornithological Notes', edited by Nora Barlow, *Bull. Brit. Mus.* (*Nat. Hist.*). *Historical Series*, vol. 2, No. 7, 1963.

'Darwin's Notebooks on Transmutation of Species', edited by Sir Gavin de Beer, *Bull. Brit. Mus.* (*Nat. Hist.*). Historical Series, Vol. 2 Nos. 2–6, 1960–1.

The following works deal with different aspects of evolution:

A. J. Cain, *Animal Species & their Evolution* (Hutchinson 1954).

Walter F. Cannon, 'The bases of Darwin's achievement: a revaluation', *Victorian Studies*, Indianapolis, December 1961, pp. 109–34.

C. D. Darlington, *The Evolution of Genetic Systems* (Oliver & Boyd 1958).

Gavin de Beer, *Embryos and Ancestors* (Oxford 1962).

T. Dobzhansky, *Genetics and the Origin of Species* (Columbia U.P. 1951).

T. Dobzhansky, *Mankind Evolving* (Yale 1962).

L. Eiseley, *Darwin's Century* (Gollancz 1959).

R. A. Fisher, *The Genetical Theory of Natural Selection* (Oxford 1930).

E. B. Ford, *Mendelism and Evolution* (Methuen 1957).

Julian Huxley, *Evolution in Action* (Chatto & Windus 1953).

Julian Huxley & others, Editors, *Evolution as a Process* (Allen & Unwin 1954).

Julian Huxley, *Evolution: The Modern Synthesis* (Allen & Unwin 1942, reprinted with new introduction 1963).

W. E. Le Gros Clark, *History of the Primates* (Brit. Mus. (Nat. Hist.) 1958).

E. Mayr, *Systematics & the Origin of Species* (Columbia 1942).

B. Rensch, *Evolution above the Species Level* (Methuen 1959).

P. M. Sheppard, *Natural Selection and Heredity* (Hutchinson 1958).

G. G. Simpson, *The Major Features of Evolution* (Columbia 1953).

Sydney Smith, 'The origin of the Origin', *Impulse*, London, No. 11, November 1959, pp. 2–4.

T. J. B. Spencer, *From Gibbon to Darwin* (Birmingham University 1959).

Robert C. Stauffer, 'On the origin of species: an unpublished version', *Science*, vol. 130, 27 November 1959, pp. 1449–52. [Darwin's large work, of which *The Origin of Species* was the 'abstract'.]

G. L. Stebbins, *Variation and Evolution in Plants* (Columbia 1957).

R. A. Stirton, *Time, Life and Man* (Chapman & Hall 1959).

A Handbook on Evolution (Brit. Mus. (Nat. Hist.) 1959).

On the state of biological knowledge before Darwin:

B. Glass & Others, *Forerunners of Darwin* (Johns Hopkins 1959).

On Darwin's life the standard sources are:

Life & Letters of Charles Darwin, edited by F. Darwin (Murray 1887).

More Letters of Charles Darwin, edited by F. Darwin & A. C. Seward (Murray 1903).

Saul Adler, 'Darwin's illness', *Nature*, London, vol. 184, 1959, pp. 1102–3.

J. H. Ashworth, 'Charles Darwin as a student in Edinburgh', *Proc. Roy. Soc. Edin.*, vol. 65, 1935, pp. 97–113.

Nora Barlow, 'Robert FitzRoy and Charles Darwin', *Cornhill Magazine*, April 1932.

The Autobiography of Charles Darwin, edited by Nora Barlow (Collins) 1958.

'Darwin's Journal', edited by Sir Gavin de Beer, *Bull. Brit. Mus. (Nat. Hist.)*. Historical Series, Vol. 2, No. 1, 1959.

Index